The Aircraft of the World

The World's Fighting Planes

William Green and Gerald Pollinger

The
Aircraft of the World

New, revised and enlarged Edition

Macdonald : London

Acknowledgements

The sources of some of the photographs appearing in this edition are as follows (Note: Each page number is followed by a numeral and a letter which indicate the position of the photo on the page: e.g., 2L indicates second photograph from the top of the page on the left-hand side): G. Apostolo, 39 (2L & 2R), 78 (3R), 122 (1R), 136 (3L), 139 (1L), 156 (3R), 169 (2R), 191 (3L). W. J. Balogh, 68 (2R), 74 (2L), 82 (1L), 147 (3L). G. Bignozzi, 111 (2L). Blandin-Regnier, 55 (2L), 56 (2R & 3R), 90 (2L), 111 (1R), 158 (1R), 169 (3L), 175 (3L), 176 (3L). W. M. Bodie, 9 (2R), 12 (1L), 24 (3L), 27 (1R), 53 (2L & 3L), 54 (1L), 90 (2R), 122 (3L), 125 (3R), 157 (1L), 173 (2L), 201 (2L). M. J. F. Bowyer, 45 (3R). E. J. Bulban, 47 (3R), 89 (3R). H. B. Burgunder, 64 (3L). Butler-Green, 9 (1L), 11 (2L), 19 (3L & 3R), 22 (1L), 24 (1L), 29 (2R), 33 (2L), 47 (1R) 49 (1L), 57 (2L & 3L), 58 (2L), 59 (1R), 69 (1L), 73 (1L), 76 (3L & 3R), 84 (3R), 85 (3L), 87 (2R & 3R), 88 (3R), 94 (2R, 2L & 3R), 95 (3L & 3R), 96 (2L & 3L), 97 (1L & 1R). 115 (2R), 117 (1L & 3L), 118 (1L), 131 (2R, 3L & 3R), 132 (1L & 1R), 133 (2L & 3L), 134 (1L), 137 (2L), 139 (3L), 149 (3L), 159 (2L), 163 (2L & 3L), 165 (2L & 3L), 167 (3L & 3R), 169 (1L), 172 (1R), 178 (1L & 3R), 181 (3L), 187 (3L), 196 (1R), 201 (1R), 203 (1L & 1R). C. W. Cain, 75 (2L). E. A. Coates, 23 (3R), 133 (2R), 157 (1R), 160 (3L), 167 (1L). R. A. Cole, 14 (3R), 39 (3L), 121 (3R). P. M. Corbell, 28 (2R), 49 (2R), 65 (1L). Crown Copyright, 95 (1L). L. Downey, 60 (1L). J. D. Dyson, 64 (2R), 68 (3R). J. C. Elholm, 164 (1L & 2L). R. Fitzpatrick, 48 (1R), 78 (3L), 87 (1R), 149 (2L), 178 (2R). M. M. Gates, 25 (2L), 41 (2L), 77 (2L), 97 (2L & 2R), 98 (3R), 102 (3R), 109 (3L), 131 (2L), 132 (2R), 171 (2L), 203 (2L). J. Goodyear, 25 (1L), 26 (3L), 39 (1R), 91 (2L), 139 (2L), 187 (2L), 201 (2R). J. M. G. Gradidge, 8 (2R), 21 (1L & 1R), 32 (1R), 33 (3L), 99 (1L), 102 (2R), 109 (2L), 112 (2L), 130 (1L), 155 (2R), 158 (2R). M. C. Gray, 41 (1L), 93 (3R). A. B. Guidotti, 13 (3L), 14 (3L), 122 (1L), 139 (1R). M. J. Hooks, 135 (3L), 155 (3R), 171 (3L). L. J. Kohn, 90 (3L), 98 (3L), 172 (3R). A. van Ishoven, 41 (1L). C. A. Johnson Collection, 9 (2L), 24 (3R), 29 (2L), 48 (1L), 49 (3L), 50 (1R), 54 (2L, 2R, 3L & 3R), 58 (2R), 67 (2L), 82 (2L), 84 (2R), 90 (1L), 92 (1R), 101 (3R), 113 (2R & 3L), 117 (1R & 2L), 122 (2L & 3R), 125 (1L), 130 (1R), 142 (2R, 3R, 2L & 3L), 143 (1L), 146 (2R & 3L), 149 (2R), 157 (2L), 181 (2R). W. T. Larkins, 10 (1R), 28 (1L & 2L), 29 (3L), 37 (1L), 38 (1L), 43 (1L), 45 (2L), 50 (1L), 53 (1R & 3R), 54 (1R), 55 (1L & 3R), 65 (3R), 69 (3L & 3R), 73 (3R), 74 (1L, 1R & 3R), 84 (3L), 86 (2L), 91 (1R), 95 (2R), 109 (1L), 110 (1L), 117 (2R & 3R), 118 (3L), 129 (3R), 134 (2R), 135 (1L), 148 (3R), 154 (3L), 155 (2L), 157 (3L), 160 (2L & 3R), 169 (3R), 171 (3R), 174 (2L), 180 (2R), 182 (2L), 184 (2R), 187 (1R). H. Levy, 194 (1L, 3L & 3R), 195 (1R), 196 (2R), E. Littauer, 93 (3L). E. Maloney, 159 (3L). A. C. Martin, 152 (1R). H. G. Martin, 42 (3R), 49 (3L), 71 (1L), 75 (3L), 91 (3L & 3R), 93 (2L), 119 (3L), 125 (3L), 126 (3L), 127 (3R), 146 (2L), 195 (3R), 202 (1L). M. Mayborn, 51 (2L), 187 (1L). K. Meechan, 19 (2R), 43 (3L), 59 (3R), 81 (3L), 133 (1L). D. A. S. McKay, 7 (1L & 1R), 41 (3L), 116 (3R), 164 (2R). J. McNulty, 58 (3L), 74 (2R & 3R), 82 (1L), 127 (3L), 143 (1R), 150 (1R), 186 (3L), 198 (2R), 200 (3R). D. J. McCutchion, 127 (2L). M. Olmsted, 15 (3R), 19 (1L). Registration Research, 7 (3R), 65 (3L), 118 (2R). J. Rosenstock, 15 (3L), 135 (2R), 166 (2L). M. A. Salo, 111 (2R), 116 (2R), 184 (2L & 3R). W. D. Shipp, 197 (1R & 3R). H. W. Smeltzer, 9 (1R). Stationery Office, Dublin, 132 (3L). R. P. Straub, 102 (1L), 109 (1R), 175 (1L). R. A. G. Stuart, 101 (2R), J. W. R. Taylor, 173 (1R). J. Villela, 23 (2L), 113 (3L), 182 (1L). N. B. Wiltshire, 87 (1L), 118 (1R), 187 (2R). G. R. Wrixon, 28 (3R), 59 (2R), 89 (1L), 178 (2L). U. S. Navy, 108 (3R). Aeroplane, 105 (2L).

In addition to the above, the authors would also like to thank the following for the use of photographs and information supplied by them: J. H. C. van Aal, S. Alberto, B. G. Ambrose, J. S. Appleby, R. D. B. Archer, P. W. Brooks, M. J. Brunning, R. M. Bueschel, L. Butt, C. Burgel, J. A. Bagley, P. Berry, L. Chamberlain, P. K. Coetgee, B. J. Colledge, L. Crew, J. Cubbage, C. J. D'Amato, W. Dollfus, P. Dow, J. H. Driscoll, J. J. Ellis, A. Furr, J. Farrell, E. Ferko, R. B. Fitzpatrick, D. Fox, H. Gunn, N. Goobie, J. S. Havers, F. A. Hudson, S. M. Hurst, P. Hylend, A. J. Jackson, B. Jamin, M. N. Jamieson, C. H. Kamphuis, B. van der Klaauw, B. C. F. Klein, H. A. Kofoed, N. B. Leicester, J. B. Lorentsen, E. A. Lucas, H. P. Macklin, R. Marriott, T. Mason, D. S. Miller, P. B. M'Cann, S. W. Nicholas, A. Pearcy, A. Pernet, W. Redden, D. F. Santie, P. M. Sargent, C. A. Savage, R. Shanks, I. Sheals, L. Smith, L. S. Stollar, E. Taylor, E. J. Toms, G. Vennai, D. N. Vincent, J. Wickenden, J. M. Wilde, C. F. Wright, W. Wincott.

The authors also wish to thank British European Airways and British Overseas Airways for the photographs of aircraft that appear in the liveries of these airlines, and the airlines, private operators, and aircraft manufacturers throughout the world who have co-operated so readily in the illustration of this publication. The kind assistance of the Antique Airplanes Association and the specialists of Air Britain is also warmly acknowledged.

First published in December 1955 by
Macdonald & Co. (Publishers), Ltd.
16 Maddox Street, W.1
Made and printed in Great Britain by
Purnell and Sons, Ltd.
Paulton (Somerset) and London

Foreword

by

Air Chief Marshal Sir BASIL E. EMBRY, K.C.B., K.B.E., D.S.O., D.F.C., A.F.C.
(Formerly Commander Allied Air Forces Central Europe)

We continue to witness the rapid and startling development of aircraft for civilian and military purposes in many different parts of the world today.

This swift progress, which continues uninterrupted, has brought the airplane and airpower to a position of such prominence that any person who aspires to an up-to-date knowledge of world affairs cannot escape coming into closer contact with aeronautical developments and problems. In fact, aeronautical science today affects most aspects of our modern life, such as transport, economics, diplomacy, military power and so on.

For these reasons I consider this book to be an invaluable reference document and aeronautical text-book in this air age and I commend it both to the serious aeronautical student and to those who need a most comprehensive and accurate guide to modern aircraft developments.

Introduction

The progress that has been made in the design of aircraft during the comparatively short span of years that has elapsed since the first primitive aircraft staggered off the ground represents one of the most remarkable achievements of the twentieth century. In the past quarter-century, which has seen the coming of age of aviation, its ever increasing dominance in military affairs and its acceptance as an important part of the lives of most of us, several thousand aircraft types, bewildering in their diversity of form, have been produced. Winged representatives of every year of the past three decades are to be found somewhere in the world's skies today; the *raison d'etre* of this book is to provide in compact form details and illustrations of this vast and varied host of aircraft.

When, two years ago this month, the first edition of *The Aircraft of the World* made its début, it represented what was probably the first serious attempt to gather together details of all the aircraft types known to be flying, irrespective of their vintage or importance in military or civil aviation. In the past twenty-four months, a multiplicity of new, and in some cases, revolutionary aircraft have been revealed, these alone would necessitate a considerable increase in the number of pages that formed the first edition of this book. But the appearance of *The Aircraft of the World* resulted in a deluge of letters informing the authors of old-stagers flying over various parts of the globe which had not found a niche in its pages. Further investigation revealed that many of these elderly aircraft were nothing more than "hangar-inventory", having spread their wings for the last time many years since, but it also unearthed many machines of all types which, still performing useful functions, were not known to be flying when the initial volume was compiled. Thus, the "new" types to be found in the pages of this edition range from antiquated, be-strutted Travel Air biplanes of the 'twenties, through relics of the Spanish Civil War such as Polikarpov's I–15 and I–16 fighters, numerous combat aircraft of the Second World War which, commonplace a decade past, are the rarities of today, to the latest shapes in supersonic warplanes such as the SAAB-35 Draken, the Chance-Vought XF8U-1 Crusader, and the English Electric P.1A, and the newest commercial machines like the Fokker Friendship and the Handley Page Herald.

The aircraft types included in this edition of *The Aircraft of the World* are those *known* to be flying at the time of closing for press. The exceptions are few, and we believe them to be confined to military aircraft that were known to be flying but of which details had not been revealed (e.g., Dassault M.D.550, Nord-SFECMAS 1501 Griffon, Lockheed F-104A), Soviet aircraft that had not been publicly revealed, relics from the First World War and earlier which appear only on rare occasions for exhibition purposes, and a number of U.S. and French "home-built" light aircraft which exist in single examples only and which, in many cases, see more of the hangar than the element for which they were designed.

In the first edition of this book the aircraft were arranged in broad structural groups, the most distinctive identification characteristic or feature of the aircraft being chosen to form the basis of the group. While this arrangement was generally agreed to be of considerable value for the purpose of isolating and identifying a specific aircraft type, it reduced the value of the book as a work of reference. It has therefore been decided to change the arrangement of the book, listing the aircraft in the alphabetical order of their manufacturers' names. Thus, all the products of a manufacturer that remain flying are grouped together. This arrangement is retained in the separate section in which all types of rotorcraft are grouped together to facilitate comparison one with another. Throughout the book silhouettes are included of selected aircraft. These are the types that are flying in the greatest numbers today; that are flying in prototype form and about to enter production, or experimental prototypes for which production orders may be anticipated.

The valuable assistance of air attachés and aircraft manufacturers throughout the world, and to numerous correspondents and photographers who have so willingly furnished information and illustrations for this book is most warmly acknowledged. The authors particularly desire to express their gratitude to "Chronicler", Mr. John W. R. Taylor, Mr. Charles W. Cain, Mr. Jacques Marmain, Mr. Gert W. Heumann, Mr. Harold G. Martin, Mr. Robert P. Straub, Mr. William T. Larkins, Mr. C. A. Johnson, Mr. W. M. Bodie, and Mr. Denis K. Fox.

London, December 1955.   THE AUTHORS

ADAM R.A.14 LOISIRS   FRANCE

The R.A.14 Loisirs two-seat light cabin monoplane was developed by Établissements Aéronautiques R. Adam for construction by aero clubs and private individuals, the company supplying drawings and fabricated parts. Design was commenced in May 1945, the prototype flying at the end of that year and becoming the first post-war design available for amateur construction. Of simple construction, the Loisirs can be fitted with a variety of engines in the 40–65 h.p. range, and examples are flying with C.N.A. D-4, Mathis 4 GB-60, Minié 4 DC-32A, and Train 6D-01 engines, but most R.A.14s have the 65 h.p. Continental A65-8.

Max. speed, 87 m.p.h.; cruising, 72 m.p.h.; empty weight, 617 lb.; loaded, 1,058 lb.; span, 35 ft. 9 in.; length, 22 ft. 11 in.; height, 7 ft. 2½ in.

ADAM R.A.15 MAJOR   FRANCE

The R.A.15 Major is basically a development of the R.A.14 Loisirs embodying several refinements, including a plywood-covered fuselage, balanced elevators and rudder, etc., and intended for engines in the 70–75 h.p. range. The R.A.15 Major is powered by a 75 h.p. Régnier 4D-2, and the R.A.151 differs in having a 75 h.p. Continental C75 engine (the photograph illustrates this version). Developments include the projected three-seat R.A.16, and the R.A.17, the latter being a single-seat crop-dusting version of the R.A.15 Major with a fuselage of reduced width and a chemical tank and spraying gear aft. The following details refer to the R.A.15 Major.

Max. speed, 109 m.p.h.; ceiling, 16,400 ft.; empty weight, 616 lb.; loaded weight, 1,145 lb.; span, 34 ft. 9 in.; length, 22 ft. 11 in.

AÉRO 101   FRANCE

Developed by the Société Indraéro and first flown in 1953, the Aéro 101 was designed by MM. Chapeau and Blanchet as a light tandem two-seat training biplane for the *Service de l'Aviation Légère et Sportive* (S.A.L.S.), and an initial production batch of thirteen machines has been completed. The Aéro 101 is powered by a 75 h.p. Minié 4 DC-32 flat-four engine and is of all-wood construction. It is generally similar in appearance to the Aéro 110 from which it was derived but, apart from its all-wood construction and flat-four engine, it differs in having a tailwheel and wheel brakes. The tandem open cockpits are fitted with dual controls.

Max. speed, 108.6 m.p.h.; cruising, 93 m.p.h.; initial climb rate, 630 ft./min.; span, 24 ft. 11 in.; length, 18 ft. 4 in.

AÉRO 110   FRANCE

The Aéro 110 is generally similar to the previously described Aéro 101, but the fuselage has a fabric-covered steel-tube framework and power is provided by a 45 h.p. Salmson 9ADB radial air-cooled engine. Produced by the Société Indraéro and flown for the first time on May 1, 1950, the Aéro 110 preceded the Aéro 101 and was also produced for the *Service de l'Aviation Légère at Sportive*. The Aéro 110 is a single-bay staggered biplane, and both upper and lower wings are of equal span and chord. A hinged panel in the upper wing provides access to the front cockpit. Full dual controls are provided.

Max. speed, 81 m.p.h.; cruising, 71.4 m.p.h.; empty weight, 594 lb.; loaded weight, 1,000 lb.; span, 24 ft. 11 in.; length, 18 ft. 4 in.

AEROCAR MODEL II   U.S.A.

The Aerocar convertible aeroplane and roadable two-seater was designed by Mr. M. B. Taylor, the prototype, the Aerocar Model I, being completed in October 1949. This was subsequently tested extensively as both an aircraft and an automobile, and a modified production model, the Aerocar Model II, flew in August 1953. The Aerocar is powered by a 135 h.p. Lycoming 0-290-D2 engine which provides front-wheel automobile drive and drives a pusher airscrew aft of the tail assembly. The wing and tail sections may be towed behind the automobile section for road transportation.

Max. speed, 112 m.p.h.; cruising, 100 m.p.h.; initial climb rate, 500 ft./min.; range, 300 miles; empty weight, 1,408 lb.; loaded, 1,950 lb.; span, 34 ft.; length, 21 ft.; height, 7 ft. 2 in.; wing area, 168 sq. ft.

AERO-FLIGHT STREAK   U.S.A.

The Streak two-seat all-metal light monoplane was developed by the Aero-Flight Aircraft Corporation of California in three versions which were similar apart from fuel capacities and engines. The three models were the AFA-1 Streak-85 powered by an 85 h.p. Continental C85-12J engine, the AFA-2 Streak-125 powered by a 125 h.p. Continental C125, and the Model AFA-3 Streak-165 powered by a 165 h.p. Franklin engine. The photographs depict the AFA-3 Streak-165, and the following specification relates to this version.

Max. speed, 219 m.p.h.; cruising, 210 m.p.h.; initial climb rate, 2,000 ft./min.; max. range, 1,065 miles; empty weight, 1,060 lb.; loaded, 1,695 lb.; span, 25 ft. 3 in.; length, 22 ft. 4 in.

AERO 2   YUGOSLAVIA

Yugoslavia's first post-war aircraft of national design, the Aero 2 tandem two-seat primary trainer was designed by Ing. Petkovic and Ing. Boris Cijan. The prototype was built by the Ikarus factory at Zemun, and flew for the first time on October 19, 1946. Several series of this trainer have since been produced for the Yugoslav Air Force, including the Aero 2C, 2D and 2F. The Aero 2C and 2F (*silhouette*) are powered by the 160 h.p. Walter Minor 6-III, and have open and enclosed cockpits respectively. The Aero 2D is powered by the 145 h.p. Gipsy Major VII, and the Aero 2H (*photo*) is a Walter Minor-powered twin-float training seaplane for the Yugoslav Navy.

Specification (Aero 2F): Tandem two-seat primary trainer. Engine: One 160 h.p. Walter Minor 6-III. Weights: Loaded, 2,156 lb. Performance: Max. speed, 139 m.p.h. at sea level. Dimensions: Span, 34 ft, 5¼ in.; length, 27 ft. 0 in.

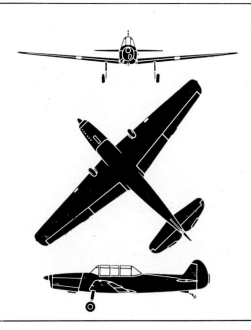

AERO AE.45-S   CZECHOSLOVAKIA

The Aero 45, built by the former Aero factory at Vysocany, flew for the first time in July 1947, and a series of one hundred aircraft of this type was laid down in the following year. The Aero 45 has since achieved considerable success, and has been exported to France, India, Switzerland, and many other countries. Construction is all-metal and dual controls are provided. The Aero 45 is essentially similar to the Super Aero 45, or AE.45-S, which features minor refinements.

Specification: Four/five-seat cabin monoplane. Engines: Two 105 h.p. Walter Minor 4-III. Weights: Empty, 1,896 lb.; loaded, 3,306 lb. Performance: Max. speed, 177 m.p.h.; cruising speed, 152 m.p.h.; initial climb rate, 980 ft./min.; service ceiling, 18,700 ft.; range, 930 miles. Dimensions: Span, 40 ft. 4 in.; length, 24 ft. 9 in.; height, 7 ft. 6 in.; wing area, 184 sq. ft.

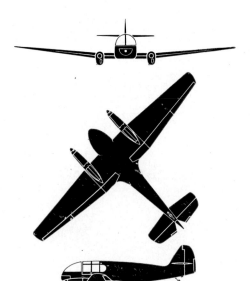

AERO COMMANDER 560A   U.S.A.

The Aero Commander 560 is a progressive development of the Commander 520 (*illustrated*), more than two hundred of which were produced. The Commander 560 differs from its predecessor in having slightly more powerful engines, increased weights, and slightly swept vertical tail surfaces. Six Commander 520s were delivered to the U.S. Army under the designation L-26. A further variant, which appeared in 1955, is the Commander 680. This has 340 h.p. Lycoming GSO-480-A1A supercharged engines, increasing top speed to 260 m.p.h.

Specification: Five/seven-seat light transport. Engines: Two 270 h.p. Lycoming Go-480-B. Weights: Empty, 3,970 lb.; loaded, 6,000 lb. Performance: Max. speed, 209 m.p.h. at sea level; cruising, 200 m.p.h. at 10,000 ft.; initial climb rate, 1,400 ft./min.; range (max. payload), 1,048 miles. Dimensions: Span, 44 ft.; length, 34 ft. 2½ in.; height, 14 ft. 9 in.; wing area, 242 sq. ft.

AERONCA C-3 (100)   (G.B.) U.S.A.

The Aeronautical Corporation of America (later Aeronca Aircraft Corp.), was the first U.S. company to market a truly light aircraft. The Aeronca C-3 was a development of the C-2 which was similar in general arrangement and construction, and produced in quantity between 1931 and 1937. The Aeronca 100 was a version built in Britain under U.S. licence (*see photo*), powered by the 36 h.p. J.A.P. J.99. The Aeronca C-3 and Aeronca 100 are externally similar, and examples of both versions are flying in the U.S.A. and the United Kingdom. The version of the C-3 flying in largest numbers is powered by the 36 h.p. Aeronca E-113A engine. More than one hundred C-3s are still in existence.
Max. speed, 93 m.p.h.; cruising, 80 m.p.h.; range, 175 miles; empty weight, 503 lb.; loaded, 925 lb.; span, 36 ft.; length, 20 ft.; height, 8 ft.

AERONCA MODEL K (AND KC) SCOUT U.S.A.

Introduced in 1937, the Aeronca K is flying in some numbers in the U.S.A., and one example is flying in Australia. The Aeronca K is powered by the 40 h.p. Aeronca E-113-CBD engine (*photo*), and is basically similar to the Aeronca KC apart from the 40 h.p. Continental A-40 engine of the latter. Other variants flying in numbers and differing from the Models K and KC only in the type of engine installed are the Models 50-C (50 h.p. Continental A-50), 50-F (50 h.p. Franklin 50), 50-L (50 h.p. Lycoming), 60-TF (65 h.p. Continental or 60 h.p. Franklin), and 65CA Super-Chief, 65TAC and 65TAF Defender (with 65 h.p. Continental), and 65LA Super-Chief (65 h.p. Lycoming).
(*Model K*) *Max. speed, 88 m.p.h.; cruising, 80 m.p.h.; range, 250 miles; empty weight, 588 lb.; loaded, 1,040 lb.; span, 36 ft.; length, 20 ft. 7 in.*

AERONCA MODEL L   U.S.A.

The Aeronca Model L two-seat cabin monoplane of 1935 was built in four versions of which three, the Model LA (70 h.p. Le Blond), the LB (85 h.p. Le Blond), and the LC (90 h.p. Warner Junior), are still flying in some numbers in the U.S.A. and Canada. Some twenty Model L monoplanes are currently registered in the U.S.A., the Warner-powered Model LC predominating. The Aeronca Model L is of mixed construction, and the enclosed cabin seats two side-by-side with dual controls. The following specification refers to the Model LB, but weights and performance are generally similar to the LC.
Max. speed, 120 m.p.h.; cruising, 105 m.p.h.; initial climb, 600 ft./min.; range, 525 miles; empty weight, 1,008 lb.; loaded, 1,680 lb.; span, 36 ft.; length, 22 ft. 6 in.; height, 7 ft.; wing area, 150 sq. ft.

AERONCA O-58B (L-3B)   U.S.A.

The Aeronca O-58B or L-3B was a two-seat liaison and observation monoplane produced for the U.S. Army. The original model, the YO-58 (two examples of which are still flying in the U.S.A.), was a light military trainer conversion of the civil Model 65TAC Defender, and the O-58, O-58A and O-58B were production models powered by the 65 h.p. Continental O-170-3. These were later redesignated L-3, L-3A and L-3B respectively, and a considerable number of O-58B/L-3B aircraft were sold to private owners as war surplus, several hundred currently flying in the U.S.A. The O58B/L-3B differs from civil production models primarily in having a more extensively glazed cabin.
Max. speed, 87 m.p.h.; cruising, 79 m.p.h.; range, 218 miles; empty weight, 835 lb.; loaded, 1,260 lb.; span, 35 ft.; length, 21 ft. 10 in.

AERONCA CHAMPION (L-16B)   U.S.A.

Introduced in 1947, the Champion had been produced in five versions (differing only in power and internal details) when production terminated in 1950. The first production Champion, the Model 7AC, was powered by a 65 h.p. Continental A65-8, and the Model 7BC differed in having an 85 h.p. Continental C85-12. The latter was ordered by the U.S. Army as the L-16A, a contract for 439 machines being placed in 1947. The Model 7CC (90 h.p. Continental C90) followed in 1948, and the Model 7DC (85 h.p.) in 1949. The final model, the 7EC, was produced in 1950, and the L-16B (*photo*) is a military conversion to which the following specification refers.
Specification: Two-seat cabin monoplane. Engine: One 90 h.p. Continental C90-12F. Weights: Empty, 890 lb.; loaded, 1,450 lb. Performance: Max. speed, 110 m.p.h.; cruising, 90 m.p.h.; initial climb rate, 800 ft./min.; range, 350 miles. Dimensions: Span, 35 ft. 2 in.; length, 21 ft. 6 in.; height, 7 ft.; wing area, 170.22 sq. ft.

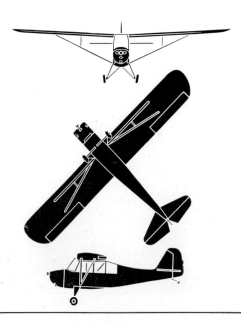

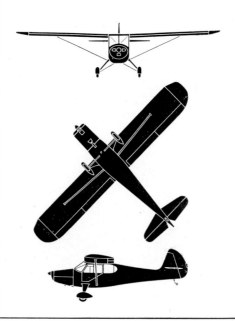

AERONCA MODEL 15AC SEDAN   U.S.A.

The Model 15AC Sedan four-seat light cabin monoplane was the last type to be produced by the Aeronca Manufacturing Corporation before this concern abandoned light-plane manufacture in 1950 to concentrate on military subcontract work. The Model 15AC Sedan was produced in considerable quantity and some four hundred machines of this type are currently registered in the U.S.A. A small number of Sedans were powered by the 165 h.p. Franklin 6A4-165-B3 engine, and a twin-float seaplane model, the S15AC, was also produced in very small numbers.

Specification: Four-seat light cabin monoplane. Engine: One 145 h.p. Continental C145. Weights: Empty, 1,150 lb.; loaded, 2,050 lb. Performance: Max. speed, 129 m.p.h.; cruising speed, 114 m.p.h. at sea level; initial climb rate, 800 ft./min.; normal range, 456 miles. Dimensions: Span, 37 ft. 6 in.; length, 25 ft. 3 in.; height, 7 ft. 0 in.; wing area, 200 sq. ft.

AERONCA MODEL 11CC SUPER-CHIEF   U.S.A.

A variation of the Champion and powered by an 85 h.p. Continental C85 engine, the Model 11CC Super-Chief was introduced in 1948. It differs from the Champion primarily in providing side-by-side seating for two. The wing, landing gear and power plant are identical to and interchangeable with the Model 7DC Champion, but the fuselage is wider, and a lower engine cowling line provides improved visibility. The Model 11AC is the version of the Super-Chief flying in the largest numbers, approximately 1,500 machines of this type currently being registered in the U.S.A. The Model 11AC is powered by the 65 h.p. Continental A-65-8 engine. The 11BC has an 85 h.p. Continental C85.

Max. speed, 100 m.p.h.; cruising, 95 m.p.h.; empty weight, 820 lb.; loaded weight, 1,350 lb.; span, 36 ft. 1 in.; length, 20 ft. 5 in.

AGUSTA P.110   ITALY

The Agusta P.110 four-seat light cabin monoplane was designed by Ing. Ermenegildo Preti. The sole prototype was built by the Centro Volo a Vela (Gliding Centre) of the Milan Polytechnic School, originally being designated C.V.V. P.110 or, alternatively, Preti CP.110. The manufacturing rights of the P.110 were acquired by Construzioni Aeronautiche Giovanni Agusta, and the type was evaluated by the Italian Air Force, but no production orders materialised. The P.110 is of all-wood construction and the enclosed cabin seats four in two pairs.

Max. speed, 170 m.p.h.; cruising, 149 m.p.h.; range, 620 miles; empty weight, 1,500 lb.; loaded, 2,425 lb.; span, 34 ft. 9 in.; length, 23 ft. 11 in.

AGUSTA P.111   ITALY

The Agusta P.111 designed by Ing. Ermenegildo Preti and built in 1951 by Construzioni Aeronautiche Giovanni Agusta, was derived from the P.110 and intended as a three-seat basic trainer and communications monoplane. Differing from its predecessor primarily in having a fixed, tailwheel-type undercarriage in place of the retractable nosewheel-type undercarriage, and a 185 h.p. Lycoming 0-435-1 engine replacing the Alfa 110ter of 145 h.p., the P.111 did not succeed in obtaining production orders, and only a sole prototype is flying.

Max. speed, 136 m.p.h.; cruising, 118 m.p.h.; range, 404 miles; loaded weight, 2,425 lb.; span, 34 ft. 9 in.; length, 24 ft. 3¼ in.; height, 9 ft.

AIRUTILITY AU18-150   U.S.A.

The AU18-150 lightweight twin-engined monoplane has been developed by the AirUtility Cargo Company as a single-seat carrier aircraft, for a variety of detachable pods which can be mounted under the centre section. It is claimed for the AU18-150 that it eliminates the necessity for an operator to possess several types of aircraft: cargo containers, chemical containers and spraying equipment for agricultural purposes, and passenger-carrying or ambulance-type pods, can be attached between the twin fuselage booms. The AU18-150 is powered by two 75 h.p. Continental A-75-8 engines, and a higher-powered model, the AU27-260, will have two 130 h.p. Lycoming 0-290-Ds.

Cruising speed, 125 m.p.h.; initial climb, 850 ft./min.; empty weight, 1,322 lb.; loaded, 2,119 lb.; span, 39 ft. 10½ in.; length, 21 ft. 11 in.

AIRSPEED A.S.6Jc ENVOY III   G.B.

The Envoy was designed in 1933 as a twin-engined successor to the Courier, and what is believed to be the sole remaining airworthy example of this type is an A.S.6Jc Envoy III registered in Sweden. This particular Envoy was originally the famous King's Flight Envoy which, at the outbreak of war, was impressed into the R.A.F., being returned to civilian status in 1946 and sold to Sweden. The Envoy was powered by a variety of engines, but the A.S.6Jc Envoy III flying in Sweden is powered by two 375 h.p. Armstrong Siddeley Cheetah A.S.9 radials.

Max. speed, 203 m.p.h.; cruising, 170 m.p.h.; range, 620 miles; empty weight, 4,340 lb.; loaded, 6,600 lb.; span, 52 ft. 4 in.; length, 34 ft. 0 in.; height, 9 ft. 6 in.

AIRSPEED A.S.10 OXFORD   G.B.

The Oxford was the standard wartime R.A.F. twin-engine trainer, and a total of 8,751 machines of this type were built, 4,961 of these by Airspeed. A number of Oxfords are flying in various parts of the world, and the type is still in service with several air forces for communications and as a twin-engine trainer. That depicted in the accompanying photograph is an Oxford Mk.2 of the Royal Netherlands Air Force. The Oxford Mk.2 differed from the Mk.1 solely in having the dorsal gun turret removed and additional navigational and radio training equipment. Two 355 h.p. A.S. Cheetah 9 or 10 radials.

Max. speed, 188 m.p.h.; climb rate at 6,300 ft., 960 ft./min.; empty weight, 5,380 lb.; loaded, 7,600 lb.; span, 53 ft. 4 in.; length, 34 ft. 6 in.; height, 11 ft. 1 in.

AIRSPEED A.S.65 CONSUL   G.B.

The Consul is a civil conversion of the Oxford trainer of which 8,751 were delivered during the war. Structurally, the Consul is similar to the A.S.10 Oxford, and most Consuls have, in fact, converted Oxford airframes with a new window arrangement, a new nose section to the fuselage and a reset tailplane. The Consul has been produced in various forms; the standard Consul has a crew of two and seats for five or six passengers; the Consul Ambulance carries, in addition to the crew, two stretcher cases and one or two sitting cases, and Consul Convertible has the ambulance door, stretcher supports, freight-lashing points and folding chairs.

Specification: Light transport. Engines: Two 395 h.p. Armstrong Siddeley Cheetah 10. Weights: Empty, 6,047 lb.; loaded, 8,250 lb. Performance: Max. cruising speed, 156 m.p.h.; initial climb rate, 1,180 ft./min.; max. range, 900 miles. Dimensions: Span, 53 ft. 4 in.; length, 35 ft. 4 in.; height, 10 ft. 1½ in.; wing area, 348 sq. ft.

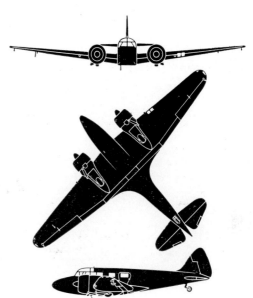

AIRSPEED A.S.57 AMBASSADOR   G.B.

The A.S.57 Ambassador is used exclusively by British European Airways by whom it has been given the Class name Elizabethan. The first of three prototypes flew on July 10, 1947, and these were followed by a production batch of twenty machines. The second prototype Ambassador was employed to air test two 3,780 e.h.p. Bristol Proteus 705 turboprops and has now been re-engined with two 4,400 e.h.p. Rolls-Royce Tyne turboprops. The third prototype has been re-engined with two 3,007 e.h.p. Napier Eland E1.1 turboprops, and plans are being considered to re-engine the remaining 19 Centaurus-Ambassadors with 3,765 e.h.p. Eland E1.4 turboprops.

Specification: Commercial (40–47 seat) transport. Engines: Two 2,625 h.p. Bristol Centaurus 661. Weights: Empty, 36,304 lb.; loaded, 52,500 lb. Performance: (10,600 lb. payload): Normal cruising, 234 m.p.h. at 15,000 ft.; initial climb rate, 1,250 ft./min.; range, 360 miles. Dimensions: Span, 115 ft.; length, 82 ft.; height, 18 ft. 3 in.

ALL AMERICAN 10-A ENSIGN U.S.A.

First flown towards the end of 1945, the Model 10-A Ensign was designed and built by All American Aircraft, Inc., a company previously specialising in sub-contract work for other manufacturers. The Ensign is an all-metal side-by-side two-seat cabin monoplane with a large Plexiglas canopy enclosing the cockpit. Power is provided by an 85 h.p. Continental C85-12 engine, and the nosewheel member of the fixed tricycle gear is steerable. The proposed production version was to have offered dual controls as optional equipment.
Max. speed, 125 m.p.h.; cruising, 110 m.p.h.; initial climb rate, 700 ft./min.; service ceiling, 12,000 ft; range, 400 miles; empty weight, 1,000 lb.; loaded, 1,550 lb.; span, 33 ft.; length, 22 ft.; height, 8 ft. 6 in.; wing area, 138 sq. ft.

A.I.S.A. HM-1B SPAIN

The HM-1 two-seat primary trainer appeared in 1943, powered by a 150 h.p. Hirth H.M.506 engine, and an order for seventy HM-1s powered by the nationally-designed 150 h.p. E.N.M.A. Tigre G-IVB engine was placed by the Spanish Air Ministry after World War II. The HM-1B differs from the original HM-1 in having enclosed tandem cockpits, and the Spanish Air Force designation is EE-4. A twin-float seaplane version, the HM-3, was produced in 1947, and a single-seat, scaled-down model, the HM-5, was also built, but neither version was produced in quantity.

Max. speed, 143 m.p.h.; cruising, 121 m.p.h.; empty weight, 1,364 lb.; loaded, 1,870 lb.; span, 31 ft. 8 in.; length, 25 ft.; height, 7 ft. 2½ in.

A.I.S.A. HM-2 SPAIN

The HM-2 tandem two-seat cabin monoplane was designed by the Instituto Nacional de Tecnica Aeronautica (I.N.T.A.), and the prototype, built and flown by Aeronautica Industrial S.A. in 1945, was powered by a Hirth H.M.506 engine. Subsequent aircraft differ from the prototype in having a cut-down rear fuselage and the nationally-designed 150 h.p. E.N.M.A. Tigre G-IVB engine. The HM-2 features retractable main undercarriage members and is of mixed construction, the wing and tail assemblies of wood and the fuselage of welded steel-tube with fabric covering.
Max. speed, 156.5 m.p.h.; cruising, 140 m.p.h.; empty weight, 1,474 lb.; loaded, 1,980 lb.; span, 31 ft. 8 in.; length, 25 ft.

A.I.S.A. HM-7 SPAIN

The HM-7, like the previously described HM-1B and HM-2, was originally designed by the Instituto Nacional de Tecnica Aeronautica (I.N.T.A.), and was first produced in 1946. The HM-7 is a four-seat touring monoplane powered by a 240 h.p. Argus As 10c engine and possessing a similar structure to that of the HM-1B with wooden wing and tail assembly and welded steel-tube fuselage. The enclosed cabin seats four with automobile-type doors, and full blind-flying equipment is fitted. No production of the HM-7 has been undertaken owing to the lack of a suitable nationally-designed power plant.
Max. speed, 162 m.p.h.; cruising, 118 m.p.h.; empty weight, 1,540 lb.; loaded, 2,640 lb.; span, 33 ft. 5½ in.; length, 25 ft. 9 in.; height, 7 ft.

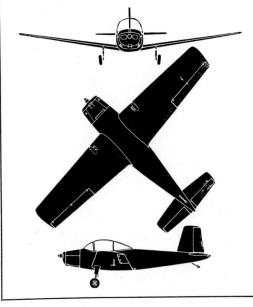

A.I.S.A. I-11B PEQUE SPAIN

Originally designed by Iberavia S.A., the design office of which was taken over by Aeronautica Industrial S.A., the I-11B Peque is being produced in quantity for Spanish aero clubs, production of an initial batch of seventy machines having been inaugurated early in 1954. The I-11B is derived from the I-11 prototype of 1950, which differed from the production model in having a fixed nosewheel undercarriage and a larger cockpit canopy. The I-11B first flew on October 16, 1953.
Specification: Two-seat light touring monoplane and trainer. Engine: One 90 h.p. Continental C90. Weights: Empty, 926 lb.; loaded, 1,422 lb. Performance: Max. speed, 128 m.p.h.; cruising speed, 112 m.p.h.; range, 435 miles. Dimensions: Span, 30 ft. 7¾ in.; length, 21 ft. 2¼ in.; height, 6 ft. 3 in.; wing area, 133.472 sq. ft.

A.I.S.A. I-115   SPAIN

Like the previously-described I-11B, the I-115 was originally designed by Iberavia S.A., and series production is being undertaken by Aeronautica Industrial S.A., a series of two hundred I-115 primary trainers currently being on order for the initial training elements of the Spanish Air Force by whom it is designated E-6. The I-115 is currently replacing the CASA-built Bucker Jungmann primary training biplane.
Specification: Two-seat primary trainer. Engine: One 150 h.p. E.N.M.A. Tigre G-IVB. Weights: Empty, 1,346 lb.; loaded, 1,980 lb. Performance: Max. speed, 149 m.p.h.; cruising speed, 130 m.p.h.; initial climb rate, 790 ft./min.; service ceiling, 14,430 ft.; duration, 3.5 hours. Dimensions: Span, 31 ft. 3 in.; length, 24 ft. 1 in.; height, 6 ft. 10 in.; wing area, 150.6 sq. ft.

A.I.S.A. I-18 (AVD-12)   SPAIN

The I-18, or AVD-12, has been designed by Emile Dewoitine, the exiled French designer, to meet the requirements of a *Ministerio del Aire* specification which, issued in 1953, called for a two/three-seat air observation post and liaison monoplane to replace the elderly Fieseler Fi 156 Storch currently employed by the Spanish Air Force. The specification called for a maximum speed of not less than 109 m.p.h., a minimum speed of not more than 37 m.p.h., and an endurance of 2.5 hours. The A.I.S.A. I-18 was flown for the first time on August 18, 1954.
Specification: Two/three-seat A.O.P. and Liaison. Engine: One 150 h.p. E.N.M.A. Tigre G-IVB. Weights: Empty, 1,322 lb.; max. loaded, 2,314 lb. Performance: Max. speed, 140 m.p.h.; cruising speed, 113 m.p.h.; initial climb rate, 900 ft./min.; service ceiling, 16,400 ft.; range, 479 miles. Dimensions: Span, 36 ft. 5 in.; length, 25 ft. 5 in.; height, 6 ft. 11 in.

ALAPARMA AM-75 BALDO   ITALY

The AM-75 Baldo is one of a series of light planes of the same basic configuration designed by Adriano Mantelli, and built by Alaparma and also, under licence, by the Officina Meccanica Aeronautica. The series has included the single-seat AM-8 (22 h.p. Macchi MB.2) and AM-9 (38 h.p. C.N.A. C.2), the two-seat AM-10 (38 h.p. C.N.A. C.2), AM-65 (65 h.p. Walter Mikron III) and the AM-75 Baldo described here. Adriano Mantelli has also produced versions in Argentina, the Mantelli AM-10 (65 h.p. Continental A65) and AM-11 Albatross (22 h.p. Ambrosini P-25).
Specification: Two-seat cabin monoplane. Engine: One 75 h.p. Praga D. Weights: Empty, 616 lb.; loaded, 1,078 lb. Performance: Max. speed, 135 m.p.h.; cruising speed, 119 m.p.h.; climb to 3,280 ft., 5 minutes; service ceiling, 15,745 ft.; cruising range, 410 miles. Dimensions: Span, 22 ft. 11 in.; length, 16 ft. 4 in.; height, 4 ft. 9 in.; wing area, 91.49 sq. ft.

AMBROSINI S.7   ITALY

The Ambrosini S.7 has been produced in both single and two-seat versions for the Italian Air Force, the latter being designated S.7B. The S.7 is actually a pre-war design which, as the S.A.I.7 and powered by a 280 h.p. Hirth H.M.508D engine, established a 100-km. closed-circuit record for aircraft in category 1. A further development of the basic design is the Super S.7, or Supersette, which is slightly larger than the S.7, and is powered by a 340 b.h.p. De Havilland Gipsy Queen 70-3 engine. The figures quoted in parentheses in the following specification relate to the Super S.7.
Specification: Single- or two-seat basic (advanced) trainer. Engine: One 225 h.p. Alfa 115ter (340 h.p. Gipsy Queen 70-3). Weights: Empty, 2,365 (3,030) lb.; loaded, 3,030 (4,300) lb. Performance: Max. speed, 224 (267) m.p.h.; initial climb rate, 1,103 (985) ft./min. Dimensions: Span, 28 ft. 10 in. (30 ft. 6 in.); length, 26 ft. 10 in.; wing area, 137.8 (148.5) sq. ft.

AMBROSINI RONDONE   ITALY

Designed by Ing. Stelio Frati, the Rondone has been produced in two versions, the two-seat F.4 Rondone I and the three-seat F.7 Rondone II (originally known as the Airone). A batch of ten Rondone I two-seaters was built by S. A. I. Ambrosini, and additional aircraft have been built by Legnami Pasotti & C. Both versions of the Rondone are generally similar externally, and the figures quoted in parentheses in following specification relate to the F.7 Rondone II. Illustrations depict Rondone I.
Specification: Two (three) seat light cabin monoplane. Engine: One 65 h.p. Walter Mikron II (90 h.p. Continental C90). Weights: Empty, 749 (1,124) lb.; loaded, 1,212 (1,742) lb. Performance: Max. speed, 143 (149) m.p.h.; cruising, 124 (130) m.p.h.; range, 466 (385) miles. Dimensions: Span, 28 ft. 2¼ in. (30 ft. 6 in.); length, 20 ft. 2 in. (22 ft. 3½ in.); wing area, 114.097 (142.083) sq. ft.

AMBROSINI S.A.I.2S   ITALY

The Ambrosini industrial group took over the Passignano factory of the Societa Aeronautica Italiana in 1934, and in the following year this concern produced the S.A.I.2 five-seat cabin monoplane for the Littorio Rally and Air Race. Subsequently, the S.A.I.2S four-seat cabin monoplane was developed from the S.A.I.2, and the post-war Grifo and Girfalco were developed directly from this aircraft. The S.A.I.2S, one example of which remains flying in Italy, is powered by a 185 h.p. Alfa 115 engine, and the enclosed cabin seats four in two pairs.

Max. speed, 161 m.p.h.; cruising, 137 m.p.h.; range, 702 miles; empty weight, 1,958 lb.; loaded, 3,124 lb.; span, 34 ft. 11 in.; length, 25 ft. 6 in.; height, 9 ft. 2 in.

AMBROSINI S.1001 GRIFO   ITALY

Derived from the previously-described S.A.I.2S, the S.1001 was produced in two versions; a four-seat tourer powered by the 130 h.p. Alfa 110 and a two-seat military trainer powered by a 145 h.p. D.H. Gipsy Major 10. A further two-seat trainer development, the S.1002 Trasimenus, is essentially a variant of the Grifo with a modified wing featuring increased span (35 ft. 9 in.) and area, and markedly increased dihedral. The fuselage of the Trasimenus is identical to that of the Grifo, and a 130 h.p. Alfa 110ter engine is employed. The following specification refers to the four-seat touring model of the Grifo.

Max. speed, 149 m.p.h.; cruising, 130.5 m.p.h.; empty weight, 1,543 lb.; loaded, 2,340 lb.; span, 32 ft. 5½ in.; length, 25 ft. 7 in.

AMBROSINI (AERFER) SAGITTARIO   ITALY

The Sagittario (Archer) was originally built to provide data for a projected transonic fighter known as the Vindex. Employing the basic fuselage of the Ambrosini Super S.7 married to a new 45° swept wing and swept tail surfaces, the Sagittario first flew on January 5, 1953 powered by an 836 lb. thrust Turboméca Marboré II turbojet. Development has been undertaken by the Aerfer concern, and three prototypes of a further development, the Ariete (Battering Ram), powered by the Rolls-Royce Derwent 9 turbojet, with a Rolls-Royce Soar turbojet for power-boosting, are currently under construction as light fighters.

Max. speed, 348 m.p.h. at 13,123 ft.; range, 354 miles; loaded weight, 5,070 lb.; span, 24 ft. 7 in.; length, 30 ft. 7 in.; wing area, 157.15 sq. ft.

ANDERSON GREENWOOD AG-14   U.S.A.

The Anderson Greenwood AG-14 two-seat light cabin monoplane was flown for the first time on October 1, 1947, and a production prototype flew on June 1, 1950, an Approved Type Certificate being granted on September 21, 1950. Four further aircraft of this type were built, but production of the AG-14 was suspended at the end of 1950 in order to give priority to sub-contract work. The AG-14 is powered by a 90 h.p. Continental C90 engine driving a pusher airscrew between the tail booms. The cabin seats two side-by-side with dual controls and construction is all-metal.

Max. speed, 120 m.p.h.; cruising, 110 m.p.h.; initial climb, 700 ft./min.; empty weight, 850 lb.; loaded, 1,400 lb.; span, 34 ft. 7 in.; length, 22 ft.; height, 7 ft. 9 in.; wing area, 120 sq. ft.

ANTONOV AN-2 KOLCHOSNIK   U.S.S.R.

The AN-2 Kolchosnik (code-named *Colt*), designed by Oleg K. Antonov, was conceived in 1947 as a rugged utility transport for use over rough terrain, and flew for the first time in 1950. In December 1953, an AN-2 established a new F.A.I. record for altitude (3,000–4,500 kg. weight category) by attaining 33,769.6 ft., further increasing the record in June 1954, by attaining 36,902 ft. Both civil and military versions are in service, the former carrying twelve passengers or 3,100 lb. freight, and the latter carrying fourteen paratroops. A twin-float seaplane variant is also in service.
Specification: Utility transport. Engine: One 760 h.p. ASh-21 or 1,000 h.p. ASh-62-IR. Weights: Loaded, 11,000 lb. Performance (ASh-62-IR): Max. speed, 137 m.p.h. at 6,890 ft.; cruising speed, 91 m.p.h.; normal range, 670 miles; ceiling, 27,890 ft. Dimensions: Span, 54 ft. 1½ in.; length, 35 ft. 3 in.

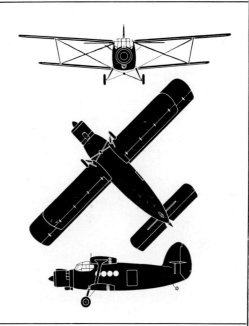

ARADO AR 79B   GERMANY

First produced in 1937 by the Arado Flugzeugwerke G.m.b.H., the Ar 79 two-seat light cabin monoplane established several international light aeroplane records prior to the war, and was later employed by the Luftwaffe for liaison and communications duties. An example of the Ar 79B is registered in the Saar, this particular aeroplane having been built in 1941. Powered by a 105 h.p. Hirth H.M.500-A1 engine, the Ar 79B seats two side-by-side with dual controls, and is of mixed wood and steel-tube construction.

Max. speed, 143 m.p.h. at sea level; cruising, 127 m.p.h.; range, 636 miles; initial climb rate, 1,020 ft./min.; empty weight, 1,014 lb.; loaded, 1,675 lb.; span, 32 ft. 9½ in.; length, 25 ft.; height, 6 ft. 10½ in.

ARADO AR 96B (C.2B-1)   GERMANY

The Ar 96B two-seat advanced trainer was adopted by the *Luftwaffe* in 1940 and, during the war years, production of this aircraft was transferred to the Letov and Avia plants in Czechoslovakia where manufacture of the type continued until the end of 1948 under the designation C.2B-1 (see *photograph*). The C.2B-1 remains a standard basic trainer in the Czechoslovak Air Force and National Security Guard, and one Czech-built Ar 96B is currently registered in Sweden. The Ar 96B is powered by a 465 h.p. Argus As 410A engine, and carries instructor and pupil in tandem enclosed cockpits.

Max. speed, 219 m.p.h.; cruising speed, 175 m.p.h.; range, 428 miles; empty weight, 2,854 lb.; loaded, 3,747 lb.; span, 35 ft. 11½ in.; length, 29 ft. 11¼ in.; height, 8 ft. 6 in.; wing area, 186.22 sq. ft.

ARMSTRONG WHITWORTH A.W.52   G.B.

The A.W.52 was designed as a research machine to determine the characteristics of large tailless aircraft and to provide data for a projected six-jet high-speed transport of generally similar configuration. Powered by two 5,000 lb. thrust Rolls-Royce Nene turbojets, the first A.W.52 flew on November 13, 1947. A second prototype, powered by Rolls-Royce Derwents, was destroyed early in its flight test programme. The A.W.52 carries a crew of two and achieves longitudinal and lateral control by means of elevons hinged on each outer wing section. Directional control of yaw is attained with wingtip fins and rudders.
Max. speed, 500 m.p.h.; max. range, 2,130 miles; initial climb rate, 4,800 ft./min.; empty weight, 19,662 lb.; loaded, 34,154 lb.; span, 90 ft.; length, 37 ft. 4 in.

ARMSTRONG WHITWORTH A.W.55   G.B.

Designed as a 26-31 passenger medium-stage airliner, the A.W.55 Apollo was the second turboprop-powered commercial aircraft to fly. The first of two prototypes, powered by four 1,135 e.h.p. A.S. Mamba A.S. Ma.1 turboprops, flew on April 10, 1949, and was followed on December 12, 1952 by a second prototype which incorporated detail modifications and was powered by four 1,475 e.h.p. Mamba A.S.Ma.3 turboprops. No production of the Apollo was undertaken, and the two prototypes are used for research by the Ministry of Supply. The following specification relates to the higher-powered second prototype.
Max. cruising speed, 310 m.p.h. at 25,000 ft.; range, 1,130 miles at 280 m.p.h. at 25,000 ft. with 7,500 lb. payload; loaded weight, 47,000 lb.; span, 92 ft.; length, 71 ft. 5½ in.; height, 26 ft.; wing area, 986 sq. ft.

AUBERT PA-204S SUPER-CIGALE   FRANCE

The PA-204S Super-Cigale four-seater is essentially a modification of the PA-20 Cigale two-seat trainer of 1938. The prototype PA-20 was destroyed during the German occupation, and a revised post-war development was designated PA-201 and powered by a 140 h.p. Renault 4 Pei. A four-seater development, the PA-204 Cigale-Major, flew on April 21, 1947, and this was externally similar to its predecessor. The second of two Cigale-Major prototypes (*see photo*) was fitted with a 170 h.p. SNECMA-Régnier 4LO-2 engine in June 1955 and redesignated PA-204S Super-Cigale, and a further version is the PA-204L Cigale with a 150 h.p. Lycoming 0-320, which flew on July 27, 1955.
PA-204S: Max. speed, 155 m.p.h.; cruising, 141 m.p.h.; empty weight, 1,499 lb.; loaded, 2,645 lb.; span, 32 ft. 9 in.; length, 25 ft. 3 in.

AUSTER PLUS MODEL D   G.B.

Produced early in 1940 by Taylorcraft Aeroplanes (England) Ltd., which changed its name to Auster Aircraft Ltd. in 1946, the Plus Model D was a licence-built version of the U.S. Taylorcraft light aeroplane with a 90 h.p. Cirrus Minor engine. Eight Plus Ds were built and used for A.O.P. trials, and the success of these resulted in the placing of an order for one hundred Plus Model D/1s, or Auster 1s, which was a fully militarised version of the original Plus D. Several Plus D and D/1 aircraft are flying, including two in Switzerland, as civilianised two-seaters. The following specification refers to the Plus Model D/1, or Auster 1 of 1941.
Max. speed, 125 m.p.h.; cruising, 107 m.p.h.; initial climb, 1,000 ft./min.; empty weight, 850 lb.; loaded, 1,400 lb.; span, 36 ft.; length, 22 ft. 11 in.

AUSTER (MODEL J) 5   G.B.

The Auster 5 is a three-seat civil conversion of the (Model J) A.O.P.5, 790 of which type were produced during the war years. The Auster 5 (*photo*) retains the 130 h.p. Lycoming 0-290-3/1 engine as does also the Auster 5A four-seat conversion, but the Auster 5D has this engine replaced by a 130 h.p. D.H. Gipsy Major and revised tail. The sole Auster 5C (currently flying in New Zealand) was a special conversion with a 145 h.p. Gipsy Major 1 for the 1950 King's Cup Race. The Auster 5 should not be confused with the Auster J/5. Subsequent to the appearance of an Auster 5A and J/5A alphabetical sub-variants of the two types were integrated. Consequently, there is no J/5C or D.
Max. speed, 130 m.p.h.; cruising, 112 m.p.h.; empty weight, 1,050 lb.; loaded, 1,850 lb.; span, 36 ft.; length, 22 ft. 5 in.; height, 6 ft. 8 in.

AUSTER MODEL B.4   G.B.

Built as a private venture, the Auster B.4 appeared in September 1951, and was intended for both civil and military roles. Following initial flight trials a number of modifications were incorporated in the prototype, the most noticeable external change being a revision of the vertical tail-surface contours. The projected production model of the B.4 was to have had the 180 h.p. Cirrus Bombardier 702 engine replaced by a 190 h.p. Bombardier 203 and seven per cent more wing area than the prototype. The following specification refers to the prototype illustrated here.
Max. speed, 121 m.p.h. at 1,000 ft.; max. cruising, 103 m.p.h.; initial climb rate, 670 ft./min.; range, 280 miles; empty weight, 1,730 lb.; loaded, 2,700 lb.; span, 24 ft. 8 in.; length, 37 ft.; height, 8 ft. 4½ in.

AUSTER MODEL J/2 ARROW G.B.

Produced in 1946, the J/2 Arrow two-seater is a scaled-down Autocrat with a 75 h.p. Continental C-75-12 engine, but two special Arrows flying in Rhodesia have 185 h.p. Continental E185-1 engines. A development of the Arrow, the J/3 Atom, was powered by the 65 h.p. Continental C65, but only two Model J/3s and one modified Model J/3A were completed. The Arrow differs externally from the Autocrat primarily in having a shorter fuselage, less window area, and cylinder heads projecting from the engine cowling. The cabin has side-by-side seating and no wing flaps are fitted.

Max. speed, 98 m.p.h.; cruising, 87 m.p.h.; initial climb rate, 430 ft./min.; empty weight, 872 lb.; loaded, 1,450 lb.; span, 36 ft.; length, 22 ft. 9 in.; height, 6 ft. 6 in.

AUSTER J/4 G.B.

The Auster J/4 is similar to the J/2 Arrow except that it is fitted with a 90 h.p. Blackburn Cirrus Minor 1 engine, the engine cowling reverting in shape to that of the Autocrat. The fuselage and wings of both types are identical, and the J/4, which was designed chiefly for operation in the United Kingdom by flying clubs and private owners, was built in some numbers. Like the Arrow, the J/4 provides accommodation for two seated side-by-side, and the Cirrus Minor engine provides the J/4 with a considerably improved performance.

Max. speed, 108 m.p.h.; cruising speed, 92 m.p.h.; initial climb rate, 746 ft./min.; range, 317 miles; empty weight, 955 lb.; loaded, 1,600 lb.; span, 36 ft.; length, 22 ft. 5¾ in.; height, 6 ft. 6 in.; wing area, 185 sq. ft.

AUSTER A.O.P.6 G.B.

The first post-war development of the wartime series of Auster air observation posts was the A.O.P.6 derived from the Lycoming-powered A.O.P.5, having a strengthened rear fuselage, increased all-up weight and power. During the several years in which production of the A.O.P.6 was undertaken, 296 machines were supplied to the R.A.F. and Belgian Air Force, and thirty-six of a modified variant were supplied to the R.C.A.F. An essentially similar machine is the T.7 two-seat trainer. The A.O.P.6 and T.7 differ internally only, the T.7 having side-by-side seating for pupil and instructor.

Specification: Two-seat air observation post. Engine: One 145 h.p. De Havilland Gipsy Major VII. Weights: Empty, 1,413 lb.; loaded, 2,160 lb. Performance: Max. speed, 124 m.p.h.; cruising, 108 m.p.h.; initial climb rate, 810 ft./min. Dimensions: Span, 36 ft.; length, 23 ft. 9 in.; height, 8 ft. 4½ in.; wing area, 184 sq. ft.

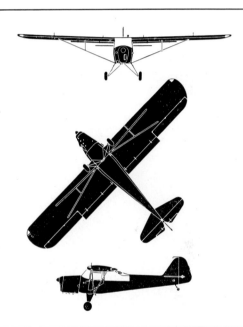

AUSTER A.O.P.9 G.B.

Ordered by the British Army for air observation post duties, the A.O.P.9 differs from earlier production Auster air observation posts in utilising an all-metal wing and various refinements. It has been developed from the private venture Model S which was the first A.O.P. to use the Cirrus Bombardier engine. The structure of the Model S was basically that of the earlier A.O.P.6, and the A.O.P.9 differs mainly in having a large 'blister' cockpit canopy, single wing struts superseding the earlier V-type struts, and the metal Fairey-Reed fixed-pitch airscrew which gives increased thrust for take-off.

Specification: Three-seat air observation post. Engine: One 185 h.p. Blackburn Cirrus Bombardier 203. Weights: Empty, 1,461 lb.; loaded, 2,050 lb. Performance: Max. speed, 127 m.p.h.; cruising speed, 110 m.p.h.; initial climb rate, 920 ft./min.; absolute ceiling, 18,500 ft.; range, 242 miles. Dimensions: Span, 36 ft. 5 in.; length, 23 ft. 8½ in.; height, 8 ft. 11 in.; wing area, 197.6 sq. ft.

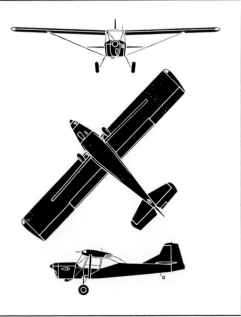

B

AUSTER MODEL J/1 AUTOCRAT   G.B.

The Autocrat was the first post-war civil light plane built by Auster Aircraft Ltd. which company was founded in November 1938, as Taylorcraft Aeroplanes (England) Ltd., changing its name in March 1946. Derived from the two-seat Plus Model D of 1940, the Autocrat was built in quantity and several hundred are in service in various parts of the world. During 1949, a four-seat Autocrat, the J/1A, was produced, and a further development, the J/5 (sometimes referred to as the Adventurer), was produced for use in Australasia and differs in having a 130 h.p. Gipsy Major 1 engine.
Specification: Three-seat cabin monoplane. Engine: One 90 h.p. Blackburn Cirrus Minor 2. Weights: Empty, 1,052 lb.; loaded, 1,850 lb. Performance: Max. speed, 120 m.p.h.; cruising, 100 m.p.h.; ceiling, 15,000 ft.; normal range, 320 miles. Dimensions: Span, 36 ft.; length, 23 ft. 5 in.; height, 6 ft. 6 in.; wing area, 185 sq. ft.

AUSTER MODEL J/5B AUTOCAR   G.B.

A four-seater developed from the J/5 Autocrat, the J/5B Autocar was first flown in August 1949. Three versions have been produced; the J/5B with a 130 h.p. Gipsy Major 1 which was followed in 1952 by the J/5G and J/5H models powered by the 155 h.p. Cirrus Major 3 and the 150 h.p. Cirrus Major 2 respectively. The wing of the Autocar is similar to that of the Autocrat but the fin and rudder assembly has been enlarged and the rear fuselage width has been increased by eight inches.
Specification: (Figures quoted in parentheses refer to the J/5G and H) Four-seat cabin monoplane. Engine: One 130 h.p. Gipsy Major 1. Weights: Empty, 1,413 (1,367) lb.; loaded, 2,400 (2,450) lb. Performance: Max. speed, 116 (127) m.p.h.; cruising, 100 (110) m.p.h.; service ceiling, 11,000 (14,000) ft.; initial climb rate, 525 (710) ft./min.; normal range, 500 (485) miles. Dimensions: Span, 36 ft.; length, 23 ft. 2 in.; height, 7 ft. 6 in.; wing area, 185 sq. ft.

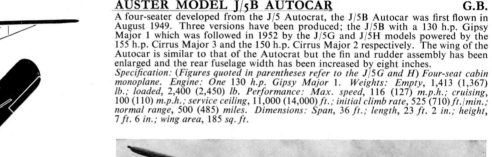

AUSTER J/5F AIGLET TRAINER   G.B.

The first version of the Aiglet, the Model J/1B, appeared in 1949 and was essentially a modified Autocrat with a redesigned fin and rudder assembly and a Gipsy Major engine. In 1951 a two-seat dual-control aerobatic trainer version, the J/5F, made its début. The airframe is basically that of the J/1B, but horn-balanced rudder and elevators are fitted, wing span has been reduced from 36 ft. to 32 ft., and fuselage width has been increased by four inches. The J/5F is also in use as a three-seat tourer, and Aiglet trainers are used by various foreign air forces.
Specification: Two-seat dual-control trainer. Engine: One 130 h.p. De Havilland Gipsy Major 1. Weights: Empty, 1,323 lb.; loaded (for aerobatics), 1,950 lb. Performance: Max. speed, 125 m.p.h.; cruising speed, 107 m.p.h.; initial climb rate, 650 ft./min.; service ceiling, 12,500 ft.; cruising range, 500 miles. Dimensions: Span, 32 ft.; length, 23 ft. 2 in.; height, 6 ft. 6 in.; wing area, 164 sq. ft.

AVIA C.210   CZECHOSLOVAKIA

The C.210 single-seat fighter was built during the early post-war years by the former Avia factory for the Czech Air Force, and remains in service in small numbers with the Czech National Security Guard as an advanced trainer. Derived from the Daimler-Benz-powered Messerschmitt Me 109G-14 and comparable with the Me 109K-16, the C.210 is powered by a 1,340 h.p. Junkers Jumo 211F engine. The Me 109G-14 was built in Czechoslovakia as the C.10 and, in two-seat trainer form, as the C.110. A number of C.210 fighters were exported to Israel but have now been withdrawn from service.

Max. speed, 432 m.p.h.; range, 350 miles; normal loaded weight, 7,800 lb.; span, 32 ft. 6½ in.; length, 29 ft. 6 in.; height, 12 ft.

AVIA LD-40   CZECHOSLOVAKIA

The Avia LD-40, designed and built by the former Avia factory of the Czechoslovak nationalised aircraft industry in 1954, is a four-seat cabin monoplane of all-metal construction and powered by a 105 h.p. Walter Minor 4-III engine. An interesting feature of this aircraft is the use of a "reverse tricycle" undercarriage, the normal nosewheel being replaced by a wheel mounted immediately aft of the wing trailing edge. The main wheels are mounted well forward below the wing and, on the ground, the Avia LD-40 remains in flying attitude. The LD-40 accommodates four people on two side-by-side bench-type seats, and the cockpit canopy slides backwards. The metal construction of the LD-40 is designed for ease of manufacture. No details of the weights, dimensions, performance, etc., are available at the time of writing.

AVIA L.60 BRIGADYR   CZECHOSLOVAKIA

The L.60 Brigadyr has been designed for use as an agricultural aircraft and for glider towing, and is being produced in quantity by the former Avia factory. The Brigadyr is powered by a 210 h.p. Praga Doris B engine, and each wing carries a full-span one-piece leading-edge slat, and double-slotted flaps are fitted between the cabin and the ailerons. These provide the Brigadyr with a minimum speed of 34 m.p.h. For agricultural spraying, a 77-gall. tank may be fitted behind the pilot. For dusting, the load is approximately 700 pounds.

Max. speed, 121 m.p.h.; max. continuous, 110–116 m.p.h.; range, 435 miles at 3,280 ft.; service ceiling, 17,390 ft.; empty weight, 1,896 lb.; loaded, 3,020 lb.; span, 45 ft. 10 in.; length, 28 ft.; height, 8 ft. 10 in.; wing area, 261 sq. ft.

AVRO TYPE 594 AVIAN IVM   G.B.

Originally designed for the 1926 Light Aeroplane Competition at Lympne, the Avian was developed in a variety of versions, but the only known airworthy example remaining is an Avian IVM in New Zealand. The Type 594 Avian IVM was a metallised version produced in 1930, the fuselage being made of welded steel-tube with plywood decking and spruce stringers. Various engines were fitted, but that flying in New Zealand is powered by a 120 h.p. de Havilland Gipsy II. Production of the Avian continued until 1932 when a total of ninety-nine were registered in Great Britain.

Max. speed, 105 m.p.h.; cruising, 90 m.p.h.; empty weight, 1,005 lb.; loaded, 1,523 lb.; span, 28 ft.; length, 24 ft. 3 in.; height, 8 ft. 6 in.

AVRO TYPE 621 TUTOR   G.B.

The Type 621 Tutor was designed in 1929 as a replacement for the famous Type 504, and several hundred Tutors were built for the R.A.F. and several foreign governments. The Tutor is a single-bay biplane of metal construction with fabric covering and powered by a 215 h.p. Armstrong Siddeley Lynx IVc radial. Several examples are flying. That illustrated is a former R.A.F. machine from the large 1932 production batch, and two examples are flying in Australia. The Type 626 Prefect is a generally similar aircraft powered by a 285 h.p. A.S. Cheetah 5a radial and differing from the Tutor in having a third cockpit. One Type 626 Prefect is flying in New Zealand.
Max. speed, 122 m.p.h.; cruising, 102 m.p.h.; empty weight, 1,800 lb.; loaded, 2,458 lb.; span, 34 ft.; length, 26 ft. 6 in.; height, 9 ft. 7 in.

AVRO TYPE 638 CLUB CADET   G.B.

The Type 638 Club Cadet and the basically similar Type 643 Cadet were produced in some numbers in the early 'thirties. Both types have identical wings, undercarriage and tail unit, but the wings of the Cadet have more stagger than those of the Club Cadet in order to provide improved view from both cockpits. Two Club Cadets are airworthy in the U.K. That illustrated here is powered by a 130 h.p. D.H. Gipsy Major 1, the other is powered by a 135 h.p. A.S. Genet Major radial. Six similarly-powered Cadets are flying in Australia. The following specification relates to the Genet Major 1A-powered Club Cadet.

Max. speed, 115 m.p.h.; cruising, 100 m.p.h.; empty weight, 1,222 lb.; loaded, 1,757 lb.; span, 30 ft.; length, 24 ft. 9 in.; height, 8 ft. 6 in.

AVRO TYPE 652A ANSON C.10   G.B.

One of the very few types of aircraft in production before the outbreak of World War 2 to continue in production after the cessation of hostilities, the type 652A Anson made its service debut in 1936 as a reconnaissance bomber, and the 11,020th and last Anson was delivered on May 27, 1952. The Anson 1 was converted for navigation and armament training early in the war, and from this version has been developed a long series of Anson trainers. The Israeli Air Force Anson 10 (*illustrated here*) is typical of the Mks.1 to 10, and is powered by two 320 h.p. Armstrong Siddeley Cheetah 9 radials.

Max. speed, 188 m.p.h.; cruising, 158 m.p.h.; empty weight, 6,510 lb.; loaded, 9,450 lb.; span, 56 ft. 6 in.; length, 42 ft. 3 in.

AVRO (FEDERAL) ANSON 5   (CANADA) G.B.

The Anson 5, built during the war years by Federal Aircraft Ltd. in Canada, differs in many respects from British-built Ansons. Featuring a Vidal moulded veneer fuselage and two 450 h.p. Pratt & Whitney R-985 AN-12B or 14B supercharged radials, production of the Anson 5 commenced in 1942 as a navigational trainer for the R.C.A.F. The Anson 6 was similar but equipped as a gunnery trainer, and 1,050 Mks. 5 and 6 were built. Many Anson 5s have been converted for use as light civil transports, and numerous such conversions are flying in North America.

Max. speed, 194 m.p.h. at 3,500 ft.; cruising, 150 m.p.h.; normal range, 650 miles; empty weight, 6,750 lb.; loaded, 9,450 lb.; span, 56 ft. 6 in.; length, 42 ft. 3 in.; height, 13 ft. 1 in.; wing area, 463 sq. ft.

AVRO TYPE 652A ANSON (MKS.18-20)   G.B.

The post-war series of Anson trainers and transports all possess the raised cabin roof first introduced on the wartime Anson C.11, and the majority of these aircraft now flying have metal wings and tailplane. The Anson 18 communications aircraft for the Royal Afghan Air Force, and the 18C civil radio/navigational trainers for India are similar to the all-metal Anson C.19 (*silhouette*). Of the 326 Mk.19 Ansons built, 143 had wooden wings and tail unit, and the remaining aircraft were all-metal. The T.20 (*photo*) is a navigational trainer version for Southern Rhodesia, and the T.21 and T.22 are R.A.F. navigational and radio trainers respectively.

Specification (T.21 and T.22): Radio/navigational trainer. Engines: Two 420 h.p. Armstrong Siddeley Cheetah 15. Weights: Empty, 7,766 lb.; loaded, 10,306 lb. Performance: Max. speed, 171 m.p.h. at 5,000 ft.; initial climb rate, 700 ft./min. Dimensions: Span, 57 ft. 6 in.; length, 42 ft. 3 in.; height, 13 ft. 10 in.; wing area, 440 sq. ft.

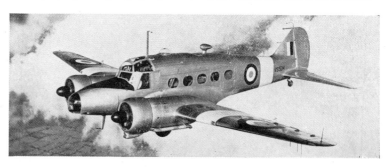

AVRO TYPE 683 LANCASTER 10-MR   (CANADA) G.B.

The Lancaster 10-MR is one of several variants of the Canadian-built Lancaster bomber currently serving with the R.C.A.F. The basic production aircraft built by Victory Aircraft in Canada was the Lancaster 10-B. Eight were converted for photo-reconnaissance as Lancaster 10-Ps in 1948, and others were converted to Lancaster 10-ASR (Air-sea rescue) and 10-BR (Bomber-reconnaissance) during 1949–50. The Lancaster 10-MR maritime reconnaissance aircraft succeeded the 10-BR, the first conversion flying on December 29, 1950. Fifty-four Lancaster B.1s and B.7s have been modified as maritime reconnaissance aircraft for French Navy.

Specification: Maritime reconnaissance bomber. Engines: Four 1,620 h.p. Packard-built Rolls-Royce Merlin 224. Weights: Empty, 41,000 lb.; loaded, 68,000 lb. Performance: Max. speed, 250 m.p.h.; cruising, 216 m.p.h.; range, 2,250 miles. Dimensions: Span, 102 ft.; length, 68 ft. 10 in.; height, 20 ft.; wing area, 1,297 sq. ft.

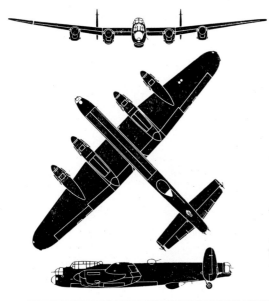

AVRO TYPE 685 YORK   G.B.

The York transport was developed from the Lancaster bomber as an interim type pending the introduction of newer designs intended from the outset for transport duties. First delivered in 1942, the York utilised many major components of the Lancaster, and production terminated in April 1948, by which time a total of 253 Yorks had been built. Numerous war surplus York transports have been sold abroad, and many post-war commercial freighters are also in service. The York is powered by four 1,620 h.p. Rolls-Royce Merlin 24 engines.

Max. speed, 306 m.p.h. at 10,800 ft.; cruising, 203 m.p.h. at sea level; initial climb rate, 1,500 ft./min.; empty weight, 39,458 lb.; loaded, 71,000 lb.; span, 102 ft.; length, 76 ft. 10 in.; height, 17 ft. 10 in.

AVRO TYPE 688 TUDOR 4B   G.B.

Designed originally for operation by B.O.A.C. and the now defunct B.S.A.A., the Tudor suffered numerous set-backs and was eventually withdrawn from service. A variety of versions of the Tudor were developed of which, at the time of writing, only a single Tudor Mk.1 and two Tudor 4B freighters have certificates of airworthiness. These are owned by Air Charter Ltd. One Tudor 4B has been adapted to have double freight-loading doors by Aviation Traders, in which form it is known as the Super Trader. The Tudor 4B is generally similar to the Tudor 1 except in having a 6 ft. increase in fuselage length. The Tudor 4B has 1,810 h.p. Rolls-Royce Merlin 623 engines.

Max. speed, 340 m.p.h.; cruising, 305 m.p.h.; loaded weight, 82,000 lb.; range, 2,800 miles; span, 120 ft.; length, 85 ft. 6 in.; height, 24 ft. 3 in.

AVRO TYPE 694 LINCOLN B.30   G.B.

The Lincoln B.30 is an Australian-built version of the Type 694 Lincoln for the R.A.A.F. The first five Lincoln B.30s were assembled largely from imported British components, the first flying on March 17, 1946, but a further sixty-eight machines were completely built in Australia, and these are now employed for maritime reconnaissance duties, a number being fitted with a lengthened nose (*see photo*) to accommodate two additional crew members and search radar. This increases fuselage length by 6 ft. The Lincoln B.30 has four Commonwealth-built Merlin 102 engines. Twenty Lincolns were purchased by Argentina in 1947, and others are used as power plant test beds.

Max. speed, 290 m.p.h.; cruising, 230 m.p.h.; range, 3,500 miles; loaded weight, 82,000 lb.; span, 120 ft.; length, 84 ft. 3½ in.; height, 17 ft. 3½ in.

AVRO TYPE 696 SHACKLETON M.R.1   G.B.

The Shackleton M.R.1 general reconnaissance bomber flew for the first time on March 9, 1949. Designed to meet specification B.5/46, the Shackleton has been developed from the Lincoln bomber and, in fact, began life as the Lincoln A.S.R.3. Using substantially the same wing and undercarriage as the Lincoln, the Shackleton M.R.1 has a completely new fuselage and tail assembly. The radar scanner is contained in a perspex "chin" housing, and the four 2,450 h.p. Rolls-Royce Griffon 57 engines drive six-blade contra-rotating airscrews. The Shackleton M.R.1 differs substantially in appearance from its successors, the M.R.2 and M.R.3. No details are available for publication, apart from the overall dimensions.

Span, 120 ft.; length, 77 ft. 6 in.; height, 17 ft. 6 in.

AVRO TYPE 696 SHACKLETON M.R.3   G.B.

The Shackleton M.R.2 and M.R.3 are progressive developments of the earlier M.R.1., differing primarily in having lengthened, cleaner fuselages and retractable ventral radomes. The Shackleton M.R.3 followed on the production line after the completion of the last Shackleton M.R.2 from which it differs primarily in having a nosewheel undercarriage, wingtip fuel tanks and revised cockpit canopy. The Shackleton M.R.3 has been ordered by the South African Air Force in addition to R.A.F. Coastal Command.

Specification: Overseas general-reconnaissance bomber. Engines: Four 2,450 h.p. Rolls-Royce Griffon 57. Weights and performance: No details available for publication. Dimensions (M.R.2): Span, 120 ft.; length, 87 ft. 4 in.; height, 16 ft. 9 in.: wing area, 1,421 sq. ft.

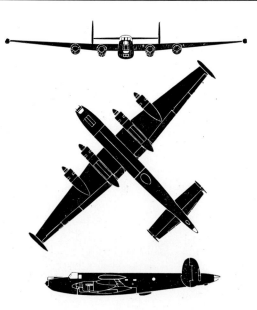

AVRO TYPE 698 VULCAN B.1 G.B.

Currently the world's largest delta-wing aircraft, the Type 698 Vulcan B.1 long-range medium bomber will enter service with R.A.F. Bomber Command during 1956. The first prototype Vulcan flew on August 30, 1952, powered by four 6,500 lb. thrust Rolls-Royce Avon R.A.3 turbojets. These were later replaced by four 8,000 lb. thrust Armstrong Siddeley Sapphires, and the second prototype flew on September 3, 1953, powered by four Bristol Olympus turbojets. Production Vulcans, the first of which were delivered in 1955, are powered by the latter turbojet, and these are possibly of the 11,000 lb. thrust Olympus 101 type. While no performance details of the Vulcan may be published, it may be assumed that, fully laden (between 120,000–150,000 lb.), the Vulcan B.1 will cruise at speeds above Mach 0.9 at altitudes up to 60,000 ft.
Specification: Long-range medium bomber. Engines: Four 11,000 lb. thrust (approx.) Bristol Olympus. Dimensions: Span, 99 ft.; length, 97 ft. 1 in.; height, 26 ft. 6 in.

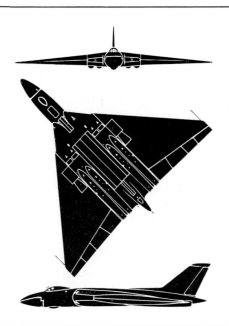

AVRO TYPE 701 ATHENA T.2 G.B.

The Avro Athena was originally designed to meet the requirements of specification T.7/45, calling for a three-seat advanced trainer powered by a turboprop. Two turboprop versions of the Athena were developed, the Athena T.1 with a 1,135 e.s.h.p. A.S. Mamba A.S.Ma.1, and the Athena T.1A with a 1,125 e.s.h.p. R.R.Dart R.Da.1. The design was then modified to meet specification T.14/47, and seventeen pre-production Athena T.2s were built, powered by the 1,280 h.p. Rolls-Royce Merlin 35. These eventually entered service as gunnery trainers at the R.A.F. Flying College, Manby, and no further production of the Athena was undertaken.
Max. speed, 297 m.p.h.; max. cruising, 276 m.p.h.; empty weight, 6,611 lb.; loaded, 8,213 lb.; span, 40 ft.; length, 37 ft. 3½ in.; height, 12 ft. 11 in.

AVRO TYPE 707 G.B.

The Type 707 was originally built as a low-speed third-scale model of the Type 698 Vulcan medium bomber, and the first prototype flew on September 4, 1949, but was destroyed during early flight testing. A second, modified aircraft, the Type 707B, flew on September 6, 1950, being followed by two Type 707As which differed primarily in having the "saddle-back" air intakes of the Types 707 and 707B replaced by wing root intakes. In July 1953, a further version, the Type 707C (*photo*) was flown. This was generally similar to the "A" but a broader, two-seat cockpit replaced the single-seat cockpit of the earlier models. The Type 707C is powered by a 3,600 lb. thrust Derwent turbojet and weighs approximately 10,000 lb. loaded.
Span, 34 ft. 2 in.; length, 42 ft. 4 in.; height, 11 ft. 7 in.

AVRO TYPE 711 ASHTON G.B.

The design of the Type 711 Ashton research aircraft was adapted from the piston-engined Tudor 2 airframe, and six machines of this type have been built to the order of the Ministry of Supply, the first flying on September 1, 1950. Powered by four 5,000 lb. thrust Rolls-Royce Nene 5 and 6 turbojets, four marks of Ashton were produced: the Mk.1 for high-altitude turbojet research, the Mk. 2 for high-altitude air conditioning tests, the Mk.3 with ventral radome and bomb containers outboard of the engine nacelles for bomb sight development, and the Mk.4 for instrument development. One of the three Mk.3s is used as a Bristol Olympus test-bed.
(Mk.1) max. speed, 439 m.p.h.; cruising, 406 m.p.h.; loaded weight, 72,000 lb.; span, 120 ft.; length, 89 ft. 6½ in.; height, 31 ft. 3 in.

AVRO CANADA C.102 JETLINER CANADA

Design work on the C.102 Jetliner was commenced in the summer of 1946 and it was initially proposed to employ two Rolls-Royce Avon turbojets, but in the autumn of 1947, when it became apparent that these units would not be available for installation, the design was modified to accommodate four 3,600 lb. thrust Rolls-Royce Derwent 5 turbojets, and in this form the Jetliner flew for the first time on August 10, 1949. The Jetliner was designed to operate over stage-lengths of the order of 1,100 miles with a maximum of fifty passengers, but no production was undertaken.
Max. cruising speed, 458 m.p.h. at 30,000 ft.; normal cruising, 403 m.p.h.; normal initial climb rate, 1,595 ft./min.; range, 1,250 miles; span, 98 ft. 1 in.; length, 82 ft. 9 in.; height, 26 ft. 5½ in.

AVRO CANADA CF-100 MK.4B   CANADA

Derived from the CF-100 Mk.3, the Mk.4 differs from its predecessor in having APG 40 radar in place of the earlier APG 33, and the eight 0.5-in. guns in a ventral tray supplemented by fifty-eight Mighty Mouse missiles in wingtip pods. In addition, the CF-100 Mk.4 has been extensively modified structurally, and has higher-powered turbojets. The prototype Mk.4 flew on October 11, 1952, and the first of 510 production machines, the Mk.4A with 6,500 lb. thrust Orenda 9s, flew on October 24, 1953. The improved final production version is designated CF-100 Mk.4C.
Specification: Two-seat all-weather fighter. Engines: Two 7,000 lb. thrust Avro Orenda Mk. 11. Weights: Empty, 24,408 lb.; normal loaded, 37,000 lb.; max. 39,750 lb. Approx. performance: Max. speed, 650 m.p.h.; initial climb rate, 10,000 ft./min.; normal range, 1,300 miles; max. range, 1,700 miles. Dimensions: Span, 52 ft.; length 54 ft. 2 in.; height, 15 ft. 6½ in.; wing area, 540 sq. ft.

AZCARATE   MEXICO

Built in 1930 by Juan F. Azcarate S.A., this two-seat reconnaissance and training sesquiplane was built in quantity for the Mexican Air Force, and several squadrons were equipped with this type until the mid 'forties. Several still serve with the Mexican School of Military Aviation. The Azcarate is powered by a 220 h.p. Wright J-5 radial engine and is primarily of wooden construction. The crew of two are seated in tandem with the instructor in the rear cockpit, and full dual controls are fitted. As a reconnaissance aircraft, a single 0.30-in. machine gun was mounted in the rear cockpit.

Max. speed, 100 m.p.h.; cruising speed, 82 m.p.h.; weights and dimensions: No details available.

BA-6   SWEDEN

Designed by Björn Andreasson and first flown in 1955, the BA-6 single-seat aerobatic sports monoplane has been developed primarily for construction by amateur groups and flying clubs. Powered by a 65 h.p. Continental A65 engine, the BA-6 is of all-wood construction and, with the exception of the fabric-covered control surfaces, has plywood covering. Fully aerobatic, the BA-6 has a Cessna-type spring-steel cantilever landing gear, and an 85 h.p. Continental engine can be fitted in place of the 65 h.p. engine installed in the two machines completed at the time of writing.
Max. speed, 145 m.p.h.; landing speed (with flaps), 34 m.p.h.; climb to 20,000 ft., 6 minutes; range, 1,200 miles; span, 23 ft.; length, 16 ft. 5 in.; height, 5 ft.

B.A. EAGLE II   G.B.

The B.A. Eagle II three-seat cabin monoplane was developed by the British Klemm Aeroplane Co. Ltd. in 1934, and taken over by the British Aircraft Manufacturing Company in the following year. The only known airworthy example of the Eagle II is currently flying in Australia. The B.A. Eagle II was produced with both fixed and retractable undercarriages and was normally powered by a 130 h.p. de Havilland Gipsy Major air-cooled engine. The cabin provides accommodation for three persons, two being seated on a bench-type seat at the rear.
Max. speed, 148 m.p.h.; cruising, 130 m.p.h.; initial climb rate, 700 ft./min.; range, 650 miles; empty weight, 1,450 lb.; loaded, 2,400 lb.; span, 39 ft. 3 in.; length, 26 ft.; height, 6 ft. 9 in.

B.A. SWALLOW II   G.B.

A development of the British Klemm monoplane built by British Aircraft Manufacturing Co. Ltd., and first flown in 1935, the Swallow II was produced with both the 80 h.p. Pobjoy Cataract II radial (*as illustrated*), and the 90 h.p. Cirrus Minor. Two Swallow IIs (one with a Cataract and the other with a Cirrus Minor) are flying in Australia, eight are flying in Eire and several examples are airworthy in the U.K. One of the latter, the Cirrus Minor-powered G-AEMW, has been fitted with a cockpit canopy, but most Swallow IIs have tandem open cockpits.
(Pobjoy): Max. speed, 104 m.p.h.; cruising, 92 m.p.h.; initial climb rate, 800 ft./min.; range, 390 miles; empty weight, 990 lb.; loaded, 1,500 lb.; span, 42 ft. 8½ in.; length, 27 ft.; height, 7 ft.

B.A.C. DRONE G.B.

The B.A.C. Drone ultra-light aircraft was the production model of the Lowe-Wylde Planette, and was first produced in 1933. B.A.C. (1935) Ltd. was formed in 1935 to take over production and development of the Drone. In 1937, the Carden Ford 10 engine of 30 h.p. was fitted, and examples powered by both this engine and the 32 h.p. Bristol Cherub 3 are believed to be airworthy. The Drone is a single-seat monoplane of wooden construction with plywood and fabric covering. The following details refer to the Carden Ford-powered Drone.

Max. speed, 73 m.p.h.; cruising, 65 m.p.h.; range, 300 miles; empty weight, 453 lb.; loaded, 680 lb.; span, 39 ft. 8 in.; length, 22 ft.; height, 8 ft. 4½ in.

BARKLEY-GROW T8P-1 U.S.A.

Built by the Barkley-Grow Aircraft Corporation in some numbers before World War II, the T8P-1 high-performance commercial monoplane was produced with both fixed, spatted land undercarriage and twin floats, and several examples are flying in Canada and South America. Powered by two 400 h.p. Pratt & Whitney Wasp Junior radials, the T8P-1 carries a crew of two and provides accommodation for eight passengers. Construction is all-metal.

Max. speed, 220 m.p.h. at 5,000 ft.; cruising speed, 185 m.p.h. at 10,000 ft.; initial climb rate, 1,400 ft./min.; cruising range, 1,000 miles; empty weight, 5,880 lb.; loaded, 8,750 lb.; span, 50 ft. 8 in.; length, 36 ft. 2 in.; height, 9 ft. 7½ in.

BAUMANN B-290 BRIGADIER U.S.A.

The B-290 Brigadier is a development of the B-250 which first flew in June 1947, differing from the earlier aircraft only in having engines of a higher power rating. Pilot production of the B-290 commenced in 1951, and a type certificate was acquired in 1952. The Brigadier is powered by two 145 h.p. Continental C145 engines driving pusher airscrews. The Baumann Aircraft Corporation adapted a B-290 airframe for the Custer "channel-wing" under the designation Custer CCW-5. The CCW-5 is powered by two 280 h.p. Continental SO-470 engines. The B-290 seats five.

Max. speed, 190 m.p.h.; cruising, 165 m.p.h.; initial climb, 1,200 ft./min.; empty weight, 2,150 lb.; loaded, 3,500 lb.; span, 41 ft.; length, 27 ft. 5 in.; height, 10 ft. 4 in.; wing area, 207 sq. ft.

BEECH MODEL 17 U.S.A.

First introduced in 1932–33, the Model 17 four-seat cabin biplane was built in large numbers and a variety of versions over the following decade. All versions are externally similar and differ primarily in the type of engine installed and internal equipment. The version flying in largest numbers is the D17S with the 450 h.p. Pratt & Whitney R-985, but also flying are the B17L (285 h.p. Jacobs L-5), the similarly powered B17B, C17B, C17L, E17B, and E17L; the F17D with the 330 h.p. Jacobs, the D17A and D17R with 350 and 450 h.p. Wright Whirlwinds respectively, and the D17S and G17S with the Pratt & Whitney. Examples are flying in Australia, Sweden, France, Britain, etc.

D17S: Cruising speed, 202 m.p.h.; empty weight, 2,460 lb.; loaded, 4,200 lb.; span, 32 ft.; length, 26 ft.; height, 8 ft. 2 in.

BEECH AT-10 WICHITA U.S.A.

The AT-10 Wichita twin-engined advanced trainer was the first all-wood aircraft to be accepted as an advanced trainer by the U.S.A.F. Employing wooden construction to counter a possible shortage of light metals, the Wichita was built both by Beech Aircraft Corp. (1,771 built), and Globe Aircraft (600 built), and was powered by two 295 h.p. Lycoming R-680-9 radials. Very few remain, seven currently being registered with civil operators in the U.S.A. One of these has been re-engined with 450 h.p. Wright Whirlwind R-975-E3 engines.

Max. speed, 198 m.p.h.; cruising, 177 m.p.h.; range, 770 miles; empty weight, 4,750 lb.; loaded, 6,130 lb.; span, 44 ft.; length, 34 ft. 4 in.; wing area, 298 sq. ft.

BEECH AT-11 KANSAN U.S.A.

The AT-11 Kansan was produced in 1941 for the specialised training of bombardiers and gunners, and in general design is similar to the C-45 (employing the same wing, tail unit and landing gear), but has a modified fuselage with a transparent nose. Of the 1,582 Kansans built 1941–43, more than one hundred are currently used by civil operators in the U.S.A., and the type serves as a trainer with the Haitian Air Corps, and the air forces of Honduras, Guatemala, Mexico, Peru, Salvador, Venezuela, Uruguay, Chile, Brazil, Bolivia and the Argentine. The AT-11 Kansan is powered by two 450 h.p. Pratt & Whitney R-985-AN-1 engines.

Max. speed, 215 m.p.h.; range, 870 miles; empty weight, 6,160 lb.; loaded, 8,730 lb.; span, 47 ft. 8 in.; length, 34 ft. 3 in.; height, 9 ft. 9 in.

BEECH (C-45) MODEL 18   U.S.A.

First flown on January 15, 1937, as a light eight-seat commercial transport, the Model 18 has been built in exceptionally large numbers: 5,204 military models being produced during World War 2, in addition to pre-war civil and post-war military and civil models. Initial production models included the 18A (350 h.p. Whirlwind R-760E-2), 18D (330 h.p. Jacobs L-6) and 18S (450 h.p. Wasp Junior), and military utility transport versions for the U.S.A.F. have included the C-45A, B, C, D, E, F, and the rebuilt C-45G and H, and U.S. Navy JRB-1, -2, -3, -4, -5, and -6, all of which are externally similar. The C-45 is known as the Expediter in the R.C.A.F.

Specification (D18S): Light transport. Engines: Two 450 h.p. Pratt & Whitney R-985-B5. Weights: Empty, 5,770 lb.; loaded, 8,750 lb. Performance: Max. speed, 230 m.p.h. at 5,000 ft.; cruising, 211 m.p.h.; range, 1,125 miles. Dimensions: Span, 47 ft. 7 in.; length, 33 ft. 11½ in.; height, 9 ft. 2½ in.; wing area, 349 sq. ft.

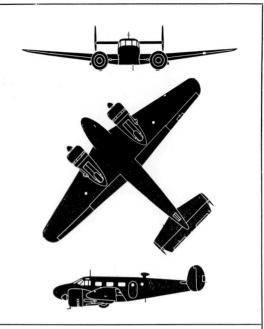

BEECH MODEL E18S SUPER 18   U.S.A.

The Super 18 is an extensively modified development of the Model D18S. It incorporates numerous structural and equipment improvements. Wing span has been increased, the flight compartment redesigned, and integral entrance steps fitted. All-up weight has been increased and all-round performance has been improved by means of external drag reduction. A military liaison and light transport variant of the Super 18 has been supplied to the Armée de l'Air. The cabin accommodates five to seven passengers.

Specification: Light commercial transport. Engines: Two 450 h.p. Pratt & Whitney R-985-14 ANB. Weights: Empty, 6,150 lb.; loaded, 9,300 lb. Performance: Max. speed, 234 m.p.h. at 5,000 ft.; cruising speed, 207 m.p.h. at 5,000 ft.; max. climb rate at sea level, 1,250 ft./min. Dimensions: Span, 49 ft. 8 in.; length, 35 ft. 2½ in.; height, 9 ft. 6 in.; wing area, 361 sq. ft.

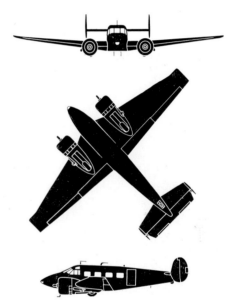

BEECH T-34 MENTOR   U.S.A.

First flown on December 2, 1948, the Model 45 Mentor has been developed from the Model 35 Bonanza, and large contracts have been placed for the type by the U.S.A.F. as the T-34A, and by the U.S. Navy as the T-34B (*photo*). In addition, the Mentor has been ordered for the Chilean and Colombian Air Forces, and is being produced under licence by the Canadian Car and Foundry Co. for both the R.C.A.F. and U.S.A.F. Licence production is also being undertaken by Fuji in Japan for the Japanese National Defence Force.

Specification: Two-seat primary trainer. Engine: One 225 h.p. Continental 0-470-13. Weights: Empty, 2,055 lb.; loaded, 2,750 lb. Performance: Max. speed, 188 m.p.h.; cruising speed, 167 m.p.h.; max. diving speed, 280 (I.A.S.) m.p.h.; initial climb rate, 1,210 ft./min.; service ceiling, 21,200 ft.; max. range, 975 miles. Dimensions: Span, 32 ft. 10 in.; length, 25 ft. 10 in.; height, 9 ft. 7 in.; wing area, 177.6 sq. ft.

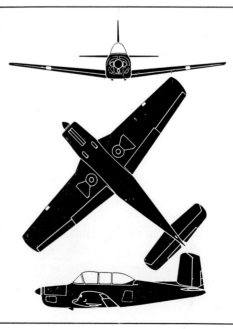

BEECH MODEL F35 BONANZA U.S.A.

Deliveries of the Bonanza commenced in mid-February 1947, since which time more than 4,000 Bonanzas have been produced, including Models A35 and B35 with the 185 h.p. Continental E185-1, the C35, D35 and E35 with the 205 h.p. Continental E185-11, and the F35 with the 225 h.p. Continental E-225-8. Each model is externally similar, featuring minor refinements, and the Model F35, introduced in 1955, can also be powered by the 205 h.p. E185-11 engine. Figures in parentheses refer to the latter.
Specification: Four-seat cabin monoplane. Engine: One 225 h.p. Continental E-225-8. Weights: Empty, 1,697 lb.; loaded, 2,750 lb. Performance: Max. speed, 194 (190) m.p.h. at sea level; recommended cruising, 184 (180) m.p.h. at 8,000 (6,000) ft.; initial climb rate, 1,300 (1,100) ft./min. Dimensions: Span, 32 ft. 10 in.; length, 25 ft. 2 in.; height, 6 ft. 6 in.; wing area, 177.6 sq. ft.

BEECH (L-23A) TWIN BONANZA U.S.A.

The Model 50 Twin Bonanza was flown for the first time in November 1949, and employs many components of the Model 35 Bonanza. Four Twin Bonanzas were acquired by the U.S. Army Field Forces for service evaluation under the designation YL-23, and the type has since been delivered in quantity as the L-23A and L-23B for staff transport and general liaison duties. Commercial production was initiated in 1953 with the Model A50, being succeeded by the similar B50 and C50 in 1954 and 1955 respectively.
Specification (C50): Six-seat light transport. Engines: Two 275 h.p. Lycoming GO-480-F6. Weights: Empty, 3,928 lb.; loaded, 6,000 lb. Performance: Max. speed, 210 m.p.h. at 2,500 ft.; cruising (65 per cent power), 197 m.p.h. at 10,000 ft.; initial climb rate, 1,450 ft./min. Dimensions: Span, 45 ft. 3⅜ in.; length, 31 ft. 6½ in.; height, 11 ft. 4 in.; wing area, 277.06 sq. ft.

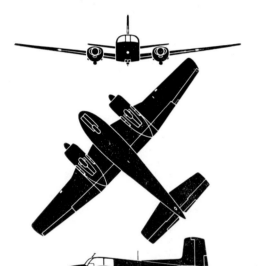

BEECRAFT HONEY BEE U.S.A.

The Honey Bee ultra-light aeroplane, which first flew on July 12, 1952 and has been developed by Beecraft Associates, Inc., is a low-cost aircraft of all-metal construction, powered by a 65 h.p. Continental A65 engine. Featuring a cantilever wing and a Vee tail with combined elevators and rudder, the Honey Bee was awarded an Approved Type Certificate on December 17, 1953. A two-seat version is projected with side-by-side seating and an 85 h.p. Continental engine. No production of the single-seat Honey Bee has been undertaken.

Max. speed, 120 m.p.h.; cruising, 110 m.p.h.; empty weight, 610 lb.; loaded, 860 lb.; span, 28 ft.; length, 16 ft. 10 in.; height, 7 ft. 8 in.

BELL V.T.O.L. U.S.A.

The Bell V.T.O.L. (vertical take-off and landing) research aircraft has been built to test the practicability of rotatable turbojets providing thrust for both vertical lift and forward propulsion. Constructed largely from existing parts, this research aircraft is powered by two 1,000 lb. thrust Fairchild J44 turbojets and one Continental-Turboméca Palouste compressor. To achieve vertical take-off, the thrust of the J44 turbojets is directed downwards, control at low airspeeds being obtained from compressed-air jets at the tail and wingtips fed by the Palouste. When clear of the ground, the J44s are gradually tilted to provide forward thrust.
Approx. loaded weight, 2,200 lb.; span, 26 ft.; length, 21 ft.; approx. wing area, 130 sq. ft.

BELL P-39Q AIRACOBRA U.S.A.

The P-39Q is one of a number of variants of the Airacobra single-seat fighter, 9,584 of which were produced during World War 2. A few remain flying in the U.S.A. for racing purposes, and a two-seat conversion is currently registered in Peru. The P-39Q is powered by a 1,200 h.p. Allison V-1710-85 engine mounted aft of the pilot's cockpit and driving the airscrew via an extension shaft. Over 4,900 P-39Qs were built, and a large proportion of these were supplied to Russia. The following details relate to the fighter prior to conversion for racing.
Max. speed, 385 m.p.h.; cruising, 240 m.p.h.; range (with external tank), 675 miles; empty weight, 5,968 lb.; loaded, 8,052 lb.; span, 34 ft.; length, 30 ft. 2 in.; wing area, 213 sq. ft.

BELL P-63C-5 KINGCOBRA U.S.A.

The Kingcobra was a development of the Airacobra which it resembled in most features. Several are registered in the U.S.A., including the P-63A-7 (1,325 h.p. Allison V-1710-93), P-63C-5 (1,325 h.p. Allison V-1710-117), P-63E-1 (1,425 h.p. Allison V-1710-109), production models. Like the remaining Airacobras, the Kingcobras are mostly used for racing. There are also several P-63 Kingcobras remaining in Peru. The following figures relate to the P-63C-5 Kingcobra prior to its conversion for racing. The photo depicts a two-seat conversion.

Max. speed, 410 m.p.h. at 25,000 ft.; empty weight, 6,694 lb.; loaded, 10,700 lb.; span, 38 ft. 4 in.; length, 32 ft. 8⅜ in.; wing area, 248 sq. ft.

BELL X-1B U.S.A.

Designed to investigate supersonic flight problems, the Bell X-1 made its first powered flight on December 9, 1946. Powered by a Reaction Motors XLR-11-RM-5 rocket motor of 6,000 lb. thrust, the X-1 was the first piloted aircraft to exceed Mach unity (October 14, 1947). The X-1A and X-1B (*illustrated*) are improved models, differing from the earlier X-1 in having a stepped canopy, a 4 ft. 7 in. longer fuselage, and a turbo-pump fuel system. The X-1A attained Mach 2.5 (1,650 m.p.h.) at 70,000 ft. on December 16, 1953, but was later destroyed. The X-1B is externally similar to the X-1A and intended to investigate thermal problems.
Full-power endurance, 4.2 min.; weight (fuel expended), 7,000 lb.; loaded, 18,000 lb.; span, 28 ft.; length, 35 ft. 7 in.; height, 10 ft. 8 in.

BELL X-2 U.S.A.

The X-2 supersonic research aircraft has been designed to attain Mach numbers in excess of those reached by the X-1 series aircraft. Powered by a throttleable Curtiss-Wright XLR-25 rocket motor of some 15,000 lb. thrust, the first of two X-2 research aircraft was destroyed on May 13, 1953 prior to its first launching from a B-50 Superfortress. A second machine was completed in 1955, and is expected to attain 2,250 m.p.h. at 100,000 ft. The X-2 has wing and tail assemblies of stainless-steel construction, and employs a skid for landing. The jettisonable cockpit can be separated from the fuselage in an emergency by an explosive charge, a ribbon-type parachute lowering the complete cockpit to a lower altitude at which the pilot can bale out in an orthodox manner.

BELLANCA CRUISAIR AND CRUISEMASTER U.S.A.

First introduced in 1937, several hundred examples of the Bellanca low-wing cabin monoplane are currently registered in the U.S.A. Both pre-war and post-war models are of basically similar design, and include the pre-war three-seat Model 14-9, examples of which are flying with both the 90 h.p. Rearwin and 100 h.p. Lycoming; the Model 14-12-F3 three-seater of 1941 with a 120 h.p. Franklin 6AC-264; the post-war Models 14-13 and 14-13-2 Cruisair Senior (150 h.p. Franklin) four-seaters, a combined total of some 400 of which are flying, and the 14-13-3 Cruisair (*photo*) and 14-19 Cruisemaster (*silhouette*) of 1948–50. These all possess generally similar characteristics.
Specification (14-19): Four-seat cabin monoplane. *Engine:* One 190 h.p. Lycoming 0-435A. *Weights:* Empty, 1,525 lb.; loaded, 2,600 lb. *Performance:* Cruising, 180 m.p.h. at 6,000 ft.; initial climb rate, 1,400 ft./min.; range, 680 miles. *Dimensions:* Span, 34 ft. 2 in.; length, 23 ft.; height, 6 ft. 2 in.

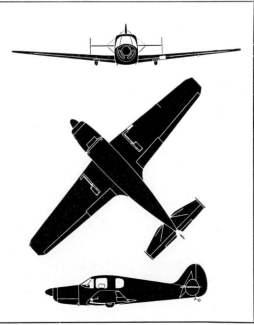

BELLANCA 66-75 AIRCRUISER   U.S.A.

The Model 66-75 Aircruiser sesquiplane was first produced in 1932 as an eleven/fourteen passenger transport powered by a 715 h.p. Wright Cyclone. As a general purpose aircraft, the Aircruiser was supplied to the Cuban government in 1935, and at least one example is still flying in Cuba. Later production aircraft were powered by the 750 h.p. Pratt & Whitney Hornet or the 875 h.p. Wright Cyclone, and a twin-float seaplane Aircruiser (*photograph*) is currently flying in Canada. The following details refer to the landplane variant.

Max. speed, 165 m.p.h.; cruising, 137 m.p.h.; empty weight, 6,300 lb.; loaded, 11,400 lb.; span, 65 ft.; length, 43 ft. 4 in.; height, 12 ft.

BELLANCA CH-300 PACEMAKER   U.S.A.

Several examples of the CH-300 Pacemaker and CH-400 Pacemaker Senior are currently airworthy in Canada, the U.S.A. and South America as light freighters. The CH-300, produced between 1928 and 1930, is powered by both the 330 h.p. Wright Whirlwind and the 450 h.p. Pratt & Whitney Wasp Junior. The CH-400 is powered by the latter engine or the 420 h.p. Wright Whirlwind. Both Pacemaker and Pacemaker Senior are six-seat cabin monoplanes and generally similar externally. The example illustrated is a twin-float CH-300 Pacemaker. (*CH-400*): *Max. speed, 165 m.p.h.; cruising, 155 m.p.h.; initial climb rate, 900 ft./min.; range, 1,360 miles; empty weight, 3,000 lb.; loaded, 5,350 lb.; span, 50 ft. 6 in.; length, 27 ft. 11 in.*

BELLANCA 31-55A SKYROCKET   U.S.A.

The Skyrocket is generally similar to the previously-described Pacemaker but carries a crew of two and six passengers. The Skyrocket was first produced in 1930, and was built with a variety of radial engines in the 450–550 h.p. range prior to World War 2. Two examples of the pre-war Model 31-42 Skyrocket are registered in the U.S.A., and others in Canada. They are externally similar to the Model 31-55A Skyrocket (*illustrated here*). This is a post-war version built under licence in 1946-7 by North-West Industries Ltd. in Canada. Powered by a 500 h.p. Pratt & Whitney Wasp S3H1, it is otherwise identical to the Model 31-42 Skyrocket of 1935.
Max. speed, 180 m.p.h.; cruising, 160 m.p.h.; empty weight, 3,760 lb.; loaded, 6,450 lb.; span, 50 ft. 6 in,; length, 27 ft. 11 in.

BHT-1 BEAUTY   SWEDEN

Completed in December 1944 by Skandinavisk Aero A.B. to the designs of E. Bratt, K. E. Hilfing and B. Tornblom, the BHT-1 Beauty is a single-seat long-range light monoplane powered by a 60 h.p. Walter Mikron 4 engine. It was originally proposed to produce a two-seat development, the BHT-2, with a new fuselage and a 90 h.p. Cirrus Minor engine, but this plan did not reach fruition, and the sole prototype of the Beauty is now registered in Norway. Construction is of wood with plywood covering, and a retractable undercarriage is fitted.
Max. speed, 155 m.p.h.; cruising, 130 m.p.h.; initial climb rate, 1,024 ft./min.; range, 1,056 miles; empty weight, 528 lb.; loaded, 803 lb.; span, 22 ft. 4½ in.; length, 19 ft.; height, 6 ft. 3 in.

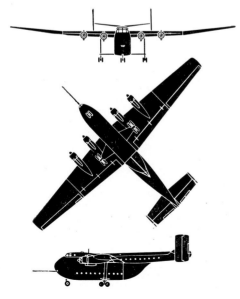

BLACKBURN BEVERLEY C.1   G.B.

The Beverley C.1 medium-range military freighter has been ordered for R.A.F. Transport Command, and an initial order for twenty machines has since been supplemented by a further order. Originally designed by General Aircraft Ltd. prior to its merger with Blackburn Aircraft Ltd., the original prototype, the Type 60, was powered by four 2,020 h.p. Hercules 730 engines, but the second prototype (Type 65) and subsequent aircraft represent an eighty per cent redesign. The Beverley C.1 is noteworthy for its short-field characteristics which can be further improved by a pair of Super Sprite rockets.
Specification: Medium-range military freighter. Engines: Four 2,850 h.p. Bristol Centaurus 173. Weights: Empty, 78,900 lb.; loaded, 135,000 lb. Performance: Max. speed, 238 m.p.h. at 5,700 ft.; cruising, 175 m.p.h.; range (29,000 lb. payload), 1,300 miles. Dimensions: Span, 162 ft.; length, 99 ft. 2 in.; height, 38 ft. 5 in.; wing area, 2,916 sq. ft.

BLACKBURN B.2   G.B.

The B.2 side-by-side two-seat training biplane was first produced in 1932 to succeed the Bluebird. It employs a semi-monocoque Alclad fuselage and fabric-covered steel wings, and has used a variety of engines. Most B.2s were scrapped during the war years, and only one is believed to have survived. This is powered by a 150 h.p. Blackburn Cirrus Major III which has replaced the Hermes and Gipsy Major with which it was successively powered. A second B.2 which survived the war, and is illustrated here, no longer possesses a current certificate of airworthiness.

Max. speed, 112 m.p.h.; cruising, 100 m.p.h.; range, 320 miles; empty weight, 1,122 lb.; loaded, 1,850 lb.; span, 30 ft. 2 in.; length, 24 ft. 3 in.; height, 9 ft.

BLAIRVACQ-PIEL C.P.30 EMERAUDE   FRANCE

Designed by MM. Blairvacq and Piel, the C.P.30 Emeraude ultra light two-seat cabin monoplane has been designed primarily for construction by amateurs and flying clubs, and is available in complete kit or plan form. A considerable number of aircraft of this type are being built in France by various groups and individuals, and construction is claimed to be relatively simple. Design of the C.P.30 owes much to experience gained with the earlier single-seat C.P.20 Pinocchio, and any suitable engine in the 40–90 h.p. range may be fitted. The prototype has a 65 h.p. Continental A65 engine.

Max. speed, 118 m.p.h. at sea level; cruising, 105 m.p.h.; initial climb rate, 882 ft./min.; range, 830 miles; empty weight, 610 lb.; loaded, 1,095 lb.; span, 29 ft. 7 in.; length, 21 ft.; height, 7 ft. 4 in.

BOEING 247D   U.S.A.

First flown in 1932, the Boeing 247 was the first all-metal aircraft of its type to be placed in production in the U.S.A., and one of the first transport aircraft to be fitted with a retractable undercarriage. The Model 247D was an improved version which appeared in 1934 and, powered by two 550 h.p. Pratt & Whitney Wasp R-1340-S1H1G radials, several examples remain airworthy in the U.S.A., and at least two further machines are flying in Central and South America. The Boeing 247D normally carries a crew of three and ten passengers.

Max. speed, 200 m.p.h.; cruising, 189 m.p.h.; range, 745 miles; initial climb rate, 1,150 ft./min.; empty weight, 9,144 lb.; loaded, 13,650 lb.; span, 74 ft.; length, 51 ft. 4 in.; height, 12 ft. 1¾ in.

BOEING 307B STRATOLINER   U.S.A.

The Boeing 307 Stratoliner first flew in 1939 and entered regular service on internal U.S. routes. The Model 307B differed from the Model 307 in having 1,100 h.p. Wright Cyclone GR-1820-G105A engines instead of G-102s, and slotted flaps in place of split trailing edge flaps. The five 307Bs originally owned by T.W.A. were extensively modified after wartime U.S.A.F. service; the cabin pressurization equipment was removed, and B-17 Fortress wings and 1,200 h.p. Wright R-1820 engines were fitted. These were eventually sold to France where they are currently flying. Of the remaining three Stratoliners built, one Model 307 is employed by the Haitian Air Corps, and one 307 and one 307B are registered in the U.S.A.

Span, 107 ft. 3 in.; length, 74 ft. 4 in.; height, 21 ft. 1 in.

BOEING B-17G FORTRESS   U.S.A.

A total of 12,731 Fortress bombers were produced between July 1935 and April 1945, but only Dominica and Israel now use the type as a first-line bomber. Several civilianised B-17Fs and B-17Gs are used in the U.S.A. as transports. The type is also employed as a transport by the Danish Air Force, and serves the U.S.A.F. as the QB-17G target and SB-17G lifeboat-carrying air/sea rescue aircraft (*photo*). The U.S. Navy still possesses a few early-warning radar-equipped B-17Gs under the designation PB-1W, and the U.S. Navy and Coast Guard rescue version similar to the SB-17G is designated PB-1G. Following data relates to B-17G bomber with four 1,200 h.p. Wright R-1820-97 engines.
Max. speed, 295 m.p.h. at 30,000 ft.; cruising, 162 m.p.h.; empty weight, 32,720 lb.; loaded, 55,000 lb.; span, 103 ft. 9 in.; length, 74 ft. 9 in.

BOEING YL-15 SCOUT   U.S.A.

The YL-15 Scout light two-seat monoplane of unconventional design was built to meet U.S. Army Field Forces requirements for a liaison aircraft which could be quickly dismantled and loaded on a standard 2½ ton truck. Two XL-15 prototypes and ten YL-15 pre-production Scouts were built for evaluation, but no additional production orders were placed, and the remaining seven YL-15 Scouts are currently employed by the Federal Fish and Wild Life Service. The Scout is powered by a 125 h.p. Lycoming 0-290 engine and can be towed as a glider at speeds up to 165 m.p.h. without having its airscrew removed.
Max. speed, 112 m.p.h.; cruising, 101 m.p.h.; initial climb rate, 628 ft./min.; empty weight, 1,509 lb.; loaded, 2,050 lb.; span, 40 ft.; length, 25 ft. 3 in.; height, 8 ft. 8½ in.

BOEING 377 STRATOCRUISER   U.S.A.

Operated by British Overseas Airways, Pan American World Airways, and North-west Airlines, the Model 377 Stratocruiser is the civil counterpart of the military Stratofreighter, and is powered by four 3,500 h.p. Pratt & Whitney R-4360-TSB3-G engines. The Stratocruiser can provide accommodation for a maximum of eighty-six passengers, and the wing, tail surfaces and landing gear are basically similar to those of the B-50 Superfortress bomber. The fuselage is of "double-bubble" section; the upper deck accommodates the control cabin and main passenger compartment.
Max. speed, 375 m.p.h.; cruising, 196 m.p.h.; normal range, 1,500 miles; empty weight, 83,500 lb.; loaded, 142,500 lb.; span, 141 ft. 3 in.; length, 110 ft. 4 in.; height, 38 ft. 3 in.

BOEING-STEARMAN MODEL 75   U.S.A.

Designed by the Stearman Aircraft Co. prior to its incorporation in the Boeing Aircraft Company, the Model 75 was built in large numbers prior to and during World War 2 (10,346 being produced during the war years under the U.S.A.F. designations PT-13, PT-17 and PT-18, and for the U.S. Navy as the N2S-1, -2, and -3, these differing primarily in the type of engine installed). Nearly four thousand Model 75s currently exist in the U.S.A., the most widely used being the A75N1 powered by the 220 h.p. Continental W-670 radial. Many are used for crop spraying and it is used as a trainer by the air forces of Israel, Iran, and several Central and S. American countries.
Max. speed, 124 m.p.h.; cruising, 106 m.p.h.; empty weight, 1,936 lb.; loaded, 2,717 lb.; span, 32 ft. 2 in.; length, 25 ft.; height, 9 ft. 2 in.

BOEING B-50D SUPERFORTRESS   U.S.A.

The B-50 was developed from the B-29 from which it differs in having higher-powered engines, lighter wings and landing gear and redesigned tail surfaces. Deliveries of the B-50 to the U.S.A.F. began in November 1949, and the last of 750 B-50s was completed in February 1953. The B-50D is a development of the initial production models, the B-50A and B. Photo-reconnaissance versions include the RB-50E, F and G, and the TB-50D and TB-50H are navigator-bombardier trainers. A Soviet copy of the B-29 is designated TU-4 and differs from the B-50 in having shorter vertical tail.
Specification: Medium bomber. Engines: Four 3,500 h.p. Pratt & Whitney R-4360-35 Wasp Majors. Weights: Empty: 80,962 lb.; loaded, 164,500 lb. Performance: Max. speed, 400 m.p.h. at 25,000 ft.; cruising, 330 m.p.h.; ceiling, 40,000 ft.; operating range (with 10,000 lb. bomb load), 6,000 miles. Armament: Thirteen 50-in. guns. Dimensions: Span, 141 ft. 3 in.; length, 99 ft.; height, 32 ft. 9 in.; wing area, 1,768 sq. ft.

BOEING KC-97G STRATOFREIGHTER   U.S.A.

More than 500 C-97 Stratofreighter transports have been delivered to the U.S.A.F. since the prototype flew on November 15, 1944. The KC-97G convertible tanker/transport differs from the KC-97F illustrated here in having the location of the refuelling tanks and related equipment changed so that they need not be removed when the aircraft is used as a transport. With refuelling equipment installed, the KC-97G can carry sixty-five fully-equipped troops. Two Stratofreighters have been fitted with four 5,700 e.h.p. Pratt & Whitney T34 turboprops and designated YC-97J.
Specification: Convertible refuelling tanker/transport. Engines: Four 3,500 h.p. Pratt & Whitney R-4360-59 Wasp Majors. Weights: Empty, 85,400 lb.; normal loaded, 153,000 lb.; max. loaded, 175,000 lb. Performance: Max. speed, 375 m.p.h.; cruising, 300 m.p.h.; service ceiling, 35,000 ft.; range, 4,300 miles. Dimensions: Span, 141 ft. 3 in.; length, 110 ft. 4 in.; height, 38 ft. 3 in.; wing area, 1,769 sq. ft.

BOEING B-47E STRATOJET   U.S.A.

This is the standard medium bomber of the U.S.A.F.'s Strategic Air Command. The XB-47 Stratojet prototype flew on December 17, 1947, since which time more than 1,500 B-47E Stratojets have been delivered. A specialised photo-reconnaissance variant, the RB-47E, has an extended fuselage nose which increases overall length to 112 ft. 8 in. and contains a heated and air-conditioned camera compartment. The QB-47E and ETB-47E are radio-controlled drone and crew-trainer variants respectively. All B-47Es have Boeing-developed flying-boom air refuelling equipment.

Specification: Three-seat medium bomber. Engines: Six 6,000 lb. thrust (7,200 lb. with water injection) General Electric J47-GE-25. Weights: Loaded, 175,000 lb.; max. 202,000 lb. Armament: Two 20-mm. guns in tail. Max. bomb load, 20,000 lb. Performance: Approx. max. speed, 630 m.p.h.; ceiling, 40,000 ft.; normal range, 2,600 miles. Dimensions: Span, 116 ft.; length, 106 ft. 8 in.; height, 27 ft. 11 in.

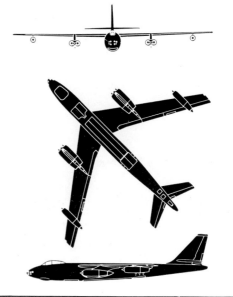

BOEING RB-52B STRATOFORTRESS   U.S.A.

One of the largest jet bombers currently in production, the RB-52B is currently being delivered to the U.S.A.F. Strategic Air Command, a total of approximately 500 being scheduled for delivery before 1958. Current Stratofortress production is centred on the RB-52B and B-52D versions, the latter carrying 40-ft. fuel tanks at the wingtips and up-rated J57 engines. Two interchangeable pressurized pods can be fitted in the bomb bay; one carrying aerial cameras and the other electronic countermeasures.

Specification: Long-range heavy bomber. Engines: Eight 9,700 lb. thrust Pratt & Whitney J57-P-3. Weights (approx.): Empty, 175,000 lb.; loaded, 350,000 lb. Armament: Two 20-mm. guns in tail. Performance: Approx. max. speed, 630 m.p.h.; service ceiling, 50,000 ft.; normal range, 3,000 miles (with 75,000 lb. bomb load); max. range, 6,000 miles (with 25,000 lb. bomb load). Dimensions: Span, 185 ft.; length, 156 ft. 6 in.; height, 48 ft. 3½ in.; wing area, 4,000 sq. ft.

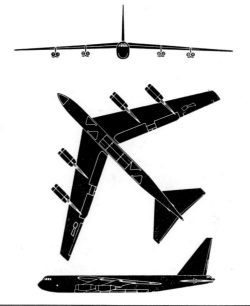

BOEING 367-80 (STRATOTANKER)   U.S.A.

The Boeing Model 367-80 is the first pure-jet transport of U.S. design and was developed as a private venture with the potential roles of military aerial refuelling tanker and long-range commercial airliner. The prototype, which flew for the first time on July 15, 1954, differs from the military tanker Model 717 Stratotanker, or KC-135, which has been ordered in quantity by the U.S.A.F., in having a shorter fuselage and a lower loaded weight. A commercial transport version will be known as the Type 707 Stratoliner, and will carry 80–130 passengers.

Specification: Military tanker/transport. Engines: Four 9,500 lb. thrust Pratt & Whitney J-57-P. (KC-135: 15,000 lb. approx. thrust J57). Weights: (Prototype) empty, 88,890 lb.; approx. loaded, 190,000 lb. (KC-135) 250,000 lb. Approx. performance: Max. speed, 630 m.p.h.; max. cruising, 550 m.p.h. at 35,000 ft. Dimensions: Span, 130 ft.; length, 127 ft. 10 in.; height, 38 ft. 3 in.; wing area, 2,400 sq. ft.

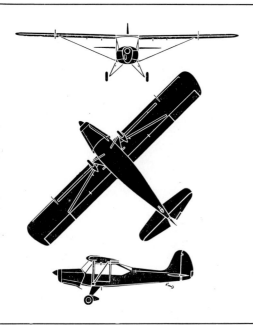

BOISAVIA B-605 MERCUREY   FRANCE

The B-605 Mercurey is the latest in a series of light planes derived from the B-50 Muscadet of 1946. The first of the Mercurey series, the B-60 with the 140 h.p. Renault 4 Pei engine, flew on April 3, 1949. Two B-60s were followed by three B-601s which differed in having the 190 h.p. Lycoming O-435-I. The B-602 has a 165 h.p. Continental E165-4, and the B-603 Mercurey-Special glider-tug variant has a 240 h.p. Salmson-Argus As 10. On April 29, 1954, the current production B-605 Mercurey flew for the first time, and an initial production batch of fourteen is in hand.

Specification: Four-seat cabin monoplane. Engine: One 170 h.p. SNECMA-Régnier 4L-02. Weights: Empty, 1,190 lb.; loaded, 2,204 lb. Performance: Max. speed, 140 m.p.h.; cruising speed, 124 m.p.h.; range, 745 miles. Dimensions: Span, 37 ft. 4 in.; length, 23 ft. 5 in.; height, 6 ft. 10 in.; wing area, 182.986 sq. ft.

BOISAVIA B-80 CHABLIS   FRANCE

The B-80 Chablis was flown for the first time in January 1951, and two machines of this type have been built. Basically a tandem two-seat parasol-wing monoplane, the Chablis is powered by a 65 h.p. Continental flat-four engine, and was designed primarily for the amateur constructor, Avions Boisavia supplying drawings, metal parts and components. Of wooden construction, with fabric and plywood covering, the Chablis can be fitted with a variety of engines in the 50–80 h.p. range.

Max. speed, 87 m.p.h.; cruising, 65 m.p.h.; initial climb, 540 ft./min.; weights: no details available; dimensions: no details available.

BOULTON PAUL P.111A   G.B.

Built for transonic flight research with delta wings, and powered by a 5,100 lb. thrust Rolls-Royce Nene turbojet, the Boulton Paul P.111A is believed to be capable of exceeding Mach unity in a shallow dive and, despite its relatively low power, will attain level speeds considerably in excess of Mach 0.95. The aircraft was originally designated P.111, and flown on October 10, 1950, but the addition of fuselage-mounted air brakes, a revised control system, etc., resulted in the designation being changed to P.111A. The modified machine flew for the first time on July 2, 1953.

Approx. empty weight, 6,500 lb.; approx. loaded, 9,600 lb.; span, 33 ft. 6 in.; length, 26 ft. 1 in.; height, 12 ft. 6½ in.; wing area, 200 sq. ft.

BOULTON PAUL BALLIOL T.2   G.B.

The P.108 Balliol was first flown on May 30, 1947, powered by a Bristol Mercury 25 radial. It had been designed to meet specification T.7/45 calling for a turboprop-powered all-purpose trainer, and the prototype was first flown with an A.S. Mamba on March 24, 1948. With the modification of R.A.F. requirements, the Balliol was modified to take the Merlin 35 piston-engine and, as the Balliol T.2, this version is currently in service with the R.A.F., a total of 187 having been built. The Sea Balliol T.21 is a deck-landing variant for the Fleet Air Arm, thirty being delivered.

Specification: Two-seat advanced trainer. Engine: One 1,280 h.p. Rolls-Royce Merlin 35. Weights: Empty, 6,730 lb.; loaded, 8,410 lb. Performance: Max. speed, 288 m.p.h.; cruising, 266 m.p.h.; initial climb rate, 1,790 ft./min.; service ceiling, 32,500 ft. Armament: One .303-in. Browning gun and four 60-lb. rockets. Dimensions: Span, 39 ft. 4 in.; length, 35 ft. 1½ in.; height, 12 ft. 6 in.; wing area, 250 sq. ft.

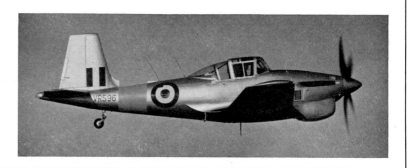

BREDA BA 42   ITALY

The Ba 42 was developed from the Ba 39 two-seat light aeroplane specially to compete in the 1934 *Challenge de Tourisme International*. With a 180 h.p. Fiat A.70S radial engine replacing the Ba 39's 130 h.p. Colombo S.63 in-line air-cooled engine, and improved fuselage contours, the Ba 42 is otherwise similar to the Ba 39, and one example, illustrated here, is currently registered in Italy. An interesting feature of the Ba 42 is the use of the Breda-Mazzini "wing-valve"—a slot in front of the ailerons and flaps which, operating in conjunction with the trailing-edge flaps, is closed by a moveable section of the wing which lowers to act as an airflow deflector.

Max. speed, 163 m.p.h.; cruising, 138 m.p.h.; empty weight, 1,232 lb.; loaded, 2,002 lb.; span, 33 ft. 1 in.; length, 25 ft. 7 in.; wing area, 170 sq. ft.

BREDA-PITTONI BP 471   ITALY

The Bp 471 twin-engined transport was designed by Mario Pittoni and was first flown in 1950. The Bp 471 is powered by two 1,200 h.p. Pratt & Whitney R-1830-92 Twin Wasp radials, and was designed primarily as an eighteen-passenger medium-range airliner or freighter. No production of the Bp 471 was undertaken, and the sole prototype is currently employed by the Italian Air Ministry as a personnel transport. The Bp 471 is unusual in having a wing of inverted gull form. All-metal construction was employed and navigational trainer, military freighter and reconnaissance variants were planned.

Max. speed, 294 m.p.h.; cruising, 256 m.p.h.; cruising range at 245 m.p.h., 1,243 miles; loaded weight, 22,046 lb.; span, 75 ft. 5 in.; length, 57 ft. 5 in.; height, 18 ft. 10 in.

BREDA-ZAPPATA BZ 308   ITALY

Designed by Filippo Zappata, the Bz 308 four-engined transport was flown for the first time on August 27, 1948, powered by four Bristol Centaurus 568 radials of 1,750 h.p. each. The Bz 308 was designed primarily for trans-Atlantic services between Italy and the Latin American countries, and four aircraft of this type were ordered by Argentina. A variety of versions were projected, including the pressurised Bz 308bis and twin-float Bz 408, and 55, 64, 74 and 80-seat layouts were planned. However, owing to the financial failure of the Breda company, development was abandoned and only one prototype completed. This is currently employed by the Italian Air Ministry.

Max. speed, 311 m.p.h.; cruising, 262 m.p.h.; empty weight, 50,706 lb.; loaded, 79,366 lb.; span, 138 ft. 2 in.; length, 110 ft.

BREGUET TYPE 731 BELLATRIX   FRANCE

Designed before the war as a military patrol flying boat, the Type 731 Bellatrix was test flown at the Berre naval air base in unoccupied France in 1942, the prototype (Type 730) having been flown just before World War 2. The Type 731 escaped destruction and, after the war, it was re-engined with four 1,480 h.p. Gnôme-Rhône 14R radials and has since been used by the French Naval Air Service. The Type 731 differs from the pre-war Type 730 in having redesigned crew accommodation, modified floats and a strengthened hull. Only one Type 731 Bellatrix was completed.

Max. speed, 239 m.p.h. at 8,530 ft.; cruising, 186 m.p.h.; empty weight, 41,226 lb.; loaded, 77,161 lb.; span, 132 ft. 5 in.; length, 79 ft. 11 in.; height, 26 ft. 10 in.; wing area, 1,851 sq. ft.

BREGUET 763 PROVENCE (DEUX PONTS)   FRANCE

The first prototype *Deux Ponts*, the Type 761, flew on February 15, 1949, powered by four 1,580 h.p. Gnome-Rhone 14R engines. Three Breguet 761 "pre-series" aircraft were built. These have been re-engined with 2,020 h.p. Pratt & Whitney R-2800-B31s and, designated Type 761S, are operated by the *Armée de l'Air*. Eleven of the twelve production-type 763 Provence airliners are used by Air France, carrying a maximum of 107 passengers on two decks. Production of the type was resumed in 1955 for the *Armée de l'Air*, with an order for twenty-three machines designated Type 765.

Specification: Commercial transport. Engines: Four 2,400 h.p. Pratt & Whitney R-2800-CA18. Weights: Empty, 55,890 lb.; loaded, 110,230 lb. Performance: Max. cruising speed, 230 m.p.h. at 9,842 ft.; initial climb rate, 740 ft./min.; range, 2,367 miles. Dimensions: Span, 140 ft.; length, 94 ft. 11 in.; height, 31 ft. 4 in.; wing area, 1,996 sq. ft.

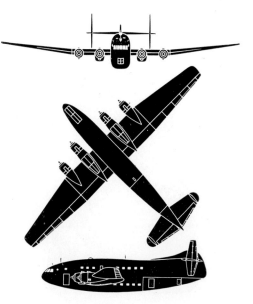

BREGUET TYPE 965 — FRANCE

The Type 965 is an aerodynamic test vehicle for the Type 1050-ASM three-seat carrier-borne attack and anti-submarine aircraft. It is, in actual fact, the second prototype Type 960 Vultur naval strike aircraft with the 1,320 h.p. Armstrong Siddeley Mamba A.S.Ma.3 turboprop retained but the 5,000 lb. thrust Hispano-Suiza Nene 104 deleted, provision made for a third crew member, and radar equipment mounted on the wing. The Type 965 flew for the first time on March 26, 1955, and a pre-production batch of five generally-similar Type 1050-ASM aircraft has been ordered. The Type 1050-ASM will be powered by the Rolls-Royce Dart R.Da.7. The following refers to the Type 1050.

Max. speed, 276 m.p.h.; endurance, 4 hours; loaded weight, 18,078 lb.; span, 51 ft. 2 in.; length, 40 ft. 4¼ in.; wing area, 387.5 sq. ft.

BRISTOL TYPE 149 BLENHEIM IV — G.B.

Several examples of the Type 149 Blenheim IV are currently employed by the Finnish Air Force for aerial photography. Originally designed as a twin-engined day bomber, the Blenheim IV, powered by 905 h.p. Bristol Mercury 15 radials, was used extensively by the R.A.F. Twenty-four Blenheims IVs were delivered to the Finnish Air Force in 1939 and, subsequently, some fifty light bombers of this type were built under licence in Finland. Thirty-six of these were still airworthy in 1946, but only a few machines now remain. The Blenheims were built at the Valtion Lentokonetehdas (State Aircraft Factory) at Tampere.

Max. speed, 295 m.p.h. at 15,000 ft.; initial climb rate, 1,500 ft./min.; range, 1,900 miles at 220 m.p.h.; empty weight, 8,250 lb.; loaded, 14,400 lb.; span, 56 ft. 4 in.; length, 42 ft. 9 in.; height, 9 ft. 10 in.

BRISTOL TYPE 156 BEAUFIGHTER T.T.10 G.B.

The Beaufighter was used in considerable numbers by the R.A.F. during the war years, a total of 5,562 machines having been built when production was terminated in September 1945. Of these, 2,231 were Beaufighter Mk.10s, and an adaptation of the type, designated T.T.10, for target-towing appeared in 1947. Modifications included the removal of most of the combat equipment, the installation of a target-towing winch on the starboard side of the fuselage, together with a seat for the winch operator. The Beaufighter T.T.10 carries two crew members and is powered by two 1,770 h.p. Bristol Hercules 18 engines.

Max. speed, 285 m.p.h.; max. cruising speed, 264 m.p.h.; still air range at 15,000 ft., 1,960 miles, (with target streamed) 1,680 miles; loaded weight, 21,250 lb.; span, 57 ft. 10 in.; length, 41 ft. 4 in.

BRISTOL TYPE 164 BRIGAND T.4 — G.B.

The Type 164 Brigand was designed as a twin-engined three-seat long-range attack aircraft, capable of fulfilling the duties of dive-bomber, torpedo-fighter, mine-carrier, or day or night fighter. The Brigand T.4, a small number of which remain in service, is an unarmed advanced trainer version based on the Brigand B.1 and employed primarily as a night fighter radar trainer. The Brigand T.4 is powered by two 2,470 h.p. Bristol Centaurus 57 radial engines, and normally carries a crew of three in tandem seats under a continuous canopy. For night fighter radar training the rear cockpit can be blacked out.

Max. speed, 358 m.p.h. at 16,000 ft.; cruising, 311 m.p.h. at 23,000 ft.; initial climb rate, 1,500 ft./min.; max. range, 2,800 miles; span, 72 ft. 4 in.; length, 46 ft. 5 in.; height, 17 ft. 6 in.

BRISTOL TYPE 170 (WAYFARER) — G.B.

Designed initially as a military transport, the Bristol Type 170 flew for the first time on December 2, 1945, and more than 200 have since been produced. The current versions are the Mk.31 freighter, the Mk.31E Wayfarer designed for the carriage of passengers, or a combination of passengers and cargo, the Mk.31M military transport supplied to Canada, New Zealand, Australia and Pakistan, and the Mk.32. The latter is an extensively modified version (*photo*) which has an increase of 5 ft. in nose length. The specification relates to the Mk.31.

Specification: Freight transport. Engines: Two 2,000 h.p. Bristol Hercules 734. Weights: Empty, 25,547 lb.; loaded, 44,000 lb. Performance: Max. cruising speed, 193 m.p.h. at 10,000 ft.; initial climb rate, 1,380 ft./min.; range (with 12,000 lb. payload), 420 miles; service ceiling, 24,500 ft. Dimensions: Span, 108 ft.; length, 68 ft. 4 in.; height, 21 ft. 6 in.; wing area, 1,487 sq. ft.

BRISTOL 175 BRITANNIA 100   G.B.

Flown for the first time on August 16, 1952, the Britannia 63–92 passenger airliner has been ordered by the British Overseas Airways Corporation and the Israeli airline El Al. The initial production model for B.O.A.C. is the Mk.100, but the Mks.200, 250 and 300 (freight, mixed freight and passenger, and passenger versions respectively) feature a 10 ft. 3 in. increase in fuselage length and are powered by 4,150 e.h.p. Proteus 755 (B.Pt.3) turboprops. The Mk.300 will accommodate a maximum of 104 passengers. A reconnaissance version is being developed by Canadair Ltd. as the CL-28.
Specification: Commercial transport. Engines: Four 3,780 e.h.p. Bristol Proteus 705. Weights: Empty, 78,598 lb.; max. loaded, 150,000 lb. Performance: Max. cruising speed, 357 m.p.h. at 26,000 ft.; economical cruising, 340 m.p.h. at 28,000 ft.; range (25,000 lb. payload), 4,100 miles. Dimensions: Span, 142 ft. 3½ in.; length, 114 ft.; height, 36 ft. 8 in.; wing area, 2,075 sq. ft.

BRISTOL TYPE 166 BUCKMASTER T.1   G.B.

The Buckmaster was produced in 1943 as a three-seat advanced trainer version of the Type 163 Buckingham bomber with the ventral gondola, turret and all armament removed, and the fuselage widened at the cockpit to permit side-by-side seating. The structure of the Buckmaster is identical to that of the Buckingham, and when contracts for the latter aircraft were reduced the components were employed for Buckmaster trainers, 110 being produced. The Buckmaster is powered by two 2,520 h.p. Bristol Centaurus 11 radials, and several machines of this type are still in service with the R.A.F.
Max. speed, 352 m.p.h. at 12,000 ft.; max. cruising speed, 325 m.p.h.; initial climb rate, 2,245 ft./min.; loaded weight, 33,700 lb.; span, 71 ft. 10 in.; length, 46 ft. 10 in.; height, 17 ft. 6 in.

BROCHET M.B.70   FRANCE

Derived from the M.B.50 Pipistrelle and M.B.60 Barbastrelle, the M.B.70 was designed and built by Avions Maurice Brochet, and obtained its *Certificat de Navigabilité* in July 1950. A two-seat cabin monoplane built to meet the requirements of the *Service de l'Aviation Légère et Sportive*, prototypes of three versions were produced, differing only in the type of engine installed. These were the M.B.70 (*photograph*), with a 45 h.p. Salmson 9ADB radial, the M.B.71 with a 75 h.p. Minié 4 DC32, and the M.B.72 with a 65 h.p. Continental A65. The following specification relates to the M.B.71 with the Minié.
Max. speed, 101 m.p.h.; cruising, 89 m.p.h.; initial climb rate, 787 ft./min.; range, 310 miles; empty weight, 765 lb.; loaded, 1,212 lb.; span, 33 ft. 11 in.; length, 21 ft. 4 in.; height, 8 ft. 2 in.

BROCHET M.B.80   FRANCE

Developed by Avions Maurice Brochet from the earlier M.B.71, the M.B.80 was first flown on November 15, 1951, and differs from the earlier machine primarily in having a wider fuselage and modified undercarriage. Powered by a 75 h.p. Minié 4 DC.32B engine and seating two, ten examples of the M.B.80 were produced for the *Service de l'Aviation Légère et Sportive*, and a *Certificat de Navigabilité* was acquired on June 6, 1952. The M.B.80 is of wooden construction, has balanced control surfaces and a landing gear of the steel spring type similar to that fitted to the later M.B.100.
Max. speed, 98 m.p.h.; cruising, 84 m.p.h.; initial climb rate, 689 ft./min.; range, 310 miles; empty weight, 849 lb.; loaded, 1,356 lb.; span, 34 ft. 3 in.; length, 21 ft. 7½ in.; height, 8 ft. 3 in.

BROCHET M.B.120   FRANCE

The Brochet M.B.120 two-seat light touring monoplane possesses the airframe of the three-seat M.B.100 remodelled as a two-seater, to which has been fitted the lighter wings and the landing flaps of the M.B.80 and a 90 h.p. Continental C90 engine. Flown for the first time on April 5, 1954, the M.B.120 has a steel-tube fuselage and a Cessna-type spring steel cantilever landing gear. The cabin accommodates two persons in side-by-side seats, and full dual controls may be fitted. Two prototypes of the M.B.120 have been completed at the time of writing.
Max. speed, 121 m.p.h.; cruising, 105.6 m.p.h.; ceiling, 16,404 ft.; range, 497 miles; empty weight, 1,113 lb.; loaded, 1,686 lb.; span, 34 ft. 11 in.; length, 21 ft. 3¾ in.; height, 6 ft. 6¾ in.

BROCHET M.B.100/101   FRANCE

The M.B.100 three-seat cabin monoplane was developed by Avions Maurice Brochet from the earlier M.B.70 and M.B.80. The M.B.101 is identical to the M.B.100 apart from the addition of an air filter and tropical finish to suit it for service in North Africa. An initial order for eight M.B.100s and twelve M.B.101s placed by the French *Service de l' Aviation Légère et Sportive* has been completed, and these have been distributed to flying clubs in France and North Africa.
Specification: Three-seat light cabin monoplane. Engine: One 100 h.p. Hirth H.M.504A-2. Weights: Empty, 1,023 lb.; loaded, 1,716 lb. Performance: Max. speed, 112 m.p.h.; cruising speed, 102 m.p.h.; initial climb rate, 590 ft./min.; service ceiling, 11,480 ft.; range, 375 miles. Dimensions: Span, 34 ft. 11 in.; length, 21 ft. 4 in.; height, 6 ft. 7 in.; wing area, 153 sq. ft.

BÜCKER BÜ 131B JUNGMANN   GERMANY

The Jungmann two-seat primary training biplane was designed by the Bücker Flugzeugbau G.m.b.H. in 1933, and was built in quantity before World War II for both *Luftwaffe* elementary training units and private owners. It was subsequently built under licence in Switzerland, where 100 were built by the former Dornier-Werke at Altenrhein, and in Spain, where it was built in considerable numbers by Construcciones Aeronauticas S.A. for the Spanish Air Force as the EE-3. Powered by a 100 h.p. Hirth HM.504 engine, the Jungmann is flying in some numbers in Spain, Switzerland, Hungary and Czechoslovakia (where it was built as the C.4 and C.104 by Aero). Others are flying in France and Sweden.
Max. speed, 115 m.p.h.; cruising, 106 m.p.h.; empty weight, 836 lb.; loaded, 1,474 lb.; span, 24 ft. 3 in.; length, 21 ft. 8 in.

BÜCKER BÜ 133C JUNGMEISTER   GERMANY

Introduced in 1935 as a single-seat advanced training biplane, the Jungmeister has been fitted with both the Hirth HM.506 in-line engine of 140 h.p. and the Siemens Sh 14A-4 radial of 160 h.p. The majority of those currently flying have the latter engine. In addition to production by the Bücker Flugzeugbau G.m.b.H., the Jungmeister has been built by Construcciones Aeronauticas S.A. in Spain for the Spanish Air Force under the designation ES-1, and forty-seven were built in Switzerland by the former Dornier-Werke for the Swiss Air Force. A number of aircraft of this type are flying in both Spain and Switzerland.
Max. speed, 134 m.p.h.; cruising, 125 m.p.h.; cruising range, 310 miles; climb to 3,280 ft., 2.8 minutes; empty weight, 925 lb.; loaded, 1,290 lb.; span, 21 ft. 7½ in.; length, 19 ft. 4 in.; height, 7 ft. 4½ in.

BÜCKER BÜ 181 BESTMANN   GERMANY

Produced in 1939, the Bestmann was used widely by the *Luftwaffe*, production being transferred to Fokker in Holland (which produced nearly 1,000) and Zlin in Czechoslovakia. The Swedish A. B. Hägglund & Söner built 125 Bestmanns for the *Flygvapnet* between 1944–46, and ninety of these have now been sold to Germany. Production continued in Czechoslovakia after World War 2 for the Czech Air Force as the C.6 and C.106 (105 h.p. Minor 4-III) and in civil form as the Zlin 381 (*photo*). The Bestmann is being built in Egypt as the "Republic of Egypt", and one civil machine is designated Gomhouria Mk.2.
Specification: Two-seat primary trainer. Engine: One 105 h.p. Hirth H.M.504. Weights: Empty, 1,056 lb.; loaded, 1,650 lb. Performance: Max. speed, 215 m.p.h.; cruising speed, 121 m.p.h.; range, 500 miles. Dimensions: Span, 34 ft. 9 in.; length, 25 ft. 5 in.; height, 6 ft. 5 in.; wing area, 145 sq. ft.

BUDD JRB-3 CONESTOGA   U.S.A.

The Edward G. Budd Manufacturing Company, which specialised in welded stainless steel products, was awarded a contract in 1942 by the U.S. Navy for the development and manufacture of a transport of stainless steel construction. A contract for 200 machines designated JRB-1 Conestoga was awarded in August 1942, and the prototype flew in October 1943. Delays in production resulted in a reduction of the U.S. Navy order to twenty-five machines, and several of these are still employed by civil operators in Central America. The JRB-3 is powered by two 1,200 h.p. Pratt & Whitney R-1830-92 Twin-Wasp radial engines.

Max. speed, 197 m.p.h. at 7,500 ft.; cruising, 165 m.p.h.; normal range, 700 miles; empty weight, 20,156 lb.; loaded, 33,860 lb.; span, 100 ft.; length, 68 ft.; height, 31 ft. 9 in.; wing area, 1,400 sq. ft.

C.5 POLAR   NORWAY

The Polar general utility monoplane was designed by Birger Hönning-stad and built by Wideröe's Flyveselskap A/S in 1948. Designed as a five-passenger taxi or charter aircraft, suitable for operation on wheels, floats or skis, the Polar is powered by a 350 h.p. Wright R-760-E2 radial engine and is of particularly rugged construction. Only one prototype was built, and this is currently employed by the Wideröe company. The following specification refers to the Polar fitted with a wheel undercarriage.

Max. speed, 150 m.p.h.; cruising, 130 m.p.h.; initial climb rate, 800 ft./min.; range, 625 miles; empty weight, 2,550 lb.; loaded, 4,150 lb.; span, 45 ft.; length, 29 ft. 6 in.; height, 8 ft. 4 in.; wing area, 269 sq. ft.

C-3603 (Fabrique Fédérale)   SWITZERLAND

Produced by the Fabrique Fédérale d'Avions Emmen, the C-3603 was developed from the C-3600 of 1939. The C-3603 was essentially a developed production version of the C-3600 prototype, from which it differed in having retractable landing gear and the 860 h.p. Hispano-Suiza 12Y engine replaced by a 1,000 h.p. Saurer/SLM Hispano-Suiza 12Y-51 engine. One hundred and fifty C-3603 attack aircraft were produced by the Fabrique Fédérale and the Dornier Flugzeugwerke, and a number of aircraft of this type remain in service with the Swiss Air Force for target-towing duties.

Max. speed, 295 m.p.h. at 15,750 ft., and 240 m.p.h. at sea level; service ceiling, 32,800 ft.; empty weight, 5,009 lb.; normal loaded, 7,600 lb.; max. 8,695 lb.; span, 45 ft. 1½ in.; length, 36 ft. 9½ in.; height, 13 ft. 1 in.

C-3604 (Fabrique Féderalé)   SWITZERLAND

The C-3604 was a higher-powered, more heavily armed development of the previously-described C-3603, but only ten machines of this type were completed, and several of these are still in service with the Swiss Air Force. Designed as a two-seat attack aircraft and carrying an armament of three 20-mm. cannon and four 7.5-mm. machine guns, the C-3604 is powered by a 1,250 h.p. Saurer/SLM Hispano-Suiza 12Y-52 engine and is of all-metal construction. Remaining machines are used primarily for the target-towing, supply-dropping and training roles.

Max. speed, 348 m.p.h. at 14,764 ft. and 298 m.p.h. at sea level; cruising, 226 m.p.h. at 15,750 ft.; empty weight, 6,260 lb.; loaded weight, 9,480 lb.; span, 45 ft. 1 in.; length, 33 ft. 7½ in.; height, 11 ft.; wing area, 307.8 sq. ft.

C.A.B. GY-20 MINICAB   FRANCE

Produced by Constructions Aéronautiques du Bearn, the Minicab flew for the first time on February 1, 1949, and the first production machine was completed early in 1952. The Minicab has since been delivered in two versions: the GY-20 and the GY-201, which differ only in equipment. Seventeen of the former version and nineteen of the latter are currently flying in France. In 1939, the Minicab won the *Coupe de Deauville* (1st in all categories), the *Grand Prix Aérien de Vichy* and the *Concours d'Elégance de Biarritz*. In July 1951, it established a world distance record (F.A.I. Category I) by flying 1,134 miles non-stop.

Specification: Two-seat cabin monoplane. Engine: One 65 h.p. Continental A65-8. Weights: Empty, 595 lb.; loaded, 1,069 lb. Performance: Max. speed, 124 m.p.h.; cruising, 112 m.p.h.; initial climb rate, 680 ft./min.; range, 466 miles. Dimensions: Span, 24 ft. 11 in.; length, 17 ft. 10½ in.; height, 5 ft. 5 in.; wing area, 107.6 sq. ft.

C.A.B. GY-30 SUPERCAB   FRANCE

Designed by M. Yves Gardan and produced by the Constructions Aéronautiques du Béarn (C.A.B.), the GY-30 Supercab is a development of the GY-20 Minicab, and was flown for the first time on February 5, 1954. Differing from its predecessor primarily in having a higher-powered engine and fully-retractable main undercarriage members, the GY-30 Supercab is powered by a 90 h.p. Continental C90 and seats two persons side-by-side. A pre-production batch of five Supercab light aircraft has been completed, two of these aircraft being ordered for evaluation by the *Service de l' Aviation Légère et Sportive* (S.A.L.S.).

Max. speed, 170 m.p.h.; cruising, 146 m.p.h.; initial climb rate, 767 ft./min.; service ceiling, 16,400 ft.; range, 746 miles; empty weight, 880 lb.; loaded, 1,348 lb.; span, 26 ft. 10 in.; length, 18 ft.; height, 5 ft. 5 in.

CAMAIR MODEL 480   U.S.A.

The Camair 480 is a twin-engine conversion of the Ryan Navion, differing in several respects from the well-known Riley Twin Navion conversion. Developed by a division of the Cameron Iron Works, Inc., of Texas, the Camair 480 is considerably more powerful than the Twin Navion, having two 240 h.p. Continental 0-470-B engines. It has increased fin and rudder area to improve single-engine flight characteristics, a longer fuselage nose, and two 29 imp. gall. fuel tanks at the wingtips to augment internal tankage. The cabin provides accommodation for four persons, and full dual controls are fitted.

Cruising speed (70 per cent), 192 m.p.h.; initial climb rate, 1,750 ft./min.; service ceiling, 22,000 ft.; range, 900 miles; empty weight, 2,730 lb.; loaded, 3,930 lb.; approx. span, 34 ft.; length, 27 ft. 11 in.

CALL-AIR 100 MODEL A-2   U.S.A.

The Call-Air Model A two-seat light cabin monoplane was first produced by the Call Aircraft Company in 1941, and production commenced in 1943. The Model A is powered by a 100 h.p. Lycoming 0-235 engine and is generally similar to the Models A-2 and A-3 which have the 125 h.p. Lycoming 0-290 and 125 h.p. Continental C125 engines respectively. An agricultural version of the Model A-2 has spray booms permanently installed within the wings and carries the liquid in a jettisonable ventral tank. The Model A provides accommodation for two in side-by-side seats. The following specification relates to the Model A-2.

Max. speed, 120 m.p.h.; cruising, 109 m.p.h.; initial climb rate, 1,000 ft./min.; range, 456 miles; empty weight, 975 lb.; loaded, 1,550 lb.; span, 35 ft. 9⅜ in.; length, 23 ft. 5⅜ in.; height, 6 ft.

CANADAIR SABRE MK.6   CANADA

Production of the North American Sabre was commenced in 1949 by Canadair Limited of Montreal, the first Canadair-built machine, an F-86A designated Sabre Mk.1, being flown on August 9, 1950. The Sabre Mk.1 served as a prototype for the subsequent Sabres Mk.2 and 4, powered by the 5,200 lb.s.t. J47-GE-13 and 5,800 lb.s.t. J47-GE-27 engines respectively. The Sabre Mk.3 was a North-American-built F-86E converted for the Avro Orenda turbojet, and the Sabres Mk.5 and Mk.6 (*photo*) are subsequent production versions powered by the 6,500 lb.s.t. Orenda 10 and 7,275 lb.s.t. Orenda 14 engines respectively. The Sabre Mks.2 and 4 have been supplied to Greece and Turkey.

Approx. max. speed, 710 m.p.h.; initial climb rate, 14,000 ft./min.; approx. loaded weight, 17,500 lb.; span, 37 ft. 1 in.; length, 37 ft. 6 in.

CANADAIR FOUR   CANADA

The Canadair Four is a progressive development of the DC-4M-2 which embodies features of both the Douglas DC-4 and the DC-6, and was adapted to take four 1,730 h.p. Merlin 620 engines. The DC-4M-2 is externally similar to the Canadair Four, and is employed by both the R.C.A.F. and Trans-Canada Air Lines. The Canadair Four has been delivered to Canadian Pacific Airlines and British Overseas Airways Corporation, the latter airline designating the type Argonaut. A total of seventy-four DC-4Ms and Canadair Fours were built by Canadair Ltd.

Specification: Forty-seat commercial transport. Engines: Four 1,760 h.p. Rolls-Royce Merlin 626. Weights: Empty, 46,832 lb.; loaded, 82,300 lb. Performance: Max. cruising speed, 325 m.p.h. at 25,200 ft.; 280 m.p.h. at 12,800 ft.; service ceiling, 29,500 ft. (Note: These performance figures refer to the aircraft at a gross weight of 70,000 lb.). Dimensions: Span, 117 ft. 6 in.; length, 93 ft. 7½ in.; height, 27 ft. 6¼ in.

CANCARGO CBY-3 LOADMASTER   CANADA

Built under the direction of Vincent J. Burnelli, the CBY-3 Loadmaster is unusual in employing an aerofoil-section fuselage which, capable of taking large concentrated loads, provides nearly fifty per cent of the lifting surface available. The fuselage is of sufficient width to allow the seating of twenty-four passengers in four rows with two aisles, and as a freighter the Loadmaster provides a useful cargo volume of 2,070 cu. ft. The sole prototype is powered by two 1,450 h.p. Pratt & Whitney R-2000-2SD13G Twin Wasp engines, and trials commenced in 1945.

Max. speed, 223 m.p.h. at 7,500 ft., and 208 m.p.h. at sea level; cruising, 193 m.p.h. at 10,000 ft.; initial climb rate, 1,050 ft./min.; range, 1,200 miles; empty weight, 16,800 lb.; loaded, 27,000 lb.; span, 86 ft.; length, 54 ft. 7 in.

C.A.P.4 PAULISTINHA   BRAZIL

Built by the Companhia Aeronautica Paulista in some numbers, the Paulistinha was produced in three versions; the C.A.P.4 tourer, the C.A.P.4B ambulance aircraft, and the C.A.P.4C military observation monoplane. The latter differs from the version illustrated here in having a cut-down rear fuselage with the side windows extended aft. All three versions are powered by the 65 h.p. Franklin 4AC-176-B2 engine. Production of the Paulistinha was terminated in 1948 when the Paulista company experienced financial difficulties.

Max. speed, 96.5 m.p.h.; cruising, 87 m.p.h.; initial climb rate, 610 ft./min.; range, 311 miles; empty weight, 706 lb.; loaded, 1,190 lb.; span, 33 ft. 1⅛ in.; length, 21 ft. 9⅞ in.; height, 6 ft. 4¾ in.

CAPRONI CA 100 CAPRONCINE   ITALY

Produced as a tandem two-seat training biplane in 1929, the Ca 100 was built in several versions, and fitted with a variety of engines in the 80–100 h.p. bracket, including the Colombo S.63, the Fiat A.50, the Walter Mars, and the Isotta Fraschini Asso. The Ca 100*bis* was a touring model powered by a 130 h.p. de Havilland Gipsy, and the Ca 100 *Idro* was a twin-float seaplane variant. Examples of both the Ca 100T and the Ca 100 *Idro* are still flying in Italy. The Ca 100 is of wooden construction, and the version illustrated and referred to in the specification is powered by a 90 h.p. Cirrus Minor engine. One example is flying in Peru.

Max. speed, 102 m.p.h.; cruising, 87 m.p.h.; ceiling, 14,763 ft.; range, 435 miles; empty weight, 882 lb.; loaded, 1,587 lb.; span, 32 ft. 10 in.; length, 23 ft. 10 in.; height, 8 ft. 11 in.

CAPRONI CA 113   ITALY

The Ca 113 two-seat advanced training and aerobatic biplane was produced in small numbers in the early 'thirties, and one example remains flying in Italy. Powered by a 370 h.p. Piaggio Stella VII radial engine, the Ca 113 is of mixed construction, the wings being of wood with fabric covering, and the fuselage and tail assembly having welded steel-tube frame-works covered with fabric. Differentially-controlled ailerons are fitted on the upper planes and small auxiliary balance surfaces are attached to the bottom planes. A special carburetter is fitted for inverted flying, and the type participated in a number of pre-war competitions.

Max. speed, 155 m.p.h.; climb to 6,560 ft. in 3.5 minutes; ceiling, 24,600 ft.; range, 186 miles; empty weight, 1,870 lb.; loaded, 2,420 lb.; span, 34 ft. 5 in.; length, 23 ft. 11 in.; height, 8 ft. 11 in.; wing area, 290.5 sq. ft.

CAPRONI CA 148   ITALY

The Caproni Ca 148 was originally a colonial development of the Ca 133 specially modified for operation in East Africa. Powered by three 460 h.p. Piaggio Stella VII R.C. radials, the Ca 148 differed from the Ca 133 primarily in having a strengthened undercarriage, and Piaggio d'Ascanio variable-pitch airscrews. In addition, the loaded weight was increased to allow a normal load of 7,716 pounds. The cabin can accommodate a maximum of sixteen passengers, and a crew of two is normally carried. Structure is of welded steel-tube with metal and fabric covering. The example illustrated was formerly employed by the Italian Air Force.

Max. speed, 174 m.p.h. at 5,575 ft.; ceiling, 21,320 ft.; range, 838 miles; empty weight, 8,580 lb.; loaded, 14,700 lb.; span, 69 ft. 8 in.; length, 50 ft. 4 in.; height, 13 ft. 1 in.; wing area, 700 sq. ft.

CAPRONI CA 164   ITALY

Produced by Aeronautica Predappio S.A., a division of the Caproni Group. in 1937, the Ca 164 tandem two-seat training and touring biplane was built in some numbers immediately prior to the war, and several examples remain airworthy in Italy. Powered by a 185 h.p. Alfa 115-1 engine, the Ca 164 is unusual in that, like the earlier Ca 100, the span of the lower planes is greater than that of the upper planes. It was employed as an elementary training biplane by the *Regia Aeronautica* during the war years.

Max. speed, 134 m.p.h.; cruising, 115 m.p.h.; range, 330 miles; empty weight, 1,873 lb.; loaded, 2,600 lb.; span, 30 ft. 10 in.; length, 22 ft. 10 in.; height, 8 ft. 6 in.

CAPRONI TRENTO F.5   ITALY

The F.5 tandem two-seat training and light touring monoplane designed by Ing. Stelio Frati, was the first light jet aircraft of Italian design, flying for the first time on May 20, 1952. Powered by a 330 lb.s.t. Turboméca Palas turbojet, the F.5 is of all-wood construction, and provides dual controls and jettisonable cockpit canopies. The construction of the F.5 is extremely simple, and is actually an adaptation of conventional glider technique. A retractable nosewheel undercarriage is fitted.

Max. speed, 224 m.p.h. at sea level; 242 m.p.h. at optimum altitude; climb to 16,400 ft., 23 minutes; service ceiling, 26,300 ft.; empty weight, 1,032 lb.; loaded, 1,650 lb.; span, 25 ft. 9 in.; length, 21 ft. 7½ in.; wing area, 107.63 sq. ft.

C.A.S.A.2111H-16-L   SPAIN

The C.A.S.A.2111H-16-L is a licence-built version of the German Heinkel He 111H-16 medium bomber produced in Spain by the Construcciones Aeronauticas S.A., 236 machines having been built for the Spanish Air Force. This obsolescent bomber, designated B.7, is currently standard equipment with Spanish bombing elements, and several early German-built He 111Es (which differ primarily in having a stepped crew compartment) are also in service in Spain for meteorological reconnaissance under the designation MB.2. Some Heinkel He 111H bombers converted for transport duties remain in service with the Rumanian Air Force. Two 1,340 h.p. Jumo 211F.

Max. speed, 250 m.p.h. at 17,000 ft.; service ceiling, 27,500 ft.; range with maximum fuel, 1,750 miles; empty weight, 17,000 lb.; loaded, 26,500 lb.; span, 74 ft. 3 in.; length, 54 ft. 6 in.; height, 13 ft. 9 in.

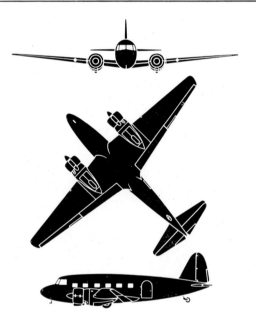

C.A.S.A.201 ALCOTAN   SPAIN

The Alcotan flew for the first time on February 11, 1949, and one hundred machines have been ordered by the Spanish Air Force under the designation T.5. Military versions include the 201-D and 201-E crew trainers powered by Cheetah 27 radials, and the Sirio-powered 201-F and 201-G. The following specification refers to the C.A.S.A.201-D navigation and radio trainer, and the 201-E bombing and photographic trainer. Figures for the 201-F and -G (two 500 h.p. E.N.M.A.Sirio-VII-A radial engines) are quoted in parentheses.

Specification: Military crew trainer. Engines: Two 475 h.p. Armstrong Siddeley Cheetah 27. Weights: Empty, 7,830 (7,920) lb.; loaded, 11,230 (12,100) lb. Performance: Max. speed, 203 (219) m.p.h.; service ceiling, 18,370 (20,000) ft.; range, 621 miles; duration, 4 hours. Dimensions: Span, 60 ft. 4 in.; length, 45 ft. 3 in.; height, 12 ft. 8 in.; wing area, 450 sq. ft.

C.A.S.A.202 HALCÓN   SPAIN

The second twin-engined aircraft of original design to be produced in Spain, the C.A.S.A.202 Halcón flew for the first time on May 21, 1953, and twenty examples are currently under construction for use on Iberia's internal routes. Powered by two 775 h.p. E.N.M.A. Beta B-4 radial engines, the Halcón can accommodate from fourteen to eighteen passengers and has a crew of three. It is possible that a military transport version of the Halcón may be ordered by the Spanish Air Force. Construction is all-metal.

Max. speed, 192.5 m.p.h. at sea level and 230 m.p.h. at 9,315 ft.; cruising speed (70 per cent power), 205 m.p.h.; service ceiling, 23,950 ft.; empty weight, 11,615 lb.; loaded, 17,090 lb.; span, 70 ft. 9 in.; length, 52 ft. 6 in.; height, 12 ft. 6 in.; wing area, 617.6 sq. ft.

C.A.S.A.207 AZOR   SPAIN

The Azor is basically a scaled-up version of the C.A.S.A.202 Halcón, and is primarily intended as a thirty/thirty-eight-seater commercial transport, although it is likely to be produced also in military transport form to replace the C.A.S.A.352-L (licence-built version of the Ju 52/3M g7e) currently serving with the Spanish Air Force transport elements. The prototype Azor, completed in August 1955, is powered by two 2,040 h.p. Bristol Hercules 730 radial engines, is of all-metal construction and carries a crew of four. The following performance figures are estimated.

Max. speed, 263 m.p.h. at 5,000 ft.; cruising speed, 215 m.p.h. at 10,000 ft.; service ceiling, 25,250 ft.; range (30 passengers), 1,100 miles; empty weight, 21,655 lb.; loaded, 33,075 lb.; span, 91 ft. 1 in.; length, 68 ft. 5 in.; height, 25 ft. 5 in.; wing area, 923.2 sq. ft.

CAUDRON C.277 LUCIOLE   FRANCE

The Luciole tandem two-seat light biplane, originally developed in the late 'twenties, was subsequently produced in considerable numbers and several versions. Versions currently flying in France include the C.270 (6) powered by the 95 h.p. Salmson 7 Ac; the C.272-3 (1) with a 120 h.p. Renault 4 Pdi; C.272-4 (1) with a 140 h.p. Renault 4 Pei; C.272-5 (1) with a 100 h.p. Renault 4 Pgi; the similarly-powered C.275 (11), and the C.277 (8) with the 140 h.p. Renault 4 Pei. All six variants of the Luciole are externally similar, and the C.277 (*illustrated*), was the final production model. The specification refers to the C.277 Luciole.

Max. speed, 107 m.p.h.; 93 m.p.h. at 3,280 ft.; range, 388 miles; empty weight, 1,067 lb.; loaded, 1,848 lb.; span, 32 ft. 5½ in.; length, 25 ft. 2 in.; height, 9 ft.; wing area, 248.2 sq. ft.

CAUDRON C.282-8 PHALÈNE VIII   FRANCE

The C.282-8 Phalène is representative of many elderly Caudron monoplanes currently flying in France. The C.282-8, five of which are flying, differs from the C.282-9 and C.282-10 (four and two examples flying respectively), primarily in the type of engine installed, the C.282-8 having a 120 h.p. Renault 4 Pdi engine and the two later models having the 140 h.p. Renault 4 Pei. The C.286-3 has a 120 h.p. Gipsy Major 1. Two examples of the C.480 Fregate are also flying. The Fregate is a development of the Phalène with a 140 h.p. Renault 4 Pei and accommodation for five persons instead of four. The photograph and specification relate to the C.282-8 Phalène four-seater.

Max. speed, 115 m.p.h.; cruising, 96 m.p.h.; ceiling, 14,760 ft.; range, 528 miles; loaded weight, 2,420 lb.; span, 38 ft. 1 in.; length, 27 ft.; height, 6 ft. 7 in.; wing area, 252 sq. ft.

CAUDRON (NORD) C.449-1 GÖELAND FRANCE

Originally produced in 1934 as the C.440, the Göeland was produced throughout the occupation of France by the Caudron-Renault concern for both the Vichy Government and the *Luftwaffe*. After the liberation of France and the incorporation of the Caudron factory into the S.N.C.A. du Nord, production of the Göeland was continued in the C.445-3 and C.449-1 versions, a total of 325 post-war machines being built. The C.445-3 and C.449-1 differed in the type of engine installed, the former having two Renault 6Q-10 or 6Q-11, and the latter having Renault 6Q-20 or 6Q-21 engines, all of 220 h.p. The Göeland accommodates six passengers.

Max. speed, 191 m.p.h.; cruising, 163 m.p.h.; service ceiling, 21,320 ft.; range, 350 miles; empty weight, 6,005 lb.; loaded, 8,140 lb.; span, 57 ft. 7 in.; length, 44 ft. 9 in.; height, 15 ft. 9 in.; wing area, 430 sq. ft.

CAUDRON C.510 PELICAN   FRANCE

The C.510 Pelican is a development of the C.282 Phalène from which it differs primarily in having a longer cabin which permits the installation of a stretcher. In the ambulance role, the Pelican carries the pilot, an attendant and a stretcher. Alternatively, accommodation is provided for four persons. The Pelican also has modified ailerons and tail unit, and is powered by a 140 h.p. Renault 4 Pei Bengali engine. Examples of the Pelican are registered in Sweden and France. The Pelican is of mixed construction and may be fitted with full dual controls.

Max. speed, 115 m.p.h.; cruising speed, 102.4 m.p.h.; minimum speed, 43.47 m.p.h.; range, 620 miles; empty weight, 1,377 lb.; loaded, 2,508 lb.; span, 38 ft. 9 in.; length, 27 ft. 11 in.; wing area, 255.5 sq. ft.

CAUDRON C.601 AIGLON   FRANCE

First produced in 1935, the Aiglon was built in two versions, the C.600 powered by a 100 h.p. Renault 4 Pgi, and the C.601 (*illustrated*) powered by a 140 h.p. Renault 4 Pei. Three examples of each type are currently registered in France, and these are to be seen with both open and enclosed cockpits. The Aiglon is a tandem two-seat light monoplane of wooden construction with stressed plywood skin. The following specification refers to the C.601 model with a 140 h.p. Renault 4 Pei Bengali Junior four-cylinder in-line inverted air-cooled engine.

Max. speed, 140 m.p.h.; cruising speed, 124 m.p.h.; landing speed, 34 m.p.h.; service ceiling, 19,680 ft.; range, 335 miles; empty weight, 1,276 lb.; loaded, 1,936 lb.; span, 37 ft. 4 in.; length, 24 ft. 11 in.; height, 6 ft. 7 in.; wing area, 156 sq. ft.

CAUDRON C.635 SIMOUN   FRANCE

The Simoun was first shown at the 1934 Paris Aero Show as the C.620, and was subsequently produced in considerable numbers, the final production model being the C.635 illustrated here. Powered by two 220 h.p. Renault 453-01 or 6Q-09 engines, the C.635 Simoun has an enclosed cabin for four persons, seated in two pairs. Aft of the cabin is a large baggage compartment, and the rear seats can be removed to suit the Simoun for use as a light freighter. Eight C.635 Simouns are currently registered in France, and several other examples are believed to be flying in North Africa.

Max. speed, 186 m.p.h.; cruising speed, 168 m.p.h.; service ceiling, 19,680 ft.; range in still air, 560 miles; empty weight, 1,760 lb.; loaded, 2,706 lb.; span, 34 ft. 1 in.; length, 28 ft. 6 in.; height, 7 ft.; wing area, 172.16 sq. ft.

CASMUNIZ 52   BRAZIL

Designed specially to operate from airfields of limited size, the Casmuniz 52 five-seat cabin monoplane is the first all-metal twin-engined aircraft to be designed in Brazil. The prototype was completed in 1953 by Cassio Muniz S.A. of São Paulo, and eighty per cent of the skin is made of unformed or single-curvature aluminium sheet panels to facilitate replacement in any locality of limited resources. The Casmuniz 52 is powered by two 185 h.p. Continental E185 engines, and the sole prototype has been sold to the Oficina de Manutençãoe Recuperaçao de Aviões, together with the manufacturing rights.

Max. speed, 200 m.p.h.; approx. cruising speed, 165 m.p.h.; range (prototype) 700 miles, (production) 900 miles; weights and dimensions: no details available at the time of writing.

CENTRAL-LAMSON L-101 AIR TRACTOR U.S.A.

The L-101 Air Tractor was designed specially for agricultural work, including dusting, spraying, seeding, fertilising, weed-killing, timber-spraying, etc., and particular attention has been paid to low maintenance costs. The prototype flew for the first time on December 10, 1953, powered by a 450 h.p. Pratt & Whitney R-985 radial engine. All four wing panels, the flaps and ailerons, interplane struts and all tail surfaces are interchangeable, and the rear fuselage is uncovered to facilitate cleaning after the use of corrosive sprays and ease the checking of control linkages.

Cruising speed, 70–90 m.p.h.; initial climb rate, 450 ft./min.; empty weight, 3,200 lb.; loaded, 5,600 lb.; span, 33 ft. 7 in.; length, 26 ft. 5 in.; height, 10 ft. 8 in.; wing area, 350 sq. ft.

C.C.F.NORSEMAN V   CANADA

First flown in 1935, the Norseman was built in quantity during the war years by Noorduyn Aircraft Ltd., and 759 Norseman IVs were delivered to the U.S.A.F. under the designations YC-64, C-64A and C-64B. Manufacturing rights for the Norseman were purchased by the Canadian Car and Foundry, which concern produced an improved version, the Norseman V. A new model, the Norseman VII with a metal wing and lengthened fuselage, was built and tested by the C.C.F., but the manufacturing rights have now been returned to Mr. R. B. Noorduyn, whose company supplies spares, etc.

Specification: Eight-seat general-purpose transport. Engine: One 600 h.p. Pratt & Whitney Wasp Junior R-1340-S3H1. Weights: Empty, 4,240 lb.; loaded, 7,400 lb. Performance: Max. speed, 155 m.p.h.; cruising, 141 m.p.h.; service ceiling, 17,000 ft.; range, 464 miles. Dimensions: Span, 51 ft. 8 in.; length, 32 ft. 4 in.; height, 10 ft. 1 in.; wing area, 325 sq. ft.

CESSNA AW   U.S.A.

The Cessna AW four-seat cabin monoplane produced between 1928 and 1930, was introduced at the 1928 National Air Races, and won the Class "A" Transcontinental Air Derby. Of mixed construction with fabric covering and powered by a 110 h.p. Warner Scarab radial engine, the Cessna AW achieved considerable popularity, and forty machines of this type were delivered to the Curtiss Flying Service. Two Cessna AW monoplanes are currently active in the U.S.A.

Max. speed, 128 m.p.h.; initial climb, 700 ft./min.; ceiling, 18,000 ft.; empty weight, 1,250 lb.; loaded, 2,300 lb.; span, 40 ft. 6½ in.; length, 23 ft. 8½ in.; height, 7 ft. 4 in.; wing area, 224 sq. ft.

CESSNA AIRMASTER   U.S.A.

The Cessna Airmaster four-seat cabin monoplane was first produced in 1934 under the model designation C-34 (indicating the year of introduction), being followed in 1937 by the C-37, and in 1938 by the C-38, all three models being powered by the 145 h.p. Warner Super-Scarab engine and differing only in detail refinements. In 1939 the Models C-145 and C-165 were introduced, the latter having a 165 h.p. Warner Super-Scarab engine. A number of C-145 and C-165 Airmasters were impressed in the U.S.A.F. as utility transports during the war under the designations UC-77 and UC-94. Specification relates to the C-145.

Max. speed, 165 m.p.h.; cruising, 151 m.p.h. at 8,200 ft.; initial climb rate, 1,000 ft./min.; ceiling, 18,000 ft.; range, 785 miles; empty weight, 1,380 lb.; loaded, 2,450 lb.; span, 34 ft. 2 in.; length, 24 ft. 8 in.

CESSNA T-50 (BOBCAT)   U.S.A.

Introduced in 1939 as a light commercial transport, the Model T-50 was adopted in 1940 as a military advanced trainer. Initially ordered by the R.C.A.F. under the name "Crane" (Jacobs R-755-9 engines), the T-50 was also ordered by the U.S.A.A.F. as a transitional trainer, and 33 were supplied in 1941 with 295 h.p. Lycoming R-680-9 engines. The Jacobs engines were later standardised, and 4,636 were delivered to the U.S.A.A.F. as the AT-17, -17A, -17B and -17C trainers, and UC-78, -78A, -78B and -78C light transports. Some fifteen hundred surplus UC-78s and AT-17s are used by commercial organisations throughout the world.
Specification: Five-seat light transport. Engines: Two 245 h.p. Jacobs R-755-9. Weights: Empty, 4,050 lb.; loaded, 5,700 lb. Performance: Max. speed, 179 m.p.h.; initial climb rate, 1,525 ft./min.; cruising range, 750 miles. Dimensions: Span, 41 ft. 11 in.; length, 32 ft. 9 in.; height, 9 ft. 11 in.; wing area, 295 sq. ft.

CESSNA MODEL 170B   U.S.A.

First introduced in 1948, the Model 170 is virtually a four-seat version of the Model 120, although it is a completely new design. Three production versions have been produced, the Models 170, 170A and 170B; all are basically similar, employing the same power plant, but the 1953 Model 170B (*illustrated here*), introduced a number of new features, the most noticeable external change being the redesigned and lengthened engine cowling. Several thousand aircraft of this type are flying in the U.S.A., Canada and Central and South America.
Specification: Four-seat cabin monoplane. Engine: One 145 h.p. Continental C-145-2. Weights: Empty, 1,205 lb.; loaded, 2,200 lb. Performance: Max. speed, 140 m.p.h.; cruising speed, 120 m.p.h.; initial climb rate, 690 ft./min.; service ceiling, 15,500 ft.; endurance, 4.5 hours. Dimensions: Span, 36 ft.; length, 24 ft. 11½ in.; height, 6 ft. 7½ in.; wing area, 175 sq. ft.

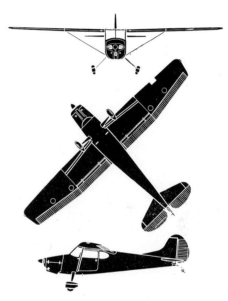

CESSNA MODEL 180   U.S.A.

Introduced at the beginning of 1953, production deliveries commencing in February of that year, the Model 180 employs the same wing as the Model 170, but has an entirely redesigned fuselage, tail assembly and considerably more power. The Model 180 employs the "para-lift" flaps originally developed for the Model 305 (L-19 Bird Dog), and a fully adjustable horizontal stabilizer is used, obviating the need for trim tabs. A twin-float seaplane version of the Model 180 has been produced, and a version modified for crop-dressing is flying in New Zealand.
Specification: Four-seat cabin monoplane. Engine: One 225 h.p. Continental O-470-A. Weights: Empty, 1,460 lb.; loaded, 2,550 lb. Performance: Max. speed, 165 m.p.h.; cruising speed, 150 m.p.h.; initial climb rate, 1,150 ft./min.; service ceiling, 19,800 ft.; endurance, 4.5 hours. Dimensions: Span, 36 ft.; length, 26 ft. 2 in.; height, 7 ft. 6⅜ in.; wing area, 175 sq. ft.

CESSNA MODELS 190-195   U.S.A.

The Cessna Models 190 and 195 are externally identical and differ primarily in the engine installed; the 190 is powered by the 240 h.p. Continental R-670-23, and the 195 has the 300 h.p. Jacobs R-755-A2. The Model 195A has the 245 h.p. Jacobs R-744-A2. The U.S.A.F. has acquired a number of Model 195s under the designation LC-126A, and these are used for Arctic rescue work (*photo*). The silhouette depicts the revised 1953 production model with close-cowled engine, airscrew spinner, and a 50 per cent increase in flap area. The specification relates to the Model 195A.
Specification: Five-seat cabin monoplane. Engine: One 245 h.p. Jacobs R-744-A2. Weights: Empty, 2,030 lb.; loaded, 3,350 lb. Performance: Max. speed, 173 m.p.h.; cruising speed, 155 m.p.h.; initial climb rate, 1,050 ft./min.; service ceiling, 16,000 ft.; range, 750 miles. Dimensions: Span, 36 ft. 2 in.; length, 27 ft. 4 in.; height, 7 ft. 2 in.; wing area, 218.125 sq. ft.

CESSNA L-19A BIRD DOG   U.S.A.

The L-19A Bird Dog (Model 305) has been produced in quantity for the U.S. Army, U.S.A.F., and U.S. Marine Corps. It has also been delivered to the R.C.A.F. and the Japanese Self-Defence Force. Developed from the civil Model 170, quantity deliveries of the Bird Dog commenced in the autumn of 1950. The U.S. Marine Corps designation for the Bird Dog is OE-1, and the U.S. Navy has ordered twenty-five of a progressive development designated OE-2. This differs principally in having a longer nose to house a 260 h.p. Continental SO-370 engine, and taller, more angular tail surfaces.
Specification: Two-seat observation and reconnaissance monoplane. Engine: One 213 h.p. Continental O-470-11. Weights: Empty, 1,400 lb.; loaded, 2,200 lb. Performance: Max. speed, 146 m.p.h. at 5,000 ft.; cruising speed, 115 m.p.h.; initial climb rate, 1,290 ft./min.; service ceiling, 21,200 ft.; range, 620 miles. Dimensions: Span, 36 ft.; length, 25 ft.; height, 7 ft. 6 in.; wing area, 174 sq. ft.

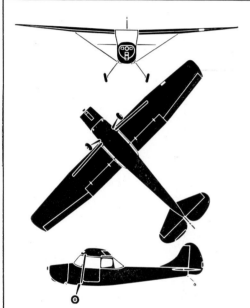

CESSNA MODEL 310   U.S.A.

The Model 310 flew for the first time on January 3, 1953, and has since been produced in quantity. Unique among light twin-engined aircraft in having all fuel housed in two 41.6 imp. gall. wingtip tanks, the Model 310 is of all-metal construction. The main undercarriage members retract inwards to lie flat in the wing undersurfaces, this method of retraction being chosen in preference to the more usual engine nacelle mainwheel housings in order to keep nacelle depth to a minimum; this effectively reduces frontal drag.
Specification: Five-seat cabin monoplane. Engines: Two 240 h.p. Continental O-470-B. Weights: Empty, 2,850 lb.; max. loaded, 4,600 lb. Performance: Max. speed, 220 m.p.h. at sea level; cruising, 205 m.p.h. at 8,000 ft.; range (60 per cent power), 875 miles at 10,000 ft.; initial climb rate, 1,700 ft./min.; service ceiling, 20,000 ft. Dimensions: Span, 36 ft.; length, 27 ft.; height, 10 ft. 6 in.

CESSNA T-37A U.S.A.

The Cessna Model 318, or XT-37, was flown for the first time on October 12, 1954, and the initial contract for eleven pre-production T-37A trainers has since been supplemented by further contracts. The T-37A was designed to meet U.S.A.F. requirements formulated in 1952 for a jet basic trainer for use as an intermediate stage between primary training on a piston-engined type and advanced training on a high-speed jet aircraft. It is unusual among U.S. military trainers in providing side-by-side seating for pupil and instructor.

Specification: Two-seat basic trainer. Engines: Two 920 lbs. .t. Continental J69-T-15. Weights: Empty, 3,116 lbs.; loaded, 5,600 lb. Performance: Max. speed, 393 m.p.h. at 35,000 ft.; cruising speed, 310 m.p.h.; initial climb rate, 3,000 ft./min.; service ceiling, 39,800 ft.; max. range, 935 miles. Dimensions: Span, 33 ft.; length, 27 ft. 1 in.; height, 8 ft. 9¼ in.; wing area, 181.8 sq. ft.

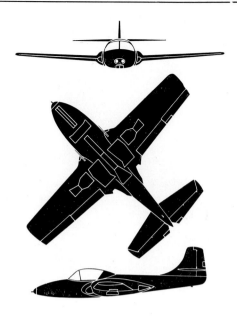

CESSNA MODEL 120 U.S.A.

The first of the Cessna Aircraft Company's post-war range of light cabin monoplanes to be produced in quantity, the Model 120 is a two-seater of all-metal construction, powered by an 85 h.p. Continental C85-12 engine. The Model 140 (*illustrated*) is identical to the Model 120, but has a number of refinements, including starter, generator and battery, and manually-operated all-metal plain-hinge flaps between ailerons and fuselage. Several thousand examples of both Models 120 and 140 are flying. The Model 140 was superseded in production in 1949 by the Model 140A. This has a 90 h.p. Continental C90 engine.

Max. speed, 123 m.p.h.; cruising, 105 m.p.h.; range, 450 miles; initial climb rate, 680 ft./min.; service ceiling, 15,500 ft.; empty weight, 770 lb.; loaded, 1,450 lb.; span, 32 ft. 10 in.; length, 21 ft. 6 in.

C.F.A. (SALMSON) D.7 CRI-CRI MAJOR FRANCE

The D.7 Cri-Cri Major is a post-war development of the pre-war D.6 Cri-Cri originally produced in 1936 by the Société des Moteurs Salmson and ordered in quantity by the *Aviation Populaire* movement. One pre-war D.6 Cri-Cri (60 h.p. Salmson 9 Adr) and two D.6-3 Cri-Cri (85 h.p. Salmson 5 AP-01) remain flying, in addition to four post-war D.7 Cri-Cri Majors (85 h.p. Salmson 5 AQ). The Cri-Cri Major differs from the pre-war machines in having enclosed tandem cockpits but is otherwise externally similar. Post-war machines have been built by the Compagnie Française d'Aviation (C.F.A.) in association with Salmson.

Max. speed, 93 m.p.h.; cruising, 80 m.p.h.; service ceiling, 13,120 ft.; empty weight, 1,023 lb.; loaded, 1,585 lb.; span, 35 ft. 11 in.; length, 23 ft. 3 in.; height, 8 ft. 6 in.; wing area, 200 sq. ft.

C.F.A. (SALMSON) D.57 PHRYGANET FRANCE

The D.57 Phryganet is basically a two-seat side-by-side adaptation of the previously-described D.7 Cri-Cri Major. Produced in prototype form only by the Compagnie Française d'Aviation (C.F.A.), the Phryganet flew for the first time on November 7, 1950. Construction and general appearance follow the earlier Cri-Cri and Cri-Cri Major, but the width of the fuselage has been increased to allow for the side-by-side seating arrangement, and a number of design refinements have been included. The D.57 Phryganet is powered by an 85 h.p. Salmson 5 AQ five-cylinder radial.

Max. speed, 99 m.p.h.; cruising speed, 87 m.p.h.; range, 310 miles; empty weight, 1,034 lb.; loaded weight, 1,625 lb.; span, 35 ft. 11 in.; height, 8 ft. 6 in.; length, 23 ft. 3 in.; wing area, 200 sq. ft.

C.F.A. D.21T-4 SUPER PHRYGANE FRANCE

The D.21T-4 Super Phrygane is a post-war development of the Salmson D.2 Phrygane first produced in 1934. Pre-war production models were the three-seat D.2 and the four-seat D.2T-4, both powered by the 135 h.p. Salmson 9 Nc radial engine. Two pre-war D.2 Phryganes and one D.2T-4 remain flying in France. The post-war D.21T-4 Super Phrygane (or Phrygane Major) flew on October 3, 1949, and is externally similar to the pre-war models of the Phrygane. Powered by a 135 h.p. Salmson 7AQ radial engine, it provides accommodation for four persons and is of wooden construction.

Max. speed, 134 m.p.h.; cruising speed, 120 m.p.h.; service ceiling, 14,300 ft.; range, 500 miles; empty weight, 1,716 lb.; loaded, 2,750 lb.; span, 38 ft. 8 in.; length, 25 ft. 11 in.; height, 7 ft. 7 in.; wing area, 241 sq. ft.

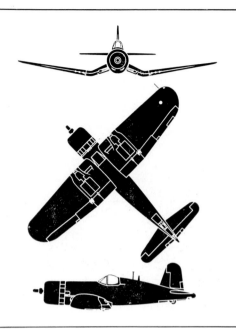

CHANCE VOUGHT AU-1 CORSAIR U.S.A.

The XF4U-1, prototype Corsair, was first flown in 1940, and the last Corsair to be built, an F4U-7, was delivered in mid-February 1953, bringing the total number of Corsairs delivered to 12,571. The F4U-5 (*photo*) and F4U-5N remain in service with reserve units of the U.S. Marine Corps, together with the AU-1 (*silhouette*), a specialised ground-attack fighter. The F4U-7, which, with the AU-1, was the final production model, is used by the French Naval Air Service and the air force of Viet Nam.

Specification: Single-seat Naval ground-attack fighter. Engine: One 2,100 h.p. Pratt & Whitney R-2800-83WA. Weights: Empty, 10,418 lb.; loaded, 13,300 lb. Performance: Max. speed, 470 m.p.h.; initial climb rate, 4,800 ft./min.; service ceiling, 40,000 ft.; range, 1,120 miles. Armament: Four 20-mm. cannon. Dimensions: Span, 40 ft. 11¾ in.; length, 34 ft. 6½ in.; height, 14 ft. 9¼ in.; wing area, 314 sq. ft.

CHANCE VOUGHT F7U-3 CUTLASS U.S.A.

The prototype Cutlass, the XF7U-1, flew for the first time on September 29, 1948. Nineteen F7U-1s, powered by two 3,000 lb.s.t. Westinghouse J34-WE-32 turbojets, were built, and this model was succeeded by the extensively redesigned F7U-3. Armament comprises four 20-mm. cannon and an underwing bomb load of 5,400 lb. An underbelly pod containing 2.75-in. Mighty Mouse unguided, folding-fin rocket missiles may be fitted. Sub-variants include the F7U-3M missile launcher, and the F7U-3P photo-reconnaissance fighter with lengthened nose.

Specification: Single-seat Naval fighter-bomber. Engines: Two 4,800 lb.s.t. (6,100 lb. with afterburning) Westinghouse J46-WE-3. Weights: Empty, 13,100 lb.; normal loaded, 20,000 lb.; max., 23,000 lb. Performance: Max. speed, 670 m.p.h. (705 m.p.h. with afterburning) at sea level; initial climb rate (with afterburning) 13,000 ft./min. Dimensions: Span, 38 ft. 8 in.; length, 40 ft. 10½ in.; height, 11 ft. 6½ in.

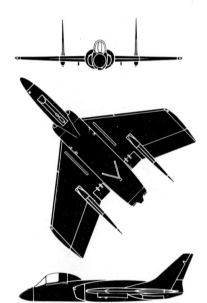

CHANCE VOUGHT XF8U-1 CRUSADER U.S.A.

The XF8U-1 carrier-borne local air superiority fighter prototype was conceived at the end of 1952, and flew for the first time in mid-April 1955. Selected from designs submitted by eight aircraft manufacturers, the XF8U-1 is powered by an afterburning Pratt & Whitney J57-P-4 turbojet, but the production F8U-1 Crusader is scheduled to receive the more powerful J57-P-21 which will give an afterburning thrust of some 16,000 lb.

Specification: Single-seat Naval interceptor fighter. Engine: One 9,700 lb.s.t. (14,000 lb.s.t. with afterburning) Pratt & Whitney J57-P-4. Approx. weights: Empty, 16,500 lb.; loaded, 22,000 lb. Approx. performance: Max. speed, 940 m.p.h. at sea level, 820 m.p.h. at 36,000 ft.; initial climb rate, 15,000 ft./min.; ceiling, 54,000 ft. Armament: Four 20-mm. cannon. Approx. dimensions: Span, 32 ft. 6 in.; length, 50 ft.; height, 14 ft. 6 in.; wing area, 350 sq. ft.

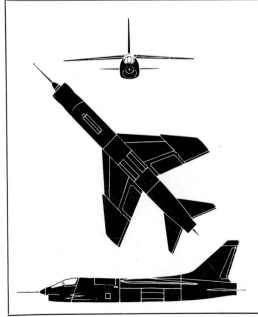

CHANCE VOUGHT OS2U-3 KINGFISHER U.S.A.

The XOS2U-1 Kingfisher prototype was delivered to the U.S. Navy in 1938, and the first production OS2U-1s went into service in 1940. The OS2U-2 and OS2U-3 production series were generally similar to the initial production model and, in service with the Fleet Air Arm were named Kingfisher. The OS2U-3 is in service with the Uruguayan Naval Air Service (*see photo*), and is powered by a 450 h.p. Pratt & Whitney Wasp Junior R-985-AN-2 engine.

Max. speed, 171 m.p.h. at 5,000 ft.; cruising, 152 m.p.h.; service ceiling, 18,200 ft.; range, 908 miles; empty weight, 3,335 lb.; loaded, 4,980 lb.; span, 35 ft. 10¼ in.; length, 33 ft. 7⅞ in.; height, 14 ft. 8 in.; wing area, 261.9 sq. ft.

CHILTON D.W.1 G.B.

First flown in April 1937 and manufactured by the Chilton Aircraft Company, the D.W.1 single-seat ultra light monoplane was produced with both the 32 h.p. Carden-Ford engine and (D.W.1A) the 44 h.p. Train 4.T. The Chilton monoplane is of wooden construction with a fixed undercarriage enclosed in streamlined fairings. Examples of both the D.W.1 and D.W.1A are flying in the United Kingdom. The photograph depicts one of the two remaining D.W.1s with a "bubble" hood over the normally open cockpit. The specification refers to the Carden-Ford powered D.W.1.

Max. speed, 112 m.p.h.; cruising, 103 m.p.h.; initial climb rate, 650 ft./min.; range, 500 miles; empty weight, 398 lb.; loaded, 640 lb.; max. permissible, 700 lb.; span, 24 ft.; length, 17 ft. 6 in.; height, 4 ft. 10 in.

CIJAN C-3 TROJKA YUGOSLAVIA

The C-3 Trojka (Three), designed by Cijan and Petrovic, won a design competition for a primary trainer suitable for use by the schools and clubs of the Yugoslav Aeronautical Union. The prototype Trojka was built by the Ikarus factory, and flew for the first time towards the end of 1946. Series production has been undertaken by the Utva factory, and the first production Trojkas were delivered in 1949. A higher powered version of the Trojka with a Walter Minor 4-III engine of 105 h.p. and a re-designed cockpit canopy appeared in 1953.

Specification: Two-seat primary trainer. Engine: One 65 h.p. Walter Mikron III. Weights: Empty, 824 lb.; loaded, 1,328 lb. Performance: Max. speed, 103 m.p.h.; cruising speed, 90 m.p.h.; service ceiling, 12,790 ft.; range, 376 miles. Dimensions: Span, 34 ft. 5 in.; length, 29 ft.; height, 6 ft. 10 in.; wing area, 166.8 sq. ft.

CHRISLEA C.H.3 SUPER ACE G.B.

First flown on August 19, 1946, the C.H.3 was produced in small series by the Chrislea Aircraft Company. The prototype (C.H.3 Series I) was fitted with a 125 h.p. Lycoming engine, a single fin and rudder and a wooden wing, but the production version, the C.H.3 Series II, was all-metal and fitted with a 145 h.p. D.H. Gipsy Major 10 engine. It also has the twin fin and rudder assembly later fitted to the prototype. The C.H.3 Series III differed primarily in having a tailwheel landing gear, and the Series IV Skyjeep is a version of the latter model with a hinged rear fuselage decking. Examples of both the Super Ace and Skyjeep are flying in Australia, New Zealand, and South America.

Max. speed, 126 m.p.h.; cruising, 112 m.p.h.; range, 400 miles; empty weight, 1,344 lb.; loaded, 2,350 lb.; span, 36 ft.; length, 21 ft. 6 in.

COLONIAL MODEL C-1 SKIMMER U.S.A.

The Colonial Aircraft Corporation was formed in 1946 to build the two-three seat Skimmer light amphibian, and a prototype was first flown on July 17, 1948. The C-1 Skimmer is of all-metal construction with a single-step hull and an enclosed cabin which normally seats two persons side-by-side, but can also accommodate a third person aft. Power is provided by a 125 h.p. Lycoming 0-290-D engine which drives a pusher airscrew and is mounted on a pylon aft of the cabin. A retractable tricycle-type undercarriage is fitted, the nosewheel of which protrudes when retracted to serve as a bumper.

Max. speed, 125 m.p.h.; cruising speed, 155 m.p.h.; initial climb rate, 700 ft./min.; range, 700 miles; empty weight, 1,300 lb.; loaded, 1,950 lb.; span, 34 ft.; length, 23 ft. 6 in.; height, 8 ft. 10 in.; wing area, 150.6 sq. ft.

COMMONWEALTH WIRRAWAY 3 AUSTRALIA

In 1937 the Commonwealth Aircraft Corporation acquired a manufacturing licence for a version of the North American NA-16 basic trainer. Two machines were supplied from the U.S.A. in 1937 for evaluation under the manufacturer's designations NA-32 and NA-33, and the first Commonwealth-built machine, named Wirraway, was delivered in July 1939. Seven hundred and seventeen Wirraway trainers had been delivered by August 31, 1945, and a considerable number remain in service with the R.A.A.F. In addition, two machines are owned by Australian commercial concerns. The Wirraway is powered by a 600 h.p. C.A.C.-built Wasp R-1340-S1H1-G radial engine.
Max. speed, 210 m.p.h.; cruising, 186 m.p.h.; initial climb rate, 1,350 ft./min.; range, 735 miles; empty weight, 3,980 lb.; loaded, 6,353 lb.; span, 43 ft.; length, 27 ft. 9 in.; wing area, 255.75 sq. ft.

COMMONWEALTH C.A.6 WACKETT
AUSTRALIA

The C.A.6 Wackett primary training monoplane, designed by Wing Commander L. J. Wackett, and the first of two prototypes powered by the D.H. Gipsy Six engine was flown early in 1940. Owing to the difficulty of obtaining engines of this type for production aircraft, the design was modified to take the 165 h.p. Warner Super Scarab 165D radial engine, and with this power plant two hundred Wackett primary trainers were produced by the Commonwealth Aircraft Corporation for the R.A.A.F. The Wackett was designed specifically for Australian climatic conditions, and has a welded chrome-molybdenum steel-tube framework with fabric covering. Although no longer used by the R.A.A.F., some twenty Wacketts are currently flying with private owners and clubs in Australia.
Max. speed, 129 m.p.h.; cruising, 110 m.p.h.; range, 390–450 miles.

COMMONWEALTH C.A.22 WINJEEL   AUSTRALIA

The C.A.22 Winjeel (the aboriginal word for Eagle) flew for the first time in 1950, and has since been placed in production for the R.A.A.F., present contracts calling for sixty-two aircraft. The two prototypes and the sixty production machines are powered by the 445 h.p. Pratt & Whitney Wasp Junior engine, but the 450 h.p. Commonwealth Cicada engine was originally intended for installation in the thirty-first production Winjeel. The Cicada is the first power plant to be completely developed in Australia, and its installation would have made the Winjeel the first aircraft to be completely designed and built in Australia.
Specification: Two/three-seat basic trainer. Engine: One 445 h.p. Pratt & Whitney R-985-SB-3 Wasp Junior. Weights: Empty, 3,240 lb.; loaded, 4,235 lb. Performance: Max. speed, 187 m.p.h.; cruising, 130 m.p.h.; initial climb rate, 1,200 ft./min. Dimensions: Span, 38 ft. 9 in.; length, 27 ft. 2 in.; height, 8 ft. 3 in.; wing area, 249 sq. ft.

COMMONWEALTH SABRE   AUSTRALIA

The C.A.27 Sabre is a licence-built development of the North American F-86F Sabre which has been extensively redesigned internally by the Commonwealth Aircraft Corporation for the installation of a 7,500 lb. thrust Rolls-Royce Avon turbojet. The front fuselage is deeper than that of the F-86F and armament comprises two 30-mm. Aden cannon. The prototype C.A.27 flew on August 3, 1953, and the first production aircraft of ninety on order for the R.A.A.F. flew on July 13, 1954. The first twenty C.A.27s have imported Avon R.A.7 turbojets, but subsequent machines have the C.A.C.-built Avon Mk.20.
Approx. max. speed, 710 m.p.h. at sea level; initial climb rate, 12,000 ft./min.; ceiling, 55,000 ft.; tactical radius, 575 miles; approx. loaded weight, 17,000 lb.; span, 37 ft. 1 in.; length, 37 ft. 6 in.; height, 14 ft. 7 in.

COMMONWEALTH 185 SKYRANGER   U.S.A.

Commonwealth Aircraft, Inc., was established in October 1942 to take over Rearwin Aircraft and Engines, Inc., and in 1945 this concern commenced production of the Model 185 Skyranger side-by-side two-seat cabin monoplane. This is externally similar to the Rearwin Models 175, 180, 180F and 190F Skyrangers introduced by the earlier company in 1940, and examples of both pre- and post-war Skyrangers are flying in the U.S.A. These differ primarily in the type of engine installed; Rearwin 175 (75 h.p. Continental), 180 (80 h.p. Continental), 180F (80 h.p. Franklin) and 190F (90 h.p. Franklin). The post-war Commonwealth 185 Skyranger is powered by an 85 h.p. Continental C85 engine.
Max. speed, 114 m.p.h.; cruising, 103 m.p.h.; empty weight, 861 lb.; loaded, 1,460 lb.; span, 34 ft.; length, 21 ft. 9 in.

COMPER CLA-7 SWIFT   G.B.

The CLA-7 Swift first flew in 1929 powered by a 40 h.p. A.B.C. Scorpion engine which was replaced in 1930 by a 50 h.p. Salmson A.D.9. Production commenced in 1930, thirty-seven Swifts being built. A variety of engines were installed, the majority having the 75 h.p. Pobjoy "R" radial, but three were fitted with 120 h.p. D.H. Gipsy III, and one of these is currently flying in Australia. Three are flying with the Pobjoy "R" engine, one having a cockpit canopy, and one (*illustrated*) has been fitted with a 90 h.p. Pobjoy Niagara engine. The following specification relates to the standard CLA-7 Swift with the Pobjoy "R".
Max. speed, 140 m.p.h.; cruising, 120 m.p.h.; initial climb, 1,400 ft./min.; service ceiling, 22,000 ft.; range, 600 miles; empty weight, 540 lb.; loaded, 985 lb.; span, 24 ft.; length, 17 ft. 8½ in.; height, 5 ft. 3½ in.

COMTE A.C.4 GENTLEMAN   SWITZERLAND

The A.C.4 Gentleman was first produced by Alfred Comte of Zürich in 1928, and six of the first version were powered by the 90 h.p. Cirrus III engine. A second series of five machines was produced in 1930; these were powered by the 110 h.p. Cirrus Hermes or the 140 h.p. Genet Major, and three remain flying in Switzerland. The A.C.4 Gentleman is a two-seat cabin monoplane of mixed construction, and the specification relates to the Hermes-powered version.

Max. speed, 109 m.p.h.; cruising, 87 m.p.h.; ceiling, 13,120 ft.; range, 434 miles; empty weight, 1,100 lb.; loaded, 1,760 lb.; span, 39 ft. 10 in.; length, 26 ft. 5 in.; height, 9 ft. 6 in.; wing area, 215 sq. ft.

COMTE A.C.8   SWITZERLAND

Produced in 1930 by Alfred Comte (Schweizerische Flugzeugfabrik) of Zurich, the A.C.8 six-seat cabin monoplane is powered by a 300 h.p. Wright J-6 radial engine. Only three examples of the A.C.8 were built, and one of these is still flying in Switzerland. The A.C.8 is of mixed construction, the wing being of spruce and plywood and the fuselage having a welded steel-tube structure. Dual control is fitted and the cabin provides accommodation for pilot and five passengers.

Max. speed, 133 m.p.h.; cruising speed, 109 m.p.h.; climb to 3,280 ft., 4.8 minutes; service ceiling, 16,400 ft.; range, 560 miles; empty weight, 2,453 lb.; loaded, 3,850 lb.; span, 47 ft. 6 in.; length, 30 ft. 2 in.; height, 9 ft. 6 in.; wing area, 301.3 sq. ft.

COMTE A.C.12 MOSKITO   SWITZERLAND

The A.C.12 Moskito cabin monoplane was first produced by Alfred Comte in 1931, and ten machines of this type were built with the 95 h.p. Argus As 8 or 120 h.p. de Havilland Gipsy III in-line engines, and the 100 h.p. Armstrong Siddeley Genet Major radial. Four A.C.12 Moskitos remain flying in Switzerland, and that illustrated is powered by the Genet Major radial. The Moskito provides accommodation for three persons. Mixed construction is employed, with wooden wing and welded steel-tube fuselage and tail assembly with plywood and fabric covering. The specification refers to the Argus-powered version.
Max. speed, 112 m.p.h.; cruising, 96 m.p.h.; climb to 3,280 ft., 6 minutes; ceiling, 16,400 ft.; empty weight, 1,100 lb.; loaded, 1,980 lb.; span, 38 ft. 2 in.; length, 24 ft. 7 in.; height, 7 ft. 5 in.; wing area, 171 sq. ft.

CONSOLIDATED FLEET TYPE 7A   U.S.A.

The Fleet tandem two-seat primary training biplane was developed from the Husky Junior, designed and first produced in 1928 and subsequently renamed "Fleet" in honour of Major R. H. Fleet, founder of the Consolidated Aircraft Corp. Powered by the 125 h.p. Kinner B-5 or 100 h.p. Kinner K-5, the Fleet 7A is basically similar to the original Fleet 1, 2, and 9. Fleet Aircraft of Canada, Ltd., was established to produce the Fleet trainer in Canada.

Max. speed, 115 m.p.h.; cruising, 90 m.p.h.; initial climb, 730 ft./min.; ceiling, 16,000 ft.; span, 28 ft.; length, 21 ft. 6 in.; height, 7 ft. 11½ in.; wing area, 194 sq. ft.

CONVAIR L-13A   U.S.A.

The Convair L-13 ambulance, observation and liaison aircraft was produced in two versions, the L-13A and L-13B, the latter being a modified version for operation in sub-zero temperatures. The wing of the L-13 is designed to fold, and the large, high-lift, slotted flaps enable it to fly at extremely low speeds. Powered by a 245 h.p. Franklin 0-425-9 engine, the L-13A can be used as an ambulance aircraft, carrying attendant and two litters. A number of L-13s have been converted for civil purposes, some being re-engined with Lycoming R-680 radials. One flying in French Guiana has been converted to seat eight people (*see photo*).
Max. speed, 115 m.p.h.; cruising speed, 92 m.p.h.; initial climb rate, 1,050 ft./min.; range, 368 miles; empty weight, 2,067 lb.; loaded, 2,900 lb.; span, 40 ft. 5½ in.; length, 31 ft. 9 in.; height, 8 ft. 5 in.

D

CONVAIR C-87 LIBERATOR — U.S.A.

The C-87 is a transport version of the B-24 Liberator bomber, two hundred and eighty-four of which were supplied to the U.S.A.F. during World War II. Converted from the B-24D, the Liberator transport was produced in two versions: the C-87 with a crew of five and accommodation for twenty passengers, and the C-87A executive sleeper with ten berths. The C-87 is powered by four 1,200 h.p. Pratt & Whitney R-1830-43 radials, and a number of surplus machines were "civilianised", although only two of these are currently registered in the U.S.A. A few B-24J Liberators remain in service for meteorological research, and a few examples of the C-87 are flying.
Max. speed, 306 m.p.h.; normal range, 1,400 miles; max. range, 3,300 miles; empty weight, 30,645 lb.; loaded, 56,000 lb.; span, 110 ft.; length, 66 ft. 4 in.

CONVAIR P4Y-2G PRIVATEER — U.S.A.

The Privateer was developed in 1943 for the U.S. Navy as a long-range maritime reconnaissance development of the B-24 Liberator. Originally designated PB4Y, the Privateer was redesignated P4Y in 1951, and several versions of this aircraft remain in service, including the P4Y-2S overseas reconnaissance aircraft with the U.S. Navy, and the P4Y-2G (*illustrated here*), used by the U.S. Coast Guard. A number of P4Y-2 Privateers are in service with the French Navy for maritime reconnaissance, and with the Chinese Nationalist Air Force as reconnaissance bombers. It is powered by four 1,350 h.p. Pratt & Whitney R-1830-94.
Max. speed, 237 m.p.h. at 13,750 ft.; economical cruising, 140 m.p.h.; initial climb rate, 1,090 ft./min.; range, 2,800 miles; empty weight, 37,485 lb.; loaded, 65,000 lb.; span, 110 ft.; length, 74 ft. 7 in.

CONVAIR T-29B — U.S.A.

Conversion of the commercial CV 240 airliner for military crew training duties was commenced in 1948, the first version being the T-29A which flew on September 22, 1949. Development of the T-29A with pressurised cabin, increased fuel capacity, etc., resulted in the T-29B (*photo*) which flew on July 30, 1952. Subsequent models include the T-29C with higher-powered engines, the T-29D for advanced navigation/bombardment training, and the VT-29E which is actually a personnel transport variant. The T-29B is intended primarily for navigational training and has two 2,400 h.p. Pratt & Whitney R-2800-97 engines.
Max. speed, 300 m.p.h.; cruising speed, 230 m.p.h.; initial climb rate, 1,370 ft./min.; range, 1,500 miles; loaded weight, 43,575 lb.; span, 91 ft. 9 in.; length, 74 ft. 8 in.; height, 27 ft. 3 in.; wing area, 817 sq. ft.

CONVAIR C-131A SAMARITAN — U.S.A.

The C-131A Samaritan air evacuation transport is one of several military transports developed from the commercial CV 240/340 airliners. Powered by two 2,500 h.p. Pratt & Whitney R-2800-99-W engines, the Samaritan can accommodate 27 litters and seven seated casualties, and twenty-six have been delivered to the U.S.A.F. The generally similar C-131B is an electronic equipment test aircraft, and the YC-131C has two Allison YT56-A-3 turboprops. The TC-131E, RC-131F and RC-131G cargo-personnel transports are generally similar to the Samaritan, and the R4Y-1 is a U.S. Navy version.
Max. speed, 313 m.p.h. at 14,500 ft.; cruising, 285 m.p.h. at 20,000 ft.; initial climb, 1,410 ft./min.; range, 875 miles; empty weight, 29,000 lb.; loaded, 43,575 lb.; span, 91 ft. 9 in.; length, 74 ft. 8 in.

CONVAIR XFY-1 — U.S.A.

Designed in 1950 to meet U.S. Navy requirements for a single-seat fighter possessing vertical take-off characteristics, the XFY-1 made the first known successful vertical take-off on August 1, 1954. Powered by a 5,850 e.h.p. Allison YT-40-A-14 turboprop (which provides a maximum power of 7,100 e.h.p. for the brief take-off period), the XFY-1 is poised on small wheels at the tips of the wing and tail surfaces for take-off, and is lowered onto these at landing, the pilot being seated in a gimbal-mounted seat which tilts forward 45° when the aircraft is in the vertical position, returning to normal when horizontal flight is attained.
Max. speed (approx.), 500 m.p.h.; approx. loaded weight, 10,000–11,000 lb.; span, 25 ft. 8 in.; length, 30 ft. 9 in.; height (tail fin, top to bottom), 22 ft. 7 in.

CONVAIR XF2Y-1 SEA DART — U.S.A.

The first water-borne aircraft of delta wing planform, the XF2Y-1 Sea Dart experimental fighter first flew on April 9, 1953, powered by two 3,400 lb. thrust Westinghouse J34-WE-42 turbojets. These engines were later replaced by two afterburning Westinghouse J46 turbojets of 4,600 lb. thrust and 6,000 lb. with afterburner operating. Initially, the XF2Y-1 had dual retractable hydro-skis (V-shaped planing surfaces), but in 1955 these were replaced by a single large hydro-ski. Four service test aircraft, designated YF2Y-1, were built, and the first of these exceeded Mach 1.0 in a shallow dive at 34,000 ft. on August 3, 1954.
Approx. max. speed, 690 m.p.h. at sea level; approx. loaded weight, 22,000 lb.; span, 30 ft. 6 in.; length, 41 ft. 2 in.; height (hydro-ski extended), 21 ft. 1 in.

CONVAIR MODEL 340-B U.S.A.

The Convair Model 340 is a development of the Model 240, from which it differs in having a 4 ft. 6 in. increase in fuselage length, increased all-up weight, and higher-powered engines. The lengthened fuselage increases passenger accommodation from forty to forty-four. The Model 340 also has a 13 ft. 7 in. increase in wing span as compared to the earlier Model 240, but apart from the "stretching", both models are externally similar. The Model 440 Metropolitan is a 52-seat development with increased loaded weight (49,100 lb.).

Specification: Forty-four/fifty-two seat airliner. Engines: Two 2,400 h.p. Pratt & Whitney R-2800-CB16. Weights: Empty, 32,399 lb.; loaded, 47,000 lb. Performance: Max. speed, 314 m.p.h. at 16,000 ft.; cruising speed, 292 m.p.h.; range, 1,150 miles. Dimensions: Span, 105 ft. 4 in.; length, 79 ft. 2 in.; height, 28 ft. 2 in.; wing area, 920 sq. ft.

CONVAIR PBY-5A CATALINA U.S.A.

The PBY-5A Catalina amphibian flying-boat was built in very large numbers during World War 2, and remains in service with the air forces of Argentina, Brazil, Chile, Denmark, Dominica, Ecuador, Indonesia, Israel, the Netherlands, Norway, Peru, and, in its licence-built version, the GST, with the Soviet Navy. The photograph depicts a Mexican Air Force Catalina, and a considerable number of civil conversions are flying with various corporations.

Specification: Patrol and air/sea rescue amphibian flying-boat. Engines: Two 1,200 h.p. Pratt & Whitney R-1830-92. Weights: Empty, 17,564 lb.; loaded, 34,000 lb. Performance: Max. speed, 196 m.p.h. at 7,500 ft.; cruising speed, 130 m.p.h. at 10,000 ft.; service ceiling, 15,800 ft.; range, 2,520 miles. Dimensions: Span, 104 ft.; length, 63 ft. 10 in.; height, 18 ft. 10 in.; wing area, 1,400 sq. ft.

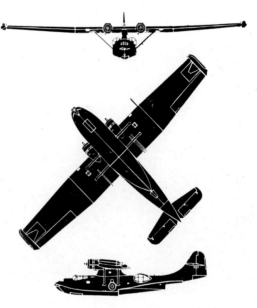

CONVAIR GRB-36J U.S.A.

Flown in prototype form on August 8, 1946, the last of some 380 B-36 heavy bombers was delivered to the U.S.A.F. on August 14, 1954. The current service version, the GRB-36J, employs the FICON system (a contraction of fighter and reconnaissance) which involves the carriage of a Republic RF-84F Thunderflash in the bomb-bay. The RF-84F can be launched and retrieved in flight, thus enabling exceptionally lengthy reconnaissance missions to be undertaken.

Specification: Long-range heavy reconnaissance bomber. Engines: Six 3,800 h.p. Pratt & Whitney R-4360-53 piston engines and four 5,200 lb.s.t. General Electric J47-GE-19 turbojets. Weights: Empty (without RF-84F), 145,000 lb.; max. loaded, 408,000 lb. Performance: Max. speed, 436 m.p.h.; cruising (piston engines only), 290 m.p.h. at 40,000 ft.; max. range, 10,000 miles. Dimensions: Span, 230 ft.; length, 162 ft. 1 in.; height, 46 ft. 9 in.; wing area, 4,772 sq. ft.

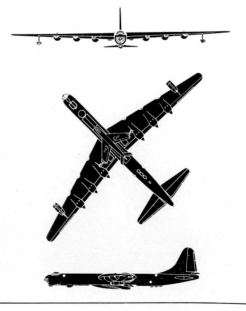

CONVAIR R3Y-2 TRADEWIND U.S.A.

The Tradewind long-range cargo flying-boat has been developed from the XP5Y-1 experimental patrol flying-boat which flew for the first time on April 18, 1950. Serving with the U.S. Navy in the Pacific, the Tradewind differs from the XP5Y-1 in having new engine nacelles with shorter airscrew drive-shafts and tailpipes, and V-shaped float struts replacing the original single struts. The R3Y-2 (*illustrated here*), flew on October 22, 1954, and features bow loading-doors. Twelve Tradewinds have been ordered by the U.S. Navy.

Specification: Naval transport flying-boat. Engines: Four 5,850 e.h.p. Allison T40-A-10. Weights: Empty, 80,000 lb.; loaded, 160,000 lb. Performance: Max. speed, 386 m.p.h. at 25,000 ft.; cruising, 300 m.p.h.; initial climb rate, 2,500 ft./min.; max. range, 4,500 miles. Dimensions: Span, 145 ft. 9 in.; length, 139 ft. 8 in.; height, 51 ft. 5 in.; wing area, 2,100 sq. ft.

CONVAIR F-102A U.S.A.

The Convair F-102A carries a Hughes automatic electronic guidance system which is used with Hughes GAR-98 Falcon missiles, six of these being housed in a retractable belly tray. The first prototype, the XF-102, flew on October 24, 1953. The production F-102A differs extensively from the initial versions, and F-102As are to be re-engined with the J57-P-35 which, with afterburning, will deliver 17,200 lb.s.t. The F-102B will be powered by the 15,000 lb. thrust (21,000 lb. with afterburning) Pratt & Whitney J75, and the TF-102A is a conversion trainer.

Specification: Single-seat interceptor fighter. Engine: One 10,900 lb.s.t. (16,000 lb.s.t. with afterburning) Pratt & Whitney J57-P-11. Weights: Approx. loaded, 25,750 lb.; max. 32,000 lb. Performance: Approx. max. speed, 990 m.p.h. above 36,000 ft. (Mach 1.5); service ceiling, 60,000 ft.; operational range, 500 miles. Dimensions: Span, 38 ft.; length, 68 ft.; height, 18 ft.; wing area, 661.5 sq. ft.

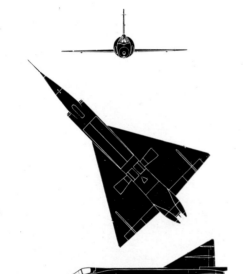

CONVAIR C-99 U.S.A.

Currently the largest transport aircraft in the world, the Convair C-99 was designed to utilise the wings, power plants and undercarriage of the B-36 bomber. The sole prototype flew on November 23, 1947, powered by six 3,000 h.p. Pratt & Whitney R-4360-25 engines driving pusher airscrews. The C-99 is employed by the U.S.A.F., and has established a number of weight lifting records. It can accommodate 400 fully armed troops on its two decks, 100,000 lb. of freight or 300 casualty litters. A crew of five plus a five-man relief crew is carried, and an electrically-operated cargo hatch in the fuselage may be opened in flight for dropping supplies.

Max. speed, approx. 300 m.p.h.; service ceiling, 30,000 ft.; max. range with 10,000 lb. cargo, 8,000 miles; empty weight, 132,000 lb.; loaded, 265,000 lb.; span, 230 ft.; length, 182 ft. 6 in.; height, 57 ft. 6 in.

C.R.D.A. CANT Z.506S AIRONE ITALY

The Z.506S is an ambulance and air/sea rescue variant of the Z.506B developed in 1936 by the Cantieri Riuniti Dell' Adriatico as a reconnaissance bomber floatplane. Both the Z.506B and Z.506S versions of the Airone were used extensively during the war years by the *Regia Aeronautica*, and a number of the latter version are still employed by the Italian Air Force for air/sea rescue duties and as general transports. The Airone is powered by three 770 h.p. Alfa-Romeo 126 RC34 radial engines and is of wooden construction. A crew of three is normally carried for air/sea rescue duties.

Max. speed, 195 m.p.h. at sea level and 229 m.p.h. at 13,120 ft.; range, 1,000 miles; endurance, 5 hours; empty weight, 18,040 lb.; loaded, 26,860 lb.; span, 86 ft. 11 in.; length, 62 ft.; height, 22 ft. 2½ in.

C.S.S.11   POLAND

The Centralne Studium Samolotow (C.S.S.) is an organisation specialising in the design and construction of prototypes, series production being undertaken by the Centralne Studium Przyrzadów, and the C.S.S. 11 is one of several tandem two-seat training monoplanes developed by this organisation. Powered by a 160 h.p. Walter Minor 6-III engine, the C.S.S.11 is a development of the earlier C.S.S.10, from which it differs primarily in having a higher-powered engine and new wing. The C.S.S.11 is of mixed construction with a wooden wing and welded steel-tube fuselage.

Max. speed, 140 m.p.h.; cruising speed, 105 m.p.h.; ceiling, 20,990 ft.; range, 680 miles; normal loaded weight, 2,070 lb.; span, 34 ft. 8 in.; length, 24 ft. 8 in.; height, 7 ft.; wing area, 168 sq. ft.

CULVER LCA CADET   U.S.A.

The Culver Aircraft Company was formed in 1939 to take over from the Dart Manufacturing Corp. the manufacture of the Dart Model G side-by-side two-seat cabin monoplane which, in turn, was originally the Monosport, the designs of which were purchased by the Dart concern from the Monocoupe Corporation in 1937. After some redesign, the Dart G was placed in production in 1940 as the Models LCA (*photo*) and LCF Cadet. These differed solely in the type of engine installed; 75 h.p. Continental (LCA) and 80 h.p. Franklin (LFA), and many of both types are flying.

Max. speed, 140 m.p.h.; cruising, 120 m.p.h.; initial climb rate, 800 ft./min.; service ceiling, 17,500 ft./min.; range, 600 miles; empty weight, 720 lb.; loaded, 1,305 lb.; span, 26 ft. 11 in.; length, 17 ft. 8 in.; height, 5 ft. 6 in.

CULVER NR-D (PQ-14)   U.S.A.

The Model NR-D radio-controlled target aircraft was designed to simulate enemy attacks. It featured an orthodox single-seat cockpit and could be controlled manually. It was produced in quantity for both the U.S. Navy and the U.S.A.F. The Navy version was powered by a 150 h.p. Franklin 6ACT-298-J5 and designated TD2C-1, a total of 1,198 being delivered. The U.S.A.F. versions were the PQ-14A and PQ-14B and, powered by the 150 h.p. Franklin 0-300-11, 150 and 594 of the respective models were delivered. There are civilian conversions of all three models.

Max. speed, 175 m.p.h. at sea level, 160 m.p.h. at 17,000 ft.; initial climb rate, 800 ft./min.; range, 512 miles at 160 m.p.h.; loaded weight, 1,830 lb.; span, 30 ft.; length, 19 ft. 5¾ in.; height, 8 ft. 4½ in.; wing area, 103 sq. ft.

CULVER V   U.S.A.

The Model V was introduced in 1946, and owed much to the experience gained by its manufacturers during the war years with a series of remotely-controlled target aircraft. Powered by an 85 h.p. Continental engine, the Model V provides accommodation for two persons seated side-by-side. Limited production was undertaken between 1946 and 1949, and approximately one hundred Model V cabin monoplanes are active in the U.S.A.

Cruising speed, 125 m.p.h.; initial climb, 600 ft./min.; service ceiling, 13,100 ft.; range, 700 miles; empty weight, 1,070 lb.; loaded, 1,600 lb.; span, 29 ft.; length, 20 ft. 8½ in.; height, 6 ft. 9½ in.; wing area, 125.9 sq. ft.

CURTISS-WRIGHT JUNIOR CW-1   U.S.A.

The Junior CW-1 two-seat ultra-light monoplane first appeared in 1931 and achieved considerable popularity, three hundred Juniors being produced in that year. Powered by a 45 h.p. Szekely engine mounted on the parasol wing, the Junior CW-1 is of mixed construction with fabric covering. A few examples remain active in the U.S.A. powered by both the Szekely engine and the 65 h.p. Lycoming, and the following specification relates to the version powered by the former engine.

Max. speed, 80 m.p.h.; initial climb, 600 ft./min.; service ceiling, 12,000 ft.; range, 200 miles; empty weight, 570 lb.; loaded, 975 lb.; span, 39 ft. 6 in.; length, 21 ft. 3 in.; height, 7 ft. 4 in.; wing area, 176 sq. ft.

CURTISS-WRIGHT ROBIN C1   U.S.A.

The Robin was first introduced in 1928, and several different versions were produced. The initial production models were three-seat cabin monoplanes, and examples of the Robin are flying with the 220 h.p. Continental, the 225 h.p. Lycoming, and the 115 h.p. Tank engine. Several Robin C1s are flying with the 185 h.p. Curtiss Challenger, and the 220 h.p. Continental, and two Robin J1s with the latter engine are also active. The Robin 4C1A was a four-seat variant. One Robin is flying in Australia.

Max. speed, 118 m.p.h.; cruising, 100 m.p.h.; initial climb, 750 ft./min.; service ceiling, 13,200 ft.; range, 338 miles; empty weight, 1,675 lb.; loaded, 2,523 lb.; span, 41 ft.; length, 25 ft. 6 in.; height, 8 ft.; wing area, 224 sq. ft.

CURTISS-WRIGHT KINGBIRD D2 — U.S.A.

The Kingbird six-passenger transport was first introduced in 1928, and a number of aircraft of this type were delivered to Eastern Air Lines, eventually being replaced in 1932 by the Curtiss-Wright Condor. One Kingbird D2, powered by two 450 h.p. Wright Whirlwind radial engines and manufactured in 1931, is currently active in the U.S.A. The two radial engines are mounted unusually close to the fuselage sides, the planes of rotation of the two airscrews passing ahead of the fuselage nose.

Max. speed, 134 m.p.h.; cruising speed, 110 m.p.h.; service ceiling, 14,700 ft.; range, 404 miles; empty weight, 3,858 lb.; loaded, 6,117 lb.; span, 54 ft. 5½ in.; length, 34 ft. 9¼ in.; height, 9 ft. 10 in.; wing area, 405 sq. ft.

CURTISS-WRIGHT HAWK 75A (P-36A) — U.S.A.

The P-36A was the initial production version of the Hawk 75A designed in 1935, an order for 210 of which was placed by the U.S.A.A.F. in 1937. Only 177 P-36A fighters were completed, the remaining machines being converted to P-36Bs with higher-powered engines. Export versions, including the Hawk 75A-1, -2, -3 and -4, were supplied to the R.A.F. (and named Mohawk), the French, Finnish, Norwegian and Netherlands East Indies Air Forces. It was also built under licence in India and, with a fixed undercarriage, as the Hawk 75A-0 in Argentina. The sole remaining P-36A has a 1,050 h.p. Pratt & Whitney R-1830-13.

Max. speed, 303 m.p.h. at 19,000 ft.; cruising speed, 259 m.p.h.; service ceiling, 32,800 ft.; range, 600 miles; loaded weight, 6,010 lb.; span, 37 ft. 4 in.; length, 28 ft. 6 in.; height, 9 ft. 3 in.; wing area, 236 sq. ft.

CURTISS-WRIGHT O-52 OWL — U.S.A.

The 0-52 Owl two-seat observation monoplane was first flown in 1941, and two hundred and three machines of this type were built for general observation, photography and army co-operation duties. Two remain in existence in the U.S.A. The Owl is powered by a 600 h.p. Pratt & Whitney R-1340-51 radial engine, and is of all-metal construction. It is unusual among single-engine, high-wing monoplanes in having a completely retractable undercarriage. Slots extend over the full span of the Owl's wing, and when the slots are opened flaps are automatically lowered.

Max. speed, 208 m.p.h.; cruising speed, 192 m.p.h.; service ceiling, 21,000 ft.; cruising range, 700 miles; empty weight, 4,231 lb.; loaded, 5,585 lb.; span, 40 ft. 4 in.; length, 26 ft. 7 in.; height, 9 ft. 3¼ in.

CURTISS-WRIGHT SEDAN 15-D — U.S.A.

The Sedan four-seat cabin monoplane of 1931 was initially produced with the 180 h.p. Curtiss Challenger and 210 h.p. Kinner C-5 engines, but the three remaining examples are powered by the 300 h.p. Wright Whirlwind (Sedan 15-D) and the 245 h.p. Jacobs (Sedan 15-N). The Sedan's cabin provides accommodation for four persons in two pairs, and dual controls are fitted. Mixed construction with fabric covering is employed.

Max. speed, 135 m.p.h.; initial climb rate, 750 ft./min.; service ceiling, 14,000 ft.; range, 500 miles; empty weight, 2,121 lb.; loaded, 3,319 lb.; span, 43 ft. 5 in.; length, 30 ft. 5 in.; height, 9 ft. 7 in.; wing area, 215.06 sq. ft.

CURTISS-WRIGHT CW-22 FALCON — U.S.A.

The Falcon was produced in 1938 as an advanced trainer, and was subsequently produced in some quantity for the U.S. Navy as the SNC-1. This type was also delivered to the Netherlands East Indies Air Force as a light attack aircraft, and to the air forces of Bolivia, Chile, Colombia and Peru. The CW-22 Falcon was virtually a low-powered, two-seat variant of the CW-21 single-seat fighter, and several examples remain airworthy in the U.S.A. The CW-22 Falcon is powered by a 450 h.p. Wright Whirlwind R-975-E3 radial engine, and is of all-metal construction.

Max. speed, 201 m.p.h. at sea level; cruising speed, 195 m.p.h. at 2,500 ft.; service ceiling, 21,900 ft.; range, 515 miles; empty weight, 2,610 lb.; loaded, 3,626 lb.; span, 35 ft.; length, 26 ft. 6 in.; height, 7 ft. 6 in.

CURTISS-WRIGHT HAWK 87A (P-40N) U.S.A.

More than fifteen thousand single-seat fighters of the Hawk 81A or 87A type were produced during World War II, the last production machine being a P-40N Warhawk. Several P-40Es and P-40Ns are flown in the U.S.A., and several examples of this fighter are still airworthy in Indonesia. The P-40N is the version flying in largest numbers, and several of these have been adapted for racing purposes while others have been converted into two-seaters. The P-40N is powered by an Allison V-1710-81 (P-40N-1-15), V-1710-99 (P-40N-20-35) or V-1710-115 (P-40N-40) of 1,200 h.p. A total of 4,219 P-40N Warhawks were built. P-40E has Allison V-1710-39 of 1,150 h.p.

Max. speed (P-40N-20-35), 375 m.p.h.; cruising speed, 300 m.p.h.; normal range, 610 miles; empty weight, 6,550 lb.; loaded, 8,850 lb.; span, 37 ft. 4 in.; length, 33 ft. 4 in.; height, 12 ft. 2 in.

CURTISS-WRIGHT C-46 (COMMANDO)　　U.S.A.

The C-46 was ordered in quantity by the U.S.A.A.F., a total of 3,180 being built. Many of these have been sold as surplus and converted for commercial purposes. These are mostly of the C-46A, C-46D (*silhouette*), C-46E and C-46F (*photo*) production models. The C-46D is the only version likely to be seen with the stepped windscreen. Approximately thirty U.S. concerns operate the C-46, and some are being modernised for the Super-46 by the installation of 2,400 h.p. R-2800-CB-16 engines which increase cruising speed by 19 m.p.h.
Specification: Thirty-seat transport or freighter. Engines: Two 2,000 h.p. Pratt & Whitney R-2800-51 or -75 Double Wasp. Weights: Empty, 29,483 lb.; loaded, 45,000 lb. Performance: Max. speed, 241 m.p.h. at 13,000 ft.; cruising, 227 m.p.h. at 10,000 ft.; service ceiling, 24,500 ft. Dimensions: Span, 108 ft. 1 in.; length, 76 ft. 4 in.; height, 21 ft. 9 in.; wing area, 1,360 sq. ft.

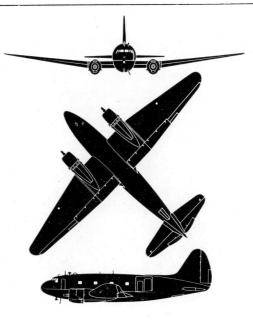

CURTISS-WRIGHT SB2C-5 HELLDIVER　　U.S.A.

The Helldiver carrier-borne attack bomber was built in large numbers during World War II but the French Naval Air Arm is now the only force still employing this type. French Helldivers are of the final production SB2C-5 type and were supplied under M.S.A. The prototype Helldiver, the XSB2C-1, was flown for the first time in November 1940, and was progressively improved in production as the SB2C-1, -3, -4, and -5. U.S.A.F. and U.S. Marine Corps variant of the SB2C-1 was designated A-25, and Canadian-built versions of the SB2C-4 and -5 were designated SBW-4, -5, and SBF-4. The SB2C-5 has a Wright R-2600-20 radial of 1,900 h.p.
Max. speed, 294 m.p.h. at 16,700 ft.; cruising, 160 m.p.h.; initial climb, 1,630 ft./min.; loaded weight, 14,042 lb.; span, 49 ft. 9 in.; length, 36 ft. 8 in.

D-3801　　SWITZERLAND

In 1938 Switzerland acquired the licence to manufacture the Morane-Saulnier M.S.406C, the type being given the designation D-3800. Production commenced at the Dornier-Werke A.G. (now renamed Flug and Fahrzeugwerke A.G.) on an improved version, the D-3801, in 1939. The D-3801 differed from the original M.S.406C in having the 860 h.p. Hispano 12Y-31 engine replaced by a 1,000 h.p. Hispano 12Y-51 built by the A. G. Adolph Saurer, with a consequent improvement in performance. A considerable number of D-3801s were delivered to the Swiss Air Force, and several remain flying in Switzerland.
Max. speed, 325 m.p.h. at 13,950 ft.; economical cruising, 190 m.p.h.; climb to 16,400 ft., 5.4 minutes; service ceiling, 35,400 ft.; empty weight, 4,694 lb.; loaded, 5,765 lb.; span, 34 ft. 9½ in.; length, 26 ft. 9½ in.

D-3802A　　SWITZERLAND

The D-3802 single-seat fighter prototype was built in 1943 by the Dornier-Werke to designs supplied by the Morane-Saulnier concern (designated M.S.450). A second prototype modified up to production standards was produced under the designation D-3802A, and orders for one hundred aircraft of this type were placed by the Swiss Air Force. With the end of the war in Europe, this order was reduced to ten machines, and several of these are still flying. The D-3802A is powered by a 1,250 h.p. Saurer/SLM-Hispano-Suiza 12Y-52 engine driving a special Escher-Wyss "paddle-blade" airscrew of Swiss design.
Max. speed, 391 m.p.h. at 21,325 ft.; climb to 19,865 ft., 7.1 minutes; ceiling, 33,500 ft.; empty weight, 6,327 lb.; loaded, 7,716 lb.; max. loaded, 8,014 lb.; span, 35 ft. 2¾ in.; length, 30 ft. 7 in.; height, 10 ft. 11 in.

DART MODEL G　　U.S.A.

The Model G side-by-side two-seat light cabin monoplane was originally the Lambert Monosport, the designs of which were purchased from the Lambert Aircraft Corp. (later Monocoupe Corp.) in 1937. Production commenced in 1938 of the Model G powered by a 90 h.p. Lambert R-266 radial, and a version powered by a 100 h.p. Continental engine, the Model GC, was produced in 1939. In the same year the Culver Aircraft Company was formed to take over the manufacture of the Dart Model GC. Production was discontinued in 1940 in favour of an improved model known as the Culver LCA.

Max. speed, 130 m.p.h.; cruising, 115 m.p.h.; initial climb rate, 900 ft./min.; range, 590 miles; empty weight, 922 lb.; loaded, 1,550 lb.; span, 29 ft. 6 in.; length, 18 ft. 6 in.; height, 7 ft. 9 in.

DASSAULT FLAMANT   FRANCE

The Flamant was designed as a light general-purpose transport for service mainly in French colonial territories and has been produced in several versions. The M.D.311 (*photo*) is a bombing and navigational trainer, thirty-nine of which were delivered to the *Armée de l'Air*. The M.D.312 is externally similar to the M.D.315 (*silhouette*), and 142 were built as six-seat liaison and communications aircraft. One hundred and thirty-seven M.D.315s were built as ten-seat light military transports. The prototype flew for the first time on February 10, 1947. The specification relates to the M.D.315.
Specification: Light military transport. Engines: Two 580 h.p. S.N.E.C.M.A.-Renault 12S 02-201. Weights: Empty, 9,350 lb.; loaded, 12,760 lb. Performance: Max. speed, 236 m.p.h.; cruising speed, 186 m.p.h.; initial climb rate, 984 ft./min.; absolute ceiling, 26,240 ft.; range, 755 miles. Dimensions: Span, 67 ft. 10 in.; length, 41 ft.; height, 14 ft. 9 in.; wing area, 508 sq. ft.

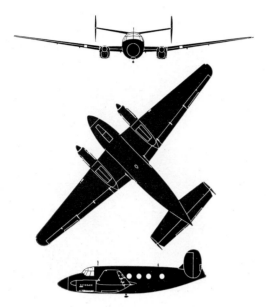

DASSAULT OURAGAN   FRANCE

Flown for the first time on February 28, 1949, the M.D.450 Ouragan is in service with the French and Indian Air Forces, three hundred and fifty fighters of this type having been built, ninety-one of these (powered by the 5,180 lb. thrust H-S.Nene 102), being supplied to India as the *Toofani*. The cannon armament of the Ouragan can be supplemented by two 1,100-lb. bombs, and several machines of this type have been used for research purposes.
Specification: Single-seat fighter-bomber. Engine: One 5,070 lb.s.t. Hispano-Suiza Nene 104B. Weights: Empty, 9,131 lb.; loaded, 14,991 lb. Performance: Max. speed, 584 m.p.h. at sea level; initial climb rate, 7,874 ft./min.; ceiling, 49,213 ft. Armament: Four 20-mm. Hispano 404 Model 50 cannon. Dimensions: Span, 40 ft. 3½ in.; length, 35 ft. 2¼ in.; height, 13 ft.; wing area, 256.18 sq. ft.

DASSAULT MYSTÈRE IIC   FRANCE

The Mystère IIC is a development of the Ouragan, retaining the fuselage of the earlier fighter but having 30° wing sweep. The Mystère I was a prototype for the Mystère II, and was flown on February 23, 1951. The Mystère IIA was a further experimental version with a 6,280 lb.s.t. Tay 250 replacing the earlier machine's 5,070 lb.s.t. Nene 104B, and three machines with two 30-mm. DEFA cannon replacing the four 20-mm. cannon installation of their predecessors were designated Mystère IIB. One hundred and fifty Mystère IIC fighters are being delivered to the *Armée de l'Air*.
Specification: Single-seat interceptor fighter. Engine: One 6,600 lb.s.t. S.N.E.C.M.A. Atar 101D-1. Weights: Empty, 11,511 lb.; loaded, 16,442 lb. Performance: Max. speed, 658 m.p.h. at sea level, 581 m.p.h. at 39,370 ft.; initial climb rate, 8,460 ft./min.; endurance, 1 hour 30 minutes. Armament: Two 30-mm. DEFA cannon. Dimensions: Span, 38 ft. 1½ in.; length, 38 ft. 4 in.; wing area 326.15 sq. ft.

DASSAULT MYSTÈRE IVA — FRANCE

Bearing only an external aerodynamic resemblance to the Mystère II, the Mystère IVA is in actual fact an entirely different design. Flown for the first time on September 28, 1952, it has an entirely new wing with a thickness chord ratio reduced from 9 to 7.5 per cent, and sweepback increased to 38° at quarter chord, and a more robust, oval-section fuselage. The first 75 Mystère IVAs are powered by the 6,280 lb.s.t. Tay 250A. A total of 325 Mystère IVAs has been ordered.
Specification: Single-seat interceptor fighter. Engine: One 7,720 lb.s.t. Hispano-Suiza Verdon. Weights: Empty, 12,518 lb.; loaded, 16,314 lb. Performance: Max. speed, 696 m.p.h. at sea level, 615 m.p.h. at 39,370 ft.; initial climb rate, 8,860 ft./min.; endurance, 1 hour 10 minutes. Armament: Two 30-mm. DEFA cannon and two 1,000-lb. bombs or twelve T-10 air-to-ground missiles. Dimensions: Span, 36 ft. 5¾ in.; length, 42 ft. 1¾ in.; height, 15 ft. 1 in.; wing area, 344.5 sq. ft.

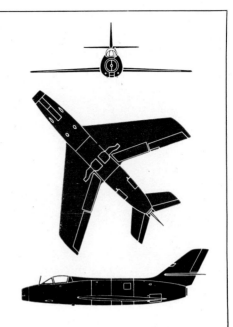

DASSAULT MYSTÈRE IVB — FRANCE

The Mystère IVB differs externally from the IVA in having a lengthened rear fuselage to house the afterburner extension of the 7,500–9,500 lb. thrust Rolls-Royce Avon R.A.7R turbojet, and a dielectric cap in a lip over the air intake. Internal changes include the revision of the air intake ducting which is led under the pilot's cockpit instead of dividing to pass either side. The Avon-powered Mystère IVB prototype flew on December 16, 1953, and a pre-production batch of six Mystère IVB fighters powered by the S.N.E.C.M.A. Atar 101G-21 (9,260 lb. thrust with afterburning) has been produced. Armament comprises two 30-mm. DEFA cannon.
Max. speed, 740 m.p.h. at sea level; initial climb rate, 22,047 ft./min.; endurance, 50 minutes; empty weight, 14,281 lb.; loaded, 18,585 lb.; span, 36 ft. 5¾ in.; length, 43 ft. 11½ in.; height, 15 ft. 1 in.

DASSAULT MYSTÈRE IVN — FRANCE

The Mystère IVN is a two-seat night and all-weather fighter derived from the single-seat Mystère IVB. The airframe of the IVN is essentially similar to that of the IVB, but 4 ft. 7 in. has been added to the fuselage length to accommodate the navigator seated behind the pilot, and a large radome is mounted in the nose with a chin-type air intake for the 7,500 lb. thrust (9,500 lb. with afterburning) Rolls-Royce Avon R.A.7R turbojet. Armament comprises two 30-mm. DEFA cannon, and these can be supplemented by fifty-two Brandt unguided air-to-air missiles housed in a retractable belly launcher.
Max. speed, 630 m.p.h. at sea level, 569 m.p.h. at 39,370 ft.; normal duration, 1 hour 45 minutes; max. 3 hours; empty weight, 15,400 lb.; normal loaded, 23,060 lb.; span, 36 ft. 5 in.; length, 48 ft. 7 in.; height, 15 ft. 3 in.

DASSAULT SUPER MYSTÈRE B1 — FRANCE

The Super Mystère B1 flew for the first time on March 2, 1955, and is more closely related to the experimental Mystère IVB than to any other of the Dassault series of fighters. The Super Mystère B1 is powered by an Avon R.A.7R turbojet, has 45° wing sweep at quarter chord and a thickness/chord ratio of six per cent. Two prototypes, five pre-production and 150 production Super Mystères are on order, and the production model, designated Super Mystère B2, will be powered by an Atar 101G-21 turbojet. A projected all-weather and night fighter variant with an Avon R.A.14 is the Super Mystère N2.
Specification: Single-seat interceptor fighter. Engine: One 7,500 lb.s.t. (9,500 lb.s.t. with afterburning) Rolls-Royce Avon R.A.7R. Weights: No details available. Performance: Limiting Mach number, 1.4; approx. max. speed, 792 m.p.h. (Mach 1.2) at 39,370 ft. Approx. Dimensions: Span, 32 ft. 9 in.; length, 46 ft.; height, 15 ft.

DASSAULT M.D.316-T   FRANCE

Developed from the M.D.315 Flamant, the M.D.316-T is a twelve-passenger light transport and crew trainer. The first prototype was powered by two 820 h.p. S.N.E.C.M.A.14X Super Mars radial engines and retained the twin fin and rudder assembly which characterises the earlier machine. This flew for the first time on July 17, 1952. The second machine illustrated here, has two 800 h.p. Wright R-1300 Cyclone C7BA1 radials and a redesigned rear fuselage with a single fin and rudder assembly.

Max. speed, 255 m.p.h. at 7,218 ft.; cruising speed, 243 m.p.h.; initial climb rate, 1,181 ft./min.; empty weight, 12,566 lb.; loaded, 16,755 lb.; span, 66 ft. 11 in.; length, 51 ft. 8 in.; height, 21 ft. 4 in.

DART KITTEN III   G.B.

The Dart Kitten was designed in 1936 for amateur construction by aero clubs and private individuals. One machine, known as the Kitten III, has been built since the war, and this, together with two pre-war-built Kittens, is currently flying in the United Kingdom. Powered by a 36 h.p. J.A.P. J.99 engine, this is a single-seat ultra-light aircraft of wooden construction. The fuselage is a simple, rectangular structure with a fabric-covered domed top, and the centre section of the parallel-chord wing is built integral with the fuselage. The wing comprises a single main spar and auxiliary rear spar, and most of the skinning is plywood.

Max. speed, 95 m.p.h. at 1,000 ft.; cruising speed, 83 m.p.h. at 2,000 ft.; initial climb rate, 600 ft./min.; range, 340 miles; empty weight, 510 lb.; loaded, 752 lb.; span, 31 ft. 9 in.; length, 21 ft. 4 in.; height, 7 ft. 11 in.

DE HAVILLAND D.H.60G GIPSY MOTH   G.B.

First flown in March 1925, the D.H.60 Moth series are among the most famous of British pre-war light planes. The first D.H.60, or Cirrus Moth, had a 60 h.p. Cirrus I, being followed by the D.H.60X with the 80 h.p. Cirrus II. In 1928 the D.H.60G Gipsy Moth (*photo*) appeared, powered by a 98 h.p. D.H. Gipsy I, to be followed in 1929 by the D.H. 60M with a metal fuselage. The D.H.60T was a trainer variant with Gipsy II engine, and the D.H.60G3 Moth Major had the 130 h.p. Gipsy Major. Apart from the engines, all D.H.60s are externally similar, and examples of all versions are flying. The specification refers to the D.H.60G.

Max. speed, 98.5 m.p.h.; cruising, 83 m.p.h.; empty weight, 970 lb.; loaded, 1,750 lb.; span, 30 ft.; length, 23 ft. 11 in.; wing area, 243 sq. ft.

DE HAVILLAND D.H.80A PUSS MOTH   G.B.

The D.H.80A Puss Moth three-seat light cabin monoplane entered production in 1930, and by the time production terminated in 1933, some 260 Puss Moths had been built. Powered by a 120 h.p. de Havilland Gipsy III engine, the Puss Moth was employed in many parts of the world and two examples remain in the United Kingdom, and single examples in Sweden, Italy, Australia, Canada, and the U.S.A. The Puss Moth is of mixed wood and metal construction with fabric covering. The two passengers are seated in staggered seats.

Max. speed, 127 m.p.h.; cruising speed, 110 m.p.h. at 1,000 ft.; initial climb rate, 630 ft./min.; service ceiling, 17,500 ft.; range, 714 miles; empty weight, 1,180 lb.; loaded, 2,050 lb.; span, 36 ft. 9 in.; length, 25 ft.; wing area, 222 sq. ft.

DE HAVILLAND D.H.82 TIGER MOTH   G.B.

Flown for the first time on October 26, 1931, the D.H.82 Tiger Moth was virtually a development of the metal-fuselage D.H.60T Moth from which it differed primarily in having staggered wings. Initial machines were fitted with the D.H. Gipsy III engine of 120 h.p., but later the 130 h.p. Gipsy Major became standard. Several thousand Tiger Moths were produced, and the type was built under licence in Australia, Canada, New Zealand and Sweden. Tiger Moths are flying in many parts of the world, and the machine illustrated is a Canadian-built D.H.82C with enclosed cockpits.

Max. speed, 109 m.p.h. at sea level; initial climb rate, 673 ft./min.; service ceiling, 13,600 ft.; empty weight, 1,115 lb.; loaded, 1,825 lb.; span, 29 ft. 4 in.; length, 23 ft. 11 in.; height, 8 ft. 9½ in.

DE HAVILLAND D.H.83 FOX MOTH   G.B.

First produced in 1932, the D.H.83 Fox Moth was initially powered by the 120 h.p. D.H. Gipsy III, but later machines (D.H.83A) have the 130 h.p. D.H. Gipsy Major. About ninety-one Fox Moths were produced by the parent company, forty-eight of these being registered in Britain and the remainder being sold abroad, but in 1945 the Canadian branch of the company returned the type to production and, as the D.H.83C with a canopy over the pilot's cockpit, built a further fifty aircraft. Two pre-war Fox Moths are flying in the U.K., and others are flying in Egypt, Rhodesia, New Zealand and Australia. Post-war Canadian-built machines are flying in both Canada and New Zealand.

Max. speed, 107 m.p.h.; cruising speed, 91 m.p.h.; initial climb, 492 ft./min.; range, 438 miles at 91 m.p.h.; empty weight, 1,100 lb.; loaded, 2,070 lb.; span, 30 ft. 10½ in.; length, 25 ft. 9 in.

DE HAVILLAND D.H.84 DRAGON G.B.

The D.H.84 feeder liner carrying six or eight passengers was introduced in 1933, the prototype having been flown on November 24, 1932. The Dragon was an immediate success owing to its high carrying capacity in relation to its low power, and by September 1933 fifty-five Dragons had been delivered to various airlines and three were privately owned. The D.H.84 Dragon is powered by two 130 h.p. de Havilland Gipsy Major engines. Two examples are flying in the United Kingdom and others are flying in Eire and Australia.

Max. speed, 134 m.p.h. at sea level; cruising speed, 109 m.p.h. at 1,000 ft.; initial climb rate, 612 ft./min.; range, 364–545 miles; empty weight, 2,385 lb.; loaded, 4,500 lb.; span, 47 ft.; length, 34 ft. 6 in.; height, 10 ft. 1 in.; wing area, 376 sq. ft.

DE HAVILLAND D.H.85 LEOPARD MOTH G.B.

Generally similar to the D.H.80A Puss Moth but differing appreciably in wing planform and undercarriage bracing struts, the D.H.85 Leopard Moth replaced the earlier machine in production and flew for the first time on May 27, 1933. A three-seat cabin monoplane powered by a 130 h.p. de Havilland Gipsy Major engine, the Leopard Moth is of wooden construction with plywood covering. Three Leopard Moths are registered in the United Kingdom, seven are flying in Switzerland, one in Rhodesia, and six in Australia.

Max. speed, 140 m.p.h. at sea level; cruising speed, 119 m.p.h.; initial climb rate, 625 ft./min.; service ceiling, 14,500 ft.; empty weight, 1,375 lb.; loaded, 2,225 lb.; span, 37 ft. 6 in.; length, 24 ft. 6 in.; height, 8 ft. 9 in.; wing area, 186 sq. ft.

DE HAVILLAND D.H.86B G.B.

The design of the D.H.86 was the direct result of a specification for a feeder line transport issued in September 1933 by the Australian Federal Government. The prototype D.H.86 flew on January 14, 1934, and differed from the production D.H.86A in having a shorter, less pointed nose. The second production version, the D.H.86B, had two outrigged, elliptically shaped fins, and one example of this type is currently flying in the United Kingdom. The D.H.86B carries 10–16 passengers, and is powered by four 204 h.p. D.H. Gipsy Six engines.

Max. speed, 166 m.p.h.; cruising, 142 m.p.h.; empty weight, 6,250 lb.; loaded, 10,250 lb.; span, 64 ft. 6 in.; length, 46 ft. 1 in.; height, 13 ft. 10 in.; wing area, 641 sq. ft.

DE HAVILLAND D.H.87B HORNET MOTH II G.B.

The D.H.87 Hornet Moth first flew early in 1934 and was designed as a potential replacement for the D.H.60 Gipsy Moth. The original D.H.87 and the initial production model, the D.H.87A Hornet Moth I, possessed wings with sharply tapered tips, but in 1936 the D.H.87B Hornet Moth II, with square-tipped wings of reduced span and larger area, succeeded the earlier model. Both versions are powered by the 130 h.p. D.H. Gipsy Major engine, but the majority of Hornet Moths flying are of the later "B" model. Sixteen D.H.87Bs are registered in the United Kingdom, two in Canada and one in Switzerland. Seven 87Bs and three 87As are flying in Australia.

Max. speed, 124 m.p.h.; range, 623 miles at 105 m.p.h.; empty weight, 1,255 lb.; loaded, 2,000 lb.; span, 31 ft. 11 in.; length, 24 ft. 11½ in.

DE HAVILLAND D.H.89A DRAGON RAPIDE G.B.

Production of the Dragon Rapide commenced in 1934, and during the war a number of D.H.89B aircraft were delivered to the R.A.F. for use as radio and navigational trainers under the name Dominie. With the end of the war, a number of D.H.89 airframes laid down for the R.A.F. were completed for commercial operators, and many ex-R.A.F. machines were converted for civil use. A total of 697 D.H.89s had been completed when production ceased in 1946. The Dragon Rapide is powered by two 205 h.p. de Havilland Gipsy Six engines and carries six or eight passengers. The Dragon Rapide is flying in numbers in many parts of the world.

Max. speed, 141 m.p.h.; cruising, 123 m.p.h.; initial climb, 860 ft./min.; empty weight, 3,520 lb.; loaded, 5,750 lb.; span, 48 ft.; length, 34 ft. 6 in.

DE HAVILLAND D.H.90 DRAGONFLY G.B.

A twin-engined, five-seat cabin biplane powered by two 130 h.p. D.H. Gipsy Major engines, the D.H.90 Dragonfly was first produced in October 1935. It can be considered as an early attempt to produce a multi-engined, multi-seat private owner type, but the comparatively small number of Dragonflies produced were used mostly on feeder lines and for charter duties. One D.H.90 Dragonfly is flying in the United Kingdom, three are flying in Australia, and another is flying in New Zealand. The Dragonfly is of wooden construction.

Max. speed, 144 m.p.h. at sea level; cruising speed, 127 m.p.h. at 1,000 ft.; initial climb rate, 875 ft./min.; cruising range, 885 miles; empty weight, 2,500 lb.; loaded, 4,000 lb.; span, 43 ft.; length, 31 ft. 8 in.; height, 9 ft. 2 in.; wing area, 288 sq. ft.

DE HAVILLAND D.H.94 MOTH MINOR   G.B.

The Moth Minor was first flown in 1938, powered by a 90 h.p. de Havilland Gipsy Minor engine. In October 1939, the Australian Department of Supply placed an order for fifty Moth Minors with de Havilland Aircraft Pty. Ltd., and fifteen of these are still flying in Australia. Eleven Moth Minors are flying in the United Kingdom, one in Switzerland, and the original prototype is still flying in New Zealand. The Moth Minor is of wooden construction and complete dual controls are fitted. The Moth Minor may be seen with either open cockpits or a hinged coupé superstructure.

Max. speed, 118 m.p.h. at sea level; cruising speed, 100 m.p.h. at 1,000 ft.; initial climb rate, 620 ft./min.; normal range, 300 miles; service ceiling, 16,600 ft.; empty weight, 970 lb.; loaded, 1,550 lb.; span, 36 ft. 7 in.; length, 24 ft. 5 in.; height, 6 ft. 4 in.; wing area, 162 sq. ft.

DE HAVILLAND D.H.98 MOSQUITO   G.B.

One of the most versatile aircraft of World War II, the Mosquito was produced in forty different variants, in Britain, Canada and Australia, a total of 7,781 machines being built. Small numbers of Mosquitos of various types are flying, but the only air forces now employing this aircraft as operational equipment are those of Burma (Mosquito F.B.6), Yugoslavia (Mosquito N.F.30), Israel (Mosquitos F.B.6 and B.9) and Sweden (Mosquito N.F.19). A few Mosquito T.3 trainers are flying in Belgium and Israel, and the *photo* depicts an Israeli F.B.6, and the specification refers to the B.35, a few of which remain with the R.A.F.

Max. speed, 422 m.p.h. at 30,000 ft.; initial climb, 1,400 ft./min.; service ceiling, 34,000 ft.; range (with 4,000 lb.), 1,750 miles; empty weight, 15,600 lb.; loaded, 25,200 lb.; span, 54 ft. 2 in.; length, 41 ft. 2 in.

DE HAVILLAND D.H.100 VAMPIRE F.B.6   G.B.

The Vampire F.B.6 is an export version of the F.B.5 from which it differs in having a 3,350 lb. thrust D.H. Goblin D.Gn.3 in place of the 3,100 lb. thrust Goblin D.Gn.2. Seventy-five Vampires of this type were delivered to Switzerland, and a further 100 machines were built in Switzerland under licence. The Vampire Mk.6 is generally similar to the Mk.50 exported to Sweden, and the Mk.52 supplied to Norway, Egypt and Venezuela. The Vampire F.B.5s and F.B.9s (tropicalised F.B.5s) in service with the R.A.F., R.N.Z.A.F., Royal South African and Royal Rhodesian Air Forces have lower performance.

Max. speed, 548 m.p.h.; initial climb rate, 4,800 ft./min.; range, 1,220 miles at 30,000 ft.; empty weight, 7,283 lb.; loaded, 12,390 lb.; span, 38 ft.; length, 30 ft. 9 in.; height, 6 ft. 2 in.; wing area, 262 sq. ft.

DE HAVILLAND VAMPIRE F.B.30   AUSTRALIA

The Vampire F.B.30, which was developed and manufactured by de Havilland Aircraft Pty. Ltd. from the British-built Vampire F.B.5, is powered by a 5,000 lb. thrust C.A.C.-built Rolls-Royce Nene 2-VH. This turbojet is about 40 per cent more powerful than the Goblin fitted to British Vampires and results in a notable increase in all-round performance. To serve the Nene's double-sided compressor an additional pair of intakes is provided on the rear fuselage decking. Eighty Vampire F.B.30s have been delivered to R.A.A.F. squadrons. Armament comprises four 20-mm. Hispano cannon.

Approx. max. speed, 570 m.p.h. at sea level; 550 m.p.h. at 20,000 ft.; climb to 40,000 ft., 10 minutes; ceiling, 49,000 ft.; empty weight, 7,600 lb.; loaded, 11,000 lb.; span, 38 ft. 0 in.; length, 30 ft. 9 in.

DE HAVILLAND D.H.103 HORNET   G.B.

The D.H. 103 was designed as a private venture and the first prototype flew on July 28, 1944. Orders were placed by the R.A.F., and the first deliveries were made in February 1945. A few examples of the Hornet F.3 and F.4 (the latter being an F.3 with an F.24 camera) remain, and these are single-seaters powered by two 2,030 h.p. Rolls-Royce Merlin 130/131 engines. A navalised version of the single-seat Hornet was produced as the Sea Hornet F.20, and this was followed by a two-seat night fighter conversion, the Sea Hornet N.F.21 (*photo*). The P.R.22 (*specification*) was a photo-reconnaissance version of the F.20. A few examples of all three Navy version remain with Fleet Requirements Units.

Max. speed, 467 m.p.h. at 22,000 ft.; initial climb, 4,000 ft./min.; range 1,500 miles; loaded weight, 18,250 lb.; span, 45 ft.; length, 36 ft. 8 in.

DE HAVILLAND D.H.106 COMET 2   G.B.

The D.H.106 Comet 2 was originally intended for medium-stage routes, carrying forty-four first-class passengers, differing from its predecessor, the Comet 1, in having Rolls-Royce Avon turbojets, a 3-ft. increase in fuselage length, and a modified wing section. The prototype (*photo*) had a Comet 1 airframe and four 6,500 lb. thrust Avon 502 turbojets. This was designated Comet 2X, flying on February 16, 1952. The first production Comet 2 with 7,150 lb. thrust Avon 503s flew on August 27, 1953, but in view of the accidents that befell the Comet 1, all Comet 2s are being modified, and R.A.F. Transport Command is to acquire an unspecified number of these for use between the U.K. and Woomera.

Cruising speed, 480 m.p.h. at 40,000 ft.; loaded weight, 120,000 lb.; span, 115 ft.; length, 96 ft.; height, 28 ft. 4½ in.; wing area, 2,015 sq. ft.

DE HAVILLAND D.H.104 DOVE
G.B.

The D.H.104 Dove has been produced to fill a variety of civil roles, the latest production versions being the eight/eleven-seat Series 5 for general transport duties, and the Series 6 five/six-seat executive transport. The Devon C.1 (*photo*) is a Series 4 Dove equipped to R.A.F. standards for use as a military personnel transport. The Devon has also been supplied to the Indian, New Zealand, South African and Swedish Air Forces. The initial production versions of the Dove, the Series 1 and 2, differed primarily in having 340 h.p. Gipsy Queen 70/4 engines.

Specification: Eight/eleven-seat light transport. Engines: Two 380 h.p. de Havilland Gipsy Queen 70 Mk.2. Weights: Empty, 5,725 lb.; loaded, 8,800 lb. Performance: Max. speed, 210 m.p.h. at 8,000 ft.; cruising, 179 m.p.h.; initial climb rate, 750 ft./min.; service ceiling, 20,000 ft.; range, 500 miles. Dimensions: Span, 57 ft.; length, 39 ft. 3 in.; height, 13 ft. 4 in.; wing area, 335 sq. ft.

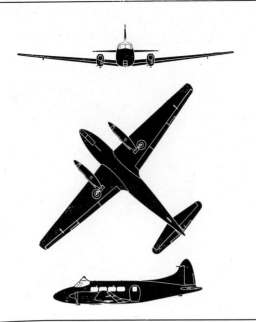

DE HAVILLAND D.H.106 COMET 4
G.B.

The Comet 4 is a developed version of the Comet 3 (*photo*), embodying structural modifications, increased fuel capacity and later series Rolls-Royce Avon turbojets. Deliveries of the Comet 4 are to commence in 1958, and this airliner will carry fifty-eight passengers in first-class accommodation over stage distances up to 2,870 miles. Twenty Comet 4s are to be delivered to B.O.A.C., and a special Comet 2 powered by four 7,300 lb.s.t. Avon Mk.117s is used for flight trials, training, etc.

Specification: Fifty-eight/seventy-six passenger commercial transport. Engines: Four 10,500 lb.s.t. Rolls-Royce Avon R.A.29. Performance: Optimum cruising speed, 489–506 m.p.h.; range (with reserves and 16,850 lb. payload), 2,870 miles. Weights: Empty, 68,000 lb.; max. loaded, 152,500 lb. Dimensions: Span, 115 ft.; length, 111 ft. 6 in.; height, 28 ft. 4½ in.; wing area, 2,121 sq. ft.

DE HAVILLAND D.H.110
G.B.

The D.H.110 has been developed to meet Naval specification N.14/49, and the first prototype flew on September 26, 1951, being followed on July 25, 1952, and June 20, 1955, by second and third prototypes. The third machine is semi-navalised, having arrester gear, long-stroke undercarriage, etc., but subsequent machines will have inward-folding wings which are not embodied in the earlier machines. The pilot's cockpit is offset to port in the fuselage nacelle, and the radar operator is seated below and to the rear of the pilot on the starboard side.

Specification: Two-seat all-weather Naval fighter and strike aircraft. Engines: 9,500 (approx.) lb.s.t. Rolls-Royce Avon. Weights: Approx. normal loaded, 30,000 lb.; max. loaded, 36,000 lb. Performance: No details available for publication. Armament: Four 30-mm. Aden cannon plus underwing ordnance loads. Dimensions: Span, 51 ft.; length, 52 ft. 1½ in.

DE HAVILLAND D.H.112 VENOM F.B.4   G.B.

Flown for the first time on September 2, 1949, the Venom is derived from the Vampire and has a new wing and other modifications in order to enable it to take advantage of the increased thrust available from a Ghost turbojet. The Venom F.B.1 is designated F.B.50 in its export version, and has been supplied to the Iraqi Air Force. In addition, 250 Venom F.B.50s are being built under licence in Switzerland. The Venom F.B.4 (*illustrated here*), differs from the F.B.1 in having power-operated ailerons and revised wing and tail surfaces, and is being supplied to the Venezuelan Air Force.

Specification: Single-seat fighter-bomber. Engine: One 4,850 lb.s.t. de Havilland Ghost 103. Weights: No details available for publication. Approx. performance: Max. speed, 640 m.p.h. at sea level; initial climb rate, 10,000 ft./min.; operational ceiling, 50,000 ft. Armament: Four 20-mm. British Hispano Mk.5 cannon. Dimensions: Span, 41 ft. 8 in.; length, 33 ft.; height, 6 ft. 8 in.; wing area, 279.8 sq. ft.

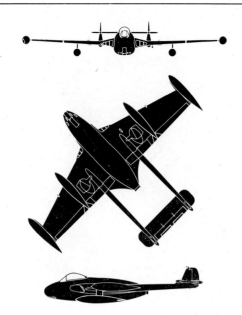

DE HAVILLAND SEA VENOM F. (A.W.) 21   G.B.

The de Havilland Sea Venom F. (A.W.) 21 is a development of the earlier F. (A.W.) 20 from which it differs in having power-operated ailerons and U.S. radar equipment supplied under M.D.A.P. The Sea Venoms F. (A.W.) 20 and 21 are respectively navalised versions of the land-based Venoms N.F.2 and N.F.3. A land-based export version, the Venom N.F.51, has been supplied to the Swedish Air Force, and the F. (A.W.) 20 is built under licence by the S.N.C.A. du Sud-Est as the *Aquilon* for the French Navy. Performance quoted in the specification relates to the French-built version.

Specification: Two-seat Naval all-weather fighter. Engine: One 4,850 lb.s.t. de Havilland Ghost 103. Weights: No details available. Performance: Max. speed, 587 m.p.h.; initial climb rate, 8,762 ft./min.; ceiling, 49,200 ft. Armament: Four 20-mm. Hispano 404 cannon. Dimensions: Span, 42 ft. 10 in.; length, 36 ft. 7¼ in.; height, 8 ft. 6¼ in.; wing area, 279.8 sq. ft.

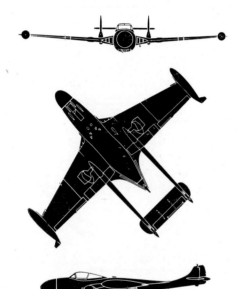

DE HAVILLAND D.H.114 HERON   G.B.

Basically a four-engined, scaled-up version of the D.H.104 Dove, the Heron was designed with particular emphasis upon simplicity of construction and maintenance. The prototype Heron Series 1 first flew on May 10, 1950, and the type is now in service in many countries. The Heron Series 2 (*silhouette*) is designed for longer stage lengths and differs from the Series 1 in having a retractable undercarriage which improves cruising speed by 20 m.p.h., but adds 165 lb. to the empty weight. The first Series 2 Heron flew on December 14, 1952.

Specification (Series 2 in parentheses): Fourteen/seventeen-seat feeder liner. Engines: Four 250 h.p. de Havilland Gipsy Queen 30 Mk.2. Weights: Empty, 7,985 (8,150) lb.; loaded, 13,000 lb. Performance: Cruising speed, 165 (183) m.p.h. at 8,000 ft.; initial climb rate, 1,060 (1,410) ft./min.; range with 2,100 lb., 805 miles (1,950 lb., 915 miles). Dimensions: Span, 71 ft. 6 in.; length, 48 ft. 6 in.; height, 15 ft. 7 in.; wing area, 487 sq. ft.

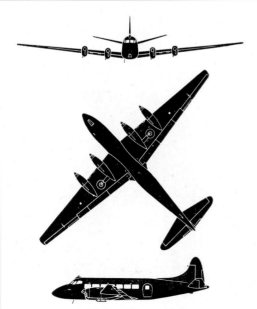

DE HAVILLAND D.H.115 VAMPIRE T.11   G.B.

Undertaken as a private venture, the D.H.115 Vampire Trainer is in service with the R.A.F. as the Vampire T.11, and in its export version as the Vampire T.55 with numerous foreign air forces. Flown for the first time on November 15, 1950, the D.H.115 Vampire Trainer has a basically similar fuselage to the D.H.113 Vampire (N.F.10) night fighter, and all essential cockpit instruments and controls are duplicated. The latest production machines differ from early aircraft in having clear-vision cockpit canopies, ejector seats and redesigned tail assemblies. A Fleet Air Arm variant is the Sea Vampire T.22, and the type is being built in Australia for the R.A.A.F.
Specification: Two-seat advanced trainer. Engine: One 3,500 lb.s.t. de Havilland Goblin 35. Weights: Empty, 7,380 lb.; loaded, 11,150 lb. Performance: Max. speed, 538 m.p.h. at sea level, 520 m.p.h. at 40,000 ft.; initial climb rate, 4,500 ft./min.: range, 840 miles at 30,000 ft. Dimensions: Span, 38 ft.; length, 34 ft. 5 in.; height, 6 ft. 2 in.

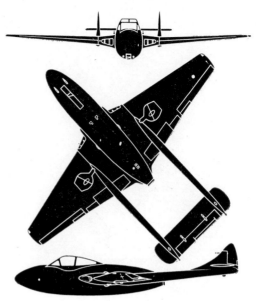

DE HAVILLAND DHC-1 CHIPMUNK   CANADA

Originally designed by the Canadian de Havilland Company and produced in both Canada and Britain, the Chipmunk serves with sixteen air forces and many flying clubs. Canadian-built Chipmunks (*photo*) are designated T.30, and the Canadian versions are the DHC-1B-1 with the Gipsy Major 1C and the DHC-1B-2 with a Gipsy Major 10-3. A total of 158 Chipmunks had been built in Canada when production temporarily ceased in December 1951, and the type was returned to production in 1955 with an order for a further 60 machines from the R.C.A.F. British versions are the T.10 and T.20 and the civil T.21 (*silhouette*).
Specification (T.10): Two-seat primary trainer. Engine: One 145 h.p. D.H. Gipsy Major 8. Weights: Empty, 1,425 lb.; loaded, 2,014 lb. Performance: Max. speed, 138 m.p.h.; cruising, 119 m.p.h.; initial climb rate, 840 ft./min.; range, 280 miles. Dimensions: Span, 34 ft. 4 in.; length, 25 ft. 5 in.; height, 7 ft.; wing area, 172 sq. ft.

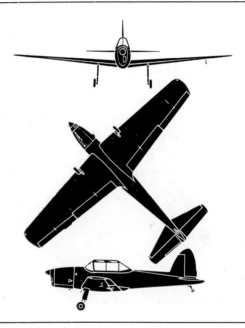

DE HAVILLAND DHC-2 BEAVER   CANADA

Designed initially for use in Northern Canada, the Beaver has been adopted for a wide variety of civil and military duties, and has been chosen by the U.S. Army and U.S.A.F. for liaison duties under the respective designations L-20 and L-20A. It is also used by the Colombian, Chilean and South Korean Air Forces, and numerous civil concerns, and one variant has been specially adapted for agricultural uses. The Beaver Series 2 is an experimental version powered by a 550 h.p. Alvis Leonides 502/4 engine, and differing externally from the standard Beaver in having a revised fin and rudder assembly.
Specification: Seven-seat utility transport. Engine: One 450 h.p. Pratt & Whitney R-985 Wasp Junior. Weights: Empty, 2,810 lb.; loaded, 4,900 lb. Performance: Max. speed, 179 m.p.h.; cruising, 142 m.p.h.; initial climb rate, 1,100 ft./min.; range, 922 miles. Dimensions: Span, 48 ft.; length, 30 ft. 3 in.; height, 10 ft. 7 in.; wing area, 375 sq. ft.

DE HAVILLAND DHC-3 OTTER — CANADA

Like its predecessor, the Beaver, the DHC-3 Otter was designed to operate in the undeveloped areas of Northern Canada, and it has been found suitable for both civil and military roles. Eighty Otters have been supplied to the R.C.A.F., four to the Colombian Air Force and others to the Royal Norwegian Air Force. The Otter has also been adopted by the U.S. Army, ninety-five machines being ordered under the designation U-1, and four have been supplied to the U.S. Navy under the designation UC-1. The Otter has nearly twice the capacity of the Beaver, carrying a maximum of fourteen passengers or over one ton of cargo.

Specification: General utility transport. Engine: One 600 h.p. Pratt & Whitney Wasp R-1340-S3H1-G. Weights: Empty, 4,165 lb.; loaded, 7,600 lb. Performance: Max. speed, 160 m.p.h.; cruising, 139 m.p.h.; initial climb rate, 1,000 ft./min.; cruising range, 1,050 miles. Dimensions: Span, 58 ft.; length, 41 ft. 10 in.; height, 10 ft. 6 in.

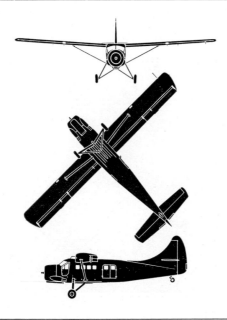

DE HAVILLAND DHA-3 DROVER 2 AUSTRALIA

The Drover, which flew for the first time on January 23, 1948, is a rugged and simple six-eight passenger transport designed by de Havilland Aircraft Pty. Ltd., and incorporating a number of structural features of the D.H.104 Dove. Limited production of the Drover was commenced in 1949 but terminated in mid-1953. Powered by three 145 h.p. D.H. Gipsy Major 10 Mk.2 engines driving fixed-pitch metal airscrews, the Drover 2 differs from the Drover 1 (*photo*) and 1F in having double-slotted flaps. Eight Drover 2s and five Drover 1s are flying, and these are used as feeder-liners, freighters and air ambulances.

Max. speed, 140 m.p.h. at sea level; cruising speed, 125 m.p.h.; initial climb rate, 670 ft./min.; range, 500 miles; empty weight, 4,100 lb.; loaded, 6,500 lb.; span, 57 ft.; length, 37 ft.; height, 9 ft. 9 in.

DESOUTTER II — G.B.

The Desoutter was the first three-seat light cabin monoplane to be produced in quantity in the U.K. Based on the Koolhoven F.K.41, production of the Desoutter commenced towards the end of 1929, and the sole survivor of the original production version, powered by a Menasco Buccaneer engine, is owned by the Shuttleworth Trust. In 1930 an improved version, known as the Desoutter II, was built, and powered by a de Havilland Gipsy Major 1 engine, one example of the latter version is flying in Australia. About forty Desoutters were built.

Max. speed, 125 m.p.h.; ceiling, 17,000 ft.; range, 500 miles; empty weight, 1,180 lb.; loaded, 1,900 lb.; span, 35 ft. 8½ in.; length, 26 ft.; height, 7 ft.; wing area, 183 sq. ft.

DEWOITINE D.26 — FRANCE

The Dewoitine D.26 single-seat fighter was one of a successful series of all-metal, high-wing monoplanes designed by Emile Dewoitine. It was exported in considerable numbers and, in 1931, a licence for the construction of this type was acquired by Switzerland. Eleven fighters of this type were built by the Konstruktionswerkstatte Thun for the Swiss Air Force and subsequently used as trainers. The D.26 is powered by a 250 h.p. Wright-Hispano radial, and six machines of this type are now flying in Switzerland, being employed by various aero clubs as glider tugs.

Max. speed, 149 m.p.h.; economical cruising, 105 m.p.h.; empty weight, 1,682 lb.; loaded, 2,354 lb.; span, 33 ft. 9 in.; length, 21 ft. 6 in.; height, 9 ft. 1 in.

DEWOITINE D.530 — FRANCE

The D.530 is a special version of the D.27 single-seat fighter of 1927, powered by a 500 h.p. Hispano-Suiza 12Md engine. Externally similar to the D.27 which, first appearing in 1927, established a World Air Speed record at 177.746 m.p.h., the D.530 became a familiar sight at post-war flying meetings in France, being flown by the late M. Doret, the internationally-known aerobatic pilot.

Max. speed, 192 m.p.h. at sea level, 180 m.p.h. at 9,840 ft.; climb to 3,280 ft., 1 minute 31 seconds; service ceiling, 30,340 ft.; empty weight, 2,134 lb.; loaded, 2,926 lb.; span, 33 ft. 9 in.; length, 21 ft. 4 in.; height, 9 ft. 6 in.; wing area, 188.3 sq. ft.

DEWOITINE D.482 — FRANCE

The D.482 side-by-side two-seat training monoplane was produced in 1932 as a higher-powered development of the D.480, the 95 h.p. Salmson 7 Ac radial engine of the earlier machine being replaced by a 135 h.p. Salmson 9 Nc radial. A number of aircraft of this type were produced by the Société Aéronautique Française in the early 'thirties, and one D.482 remains flying in France. This is used for advertising purposes by a French biscuit manufacturing concern and has been used as an exhibition aircraft by M. Marcel Doret.

Max. speed, 109 m.p.h.; economical cruising, 87 m.p.h.; service ceiling, 14,673 ft.; range, 373 miles; empty weight, 1,424 lb.; loaded, 2,005 lb.; span, 41 ft. 8 in.; length, 24 ft. 3¼ in.; height, 9 ft. 3 in.; wing area, 204.5 sq. ft.

DITTMAR HD 153 MOTOR-MÖVE — GERMANY

A motorised development of the Segelmöve sailplane designed by Heini Dittmar, the HD 153 Motor-Möve was first flown in mid-1954, and can be powered by Continental motors of either 65 or 85 h.p. The HD 153 is a side-by-side two-seater of wooden construction, and the prototype is powered by a 65 h.p. Continental A65 engine. A second machine is powered by a 60 h.p. Hirth engine. The wing and tail assembly can be detached for road transportation, and the type can be employed as a glider tug.

Max. speed, 102.5 m.p.h.; 90 m.p.h.; time to 3,280 ft., 7 minutes; endurance, 4 hours, 30 minutes; empty weight, 816 lb.; loaded, 1,543 lb.; span, 39 ft. 4½ in.; length, 21 ft. 4 in.; height, 5 ft. 3 in.; wing area, 196.979 sq. ft.

DORNIER DO 27 — GERMANY

The Do 27 has been developed from the Do 25 (designed to meet a Spanish Air Ministry specification for an air observation post and liaison monoplane) by the Oficinas Técnicas Dornier, and built by the Cadiz factory of the Construcciones Aeronauticas S.A. The Dornier Do 25 flew for the first time on June 25, 1954, powered by a 150 h.p. E.N.M.A. Tigre G-IVB engine, and the Do 27, powered by a 225 h.p. Continental O-470-J, was also built in Spain but assembled by the Dornier-Werke G.m.b.H. in Germany, and flown on April 8, 1955. Quantity production of the Do 27 will be inaugurated by the Dornier-Werke in 1956.

Specification: Two/three-seat air observation post and liaison monoplane. Engine: One 225 h.p. Continental 0-470-J. Weights: Empty, 1,962 lb.; loaded, 2,976 lb. Performance: Max. speed, 152 m.p.h. at 3,280 ft.; cruising, 130 m.p.h.; climb to 3,280 ft., 3 minutes; range, 410 miles. Dimensions: Span, 39 ft. 4½ in.; length, 30 ft. 9¾ in.

DOUGLAS A-20G HAVOC — U.S.A.

Descended from the DB-7 ordered by France for the *Armée de l'Air* in 1939, the A-20 Havoc was produced in a number of versions for the U.S.A.F., the A-20G model being built in largest numbers (2,850 built). Several of these have been converted for civil use (*photo*), and these are powered by two 1,600 h.p. Wright Cyclone R-2600-23 radial engines. A total of 7,097 of the various versions of the A-20 were produced between 1939 and 1944, and a considerable proportion of these were supplied to the R.A.F. and the Soviet Air Force. The A-20 Havoc no longer forms part of the operational equipment of any air force.

Max. speed, 317 m.p.h. at 6,700 ft.; cruising speed, 243 m.p.h.; range, 1,000 miles; service ceiling, 26,000 ft.; loaded weight, 25,700 lb.; span, 61 ft. 4 in.; length, 48 ft.; height, 15 ft. 10 in.; wing area, 464.8 sq. ft.

DOUGLAS A-24B DAUNTLESS — U.S.A.

The A-24B Dauntless was a land-based variant of the SBD-5 Dauntless (*photo*) carrier-based dive-bomber, from which it differed only in minor items of equipment and by the elimination of the arrester hook. Eight hundred and sixty-three A-24s were delivered to the U.S.A.F. between 1941 and 1943 when production ceased, and several of these are owned privately in the U.S.A. The only air force now employing the A-24B as first-line equipment is Mexico. A few SBD-5s are also in existence. The Mexican Air Force A-24Bs carry a maximum bomb load of 1,200 lb., and a defensive armament of two 0.50-in. and two 0.30-in. guns.

Max. speed, 255 m.p.h. at 14,000 ft.; cruising speed, 185 m.p.h.; range, 456 miles; empty weight, 6,535 lb.; loaded, 9,519 lb.; span, 41 ft.; length, 32 ft.; height, 13 ft.; wing area, 325 sq. ft.

E

DOUGLAS AD-4W SKYRAIDER (A.E.W.1) U.S.A.

Produced in a variety of versions since the prototype first flew in April 1945, the AD-4 differed from its predecessor, the AD-3, in having an auto pilot, improved radar, redesigned windshield, and modified arrester hook. Variants included the three-seat AD-4N (night attack), the two-seat AD-4Q (radar countermeasures), and the three-seat AD-4W (anti-submarine), in addition to the single-seat AD-4 day attack variant to which the specification refers. The AD-4W has been supplied to the Royal Navy under the designation Skyraider A.E.W.1 (*photo*), and this is powered by a 2,700 h.p. Wright R-3350-26W engine.
Max. speed, 359 m.p.h. at 15,000 ft.; initial climb rate, 2,850 ft./min.; max. range, 1,500 miles; empty weight, 10,550 lb.; max. loaded, 18,500 lb.; span, 50 ft.; length, 38 ft. 9½ in.; height, 15 ft. 7½ in.

DOUGLAS A2D-1 SKYSHARK U.S.A.

Designed originally as a successor to the Skyraider, the prototype Skyshark, the XA2D-1, flew for the first time on June 1, 1950. Two prototypes were completed, and quantity orders for the Skyshark were placed by the U.S. Navy, but continual power-plant failures led to the reduction of production orders to ten machines. These are powered by the 5,850 e.h.p. Allison XT40-A-6 airscrew turbine. The A2D-1 was designed to carry an underwing load of bombs, rockets and fuel totalling 8,000 lb., but a maximum underwing load of 15,000 lb. is permissible.
Max. speed, 460 m.p.h.; range, 1,600 miles; ceiling, 40,000 ft.; empty weight, 16,500 lb.; max. loaded (exceeds) 30,000 lb.; span, 50 ft.; length, 38 ft. 3¾ in.; height, 15 ft. 10 in.

DOUGLAS AD-5 SKYRAIDER U.S.A.

The AD-5 is a multi-purpose version of the Skyraider which has been in continuous production since the prototype flew in March 1945. The basic airframe of the AD-5 is quickly convertible for twelve different operational roles, ranging from ten-passenger transport to airborne early warning and anti-submarine search aircraft. The AD-5N is a night attack machine with a strike radar pod under the port wing and heavy underwing ordnance loads; the AD-5W is a three-seat airborne early warning aircraft; the AD-5Q is an electronic countermeasures aircraft, and the AD-5U is a target tug. The AD-6 is a single-seat attack bomber variant introduced in production in May 1952.
Specification: General-purpose Naval aircraft. Engine: One 2,700 h.p. Wright R-3350-26W. Weights: Empty, 11,800 lb.; loaded, 17,800 lb. Performance: Max. speed, 350 m.p.h. at 15,000 ft.; initial climb rate, 2,850 ft./min.; range, 1,000 miles. Dimensions: Span, 50 ft.; length, 38 ft. 9½ in.; height, 15 ft. 7½ in.

DOUGLAS A3D-1 SKYWARRIOR U.S.A.

Designed to operate from the giant Forrestal Class aircraft carriers, the A3D-1 Skywarrior attack bomber is the largest deck-landing jet aircraft to be accepted for carrier service. The prototype Skywarrior, the XA3D-1, flew on October 28, 1952, and entered production for the U.S. Navy in 1953. The internal weapons bay can accommodate a variety of bombs, depth charges, mines or torpedoes and, for the reconnaissance role, a modified camera nose may be fitted. A progressive development with more powerful turbojets, the A3D-2, is now in production.
Specification: Three-seat Naval attack bomber. Engines: Two 9,700 lb.s.t. Pratt & Whitney J57-P-12. Weights: Normal loaded, 70,000 lb.; max. loaded, 73,000 lb. Approx. performance: Max. speed, 575–610 m.p.h.; max. range, 2,300 miles. Defensive armament: Two 20-mm. cannon in radar-directed tail turret. Dimensions: Span, 73 ft.; length, 74 ft. 6 in.; height, 26 ft. 6 in.; wing area, 680 sq. ft.

DOUGLAS A4D-1 SKYHAWK   U.S.A.

The A4D-1 represents an attempt to depart from the present trend towards increasingly heavier and more complex combat aircraft by simplifying the airframe and operational equipment. The prototype Skyhawk, the XA4D-1, flew for the first time on June 22, 1954, and production for the U.S. Navy has since been inaugurated. The XA4D-1 was powered by a 7,200 lb.s.t. Wright J65-W-2 turbojet, and was the first U.S. aircraft of delta planform to utilise a tailplane. This was necessitated by the use of slats and flaps, and the need to balance out the trim changes necessitated by the extension of these. A built-in armament of two 20-mm. guns is carried.
Specification: Single-seat Naval fighter-bomber. Engine: One 7,800 lb.s.t. Wright J65-W-4. Approx. weights: Empty, 11,000 lb.; loaded (as interceptor), 15,000 lb.; max. 21,000 lb. Approx. performance: Max. speed, 675 m.p.h. at sea level; endurance, 2 hours, 45 minutes. Dimensions: Span, 27 ft.; length, 35 ft. height, 15 ft.

DOUGLAS B-18A BOLO   U.S.A.

A military version of the DC-3 transport, the DB-1, or B-18, appeared in 1936 and, powered by two 930 h.p. Wright R-1820-45 radial engines, one hundred and thirty-three were produced for U.S.A.A.F. bomber elements. These were followed by two hundred and seventeen B-18As which had 1,000 h.p. Wright R-1820-53 engines and a power-operated dorsal turret, and one hundred and twenty-two of these were converted to B-18Bs by the addition of anti-submarine gear. Many 18s were converted for use as transports, and B-18, B-18A and B-18B conversions are flying in the U.S. with civil concerns. The B-18A illustrated has a crop-spraying bar under the elevators.

Max. speed, 214 m.p.h.; initial climb, 1,050 ft./min.; range, 1,200 miles; loaded weight, 25,746 lb.; span, 89 ft. 6 in.; length, 56 ft. 8 in.

DOUGLAS UC-67 DRAGON   U.S.A.

Basically a development of the B-18A Bolo which, in turn, was a bomber adaptation of the DC-3 commercial transport, the Dragon first appeared in 1940 as the B-23, and thirty-eight bombers of this type were delivered to the U.S.A.F. Twelve of these were converted to UC-67 transports, and the remaining B-23s were used as glider tugs and for training purposes. Fifteen "civilianised" B-23s and four UC-67s are used by various commercial concerns as executive transports. Both the B-23 and the UC-67 are powered by two 1,600 h.p. Wright Cyclone R-2600-29 radial engines, and a crew of two and eleven to fourteen passengers are carried.

Max. speed, 286 m.p.h.; cruising speed, 261 m.p.h.; range, 2,200–3,000 miles; service ceiling, 28,200 ft.; loaded weight, 27,000–29,900 lb.; span, 92 ft.; length, 58 ft. 6 in.; height, 18 ft. 4 in.; wing area, 993 sq. ft.

DOUGLAS B-66B   U.S.A.

Basically a land-based variant of the carrier-borne A3D-1 Skywarrior, the prototype B-66 flew for the first time on June 28, 1954. The basic external differences between the B-66B and the Skywarrior include the former's revised wing planform with compound sweep on the trailing edge and increased area, longer turbojet nacelles and revised crew enclosure. Initially, production models have the Allison J71-A-9 turbojets, but latest production machines have the improved J71-A-11 with revised fuel system. Two basic variants are being produced, the B-66B and the RB-66B reconnaissance aircraft.
Specification: Three-seat light bomber and night interdictor. Engines: Two 9,700 lb.s.t. Allison J71-A-11. Weights: Empty, 40,330 lb.; loaded, 78,000 lb. (RB-66B: Empty, 39,686 lb.; loaded, 70,000 lb.). Performance: Approx. max. speed, 620 m.p.h.; range, 1,500–1,750 miles. Dimensions: Span, 72 ft. 6 in.; length, 75 ft. 1¼ in.; height, 23 ft. 7 in.; wing area, 779 sq. ft.

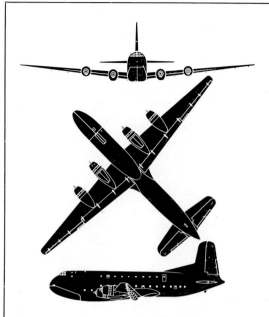

DOUGLAS C-124C GLOBEMASTER II   U.S.A.

Largest military transport in series production, the Globemaster II has been developed from the C-74 Globemaster I, using the same wing, tail unit and power plants. The initial production version was the C-124A powered by R-4360-20W engines developing 3,500 h.p. for take-off. This was followed by the improved C-124C which can carry 200 troops and has higher-powered engines. The YC-124B is an experimental turbo-prop-powered variant with four 5,500 e.h.p. Pratt & Whitney YT34-P-1 engines.
Specification: Military cargo and troop transport. Engines: Four 3,800 h.p. Pratt & Whitney R-4360-63A Wasp Majors. Weights: Empty, 100,821 lb.; normal loaded, 175,000 lb.; maximum, 195,000 lb. Performance: Max. speed, 298 m.p.h. at 20,800 ft.; cruising, 264 m.p.h.; initial climb rate, 800 ft./min.; range, 6,280 miles. Dimensions: Span, 173 ft. 3 in.; length, 130 ft.; height, 48 ft. 3 in.; wing area, 2,510 sq. ft.

DOUGLAS C-74 GLOBEMASTER I   U.S.A.

The prototype of the Globemaster I, the XC-74, was flown for the first time on September 5, 1945, and fourteen C-74s were subsequently delivered to the U.S.A.F. Initially a civil transport version was projected but orders for this were cancelled in view of the high initial cost. The type was subsequently developed with a new fuselage as the C-124 Globemaster II. The C-74 is powered by four 3,500 h.p. Pratt & Whitney Wasp Major R-4360-49 radial engines, and can carry two 75-mm. or 105-mm. howitzers with tractors, ammunition carriers and crews, or seat 125 troops.

Approx. cruising speed, 300 m.p.h.; max. range, 7,800 miles; empty weight, 85,000 lb.; loaded, 165,000 lb.; span, 173 ft. 3 in.; length, 124 ft. 1½ in.; height, 43 ft. 9 in.

DOUGLAS D-558-1 SKYSTREAK   U.S.A.

The first of three D-558-1 Skystreak research aircraft was flown on May 28, 1947, and some three months later, on August 20, raised the World Air Speed Record to 640.663 m.p.h., increasing this figure to 650.606 m.p.h. five days later. The Skystreak was initially powered by the 4,000 lb. thrust Allison J35-A-23 turbojet, and this was later replaced by a 5,000 lb. thrust Allison J35-A-11. The three Skystreaks have been used extensively by the National Advisory Committee for Aeronautics, and 640 lb. of research equipment is carried. The nose section of the fuselage can be jettisoned in an emergency.

Max. speed, 651 m.p.h.; loaded weight, 9,750 lb.; span, 25 ft.; length, 35 ft. 1 in.; height, 12 ft. 2 in.; wing area, 150 sq. ft.

DOUGLAS D-558-2 SKYROCKET   U.S.A.

The first of three D-558-2 Skyrockets flew on February 4, 1948. It was originally intended as a swept-wing version of the Skystreak, and the 3,000 lb. thrust Westinghouse J34-WE-22 was supplemented by a 6,000 lb. thrust Reaction Motors XLR-8 bi-fuel rocket. With this power combination, the Skyrocket attained Mach 1.0 in October 1947. In August 1951 the turbojet was removed from one Skyrocket and its rocket fuel capacity doubled. In this form it attained Mach 1.7 at 68,000 ft. (1,143 m.p.h.) on August 21, 1951. On November 21, 1953, a Skyrocket attained Mach 2.01 at 65,000 ft. (1,327 m.p.h.). These performances are particularly noteworthy in view of the fact that the Skyrocket employs a conventional sub-sonic aerofoil.
Span, 25 ft.; length, 45 ft. 3 in.; height, 11 ft. 6 in.

DOUGLAS DC-2   U.S.A.

The DC-2 was a direct development of the sole DC-1, and flew for the first time in May 1934, powered by two 710 h.p. Wright Cyclone SGR-1820-F3 radial engines. These were later supplanted by 760 h.p. SRG-1820-F52 radials, and twenty-four machines were delivered to the U.S.A.A.F. as the C-32A and, with a cargo door, eighteen as the C-33. Thirty-five were delivered to the U.S.A.A.F. in 1939 with the DC-2 fuselage and DC-3 wing and tail assemblies. Powered by 975 h.p. Wright R-1820-25 engines, these were designated C-39. One DC-2 is flying in Australia, another (with Bristol Mercury 8s) in Finland, one in the U.S.A., three C-39s in Mexico, and two C-39s in Argentina.
Max. speed, 210 m.p.h.; cruising, 190 m.p.h.; initial climb, 1,000 ft./min.; empty weight, 12,408 lb.; loaded, 18,560 lb.; span, 85 ft.; length, 61 ft. 11¾ in.

DOUGLAS DC-3C   U.S.A.

Flown for the first time on December 22, 1935, the DC-3 was adopted as the standard transport of the Allied Air Forces, and 10,926 had been built in the U.S.A. when production terminated. The military version of the DC-3 was designated C-47 Skytrain (Dakota in R.A.F. service), and it is still employed by many of the world's air forces. Surplus C-47s are used by most of the world's smaller air lines. The DC-3A is the model originally built as a commercial transport, but the most widely employed model is the DC-3C (converted surplus C-47A and B). The DC-3D and -3G differ in power plants.
Specification (DC-3G): Commercial transport. Engines: Two 1,200 h.p. Wright Cyclone GR-1820-G-202A. Weights: Empty, 16,480 lb.; loaded, 25,200–26,900 lb. Performance: Max. speed, 216 m.p.h.; cruising, 167 m.p.h. Dimensions: Span, 95 ft.; length, 64 ft. 5½ in.; height, 16 ft. 11 in.; wing area, 987 sq. ft.

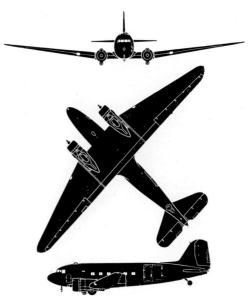

DOUGLAS R4D-8   U.S.A.

The Douglas R4D-8 is an extensive conversion of the C-47. The modernisation programme involved the fitting of new wings, a new tail unit, modified landing gear and more powerful engines, and the result was practically a new aircraft. The commercial version, the Super DC-3, was utilised for a short period by Capital Airlines, but all Super DC-3s currently in service are military transports. The U.S. Navy has had a large number of R4D (C-47) transports converted to R4D-8 standards.
Specification: Military transport. Engines: Two 1,535 h.p. Wright R-1820-80. Weights: Empty, 19,537 lb.; loaded, 31,000 lb. Performance: Max. speed, 270 m.p.h. at 5,900 ft.; cruising speed, 251 m.p.h. at 15,400 ft.; initial climb rate, 1,300 ft./min.; normal range, 1,425 miles; max. range, 2,200 miles. Dimensions: Span, 90 ft.; length, 67 ft. 8½ in.; height, 18 ft. 3 in.; wing area, 969 sq. ft.

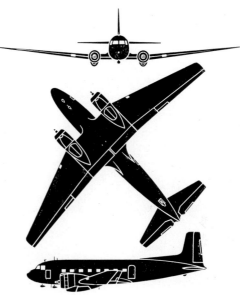

DOUGLAS B-26C INVADER   U.S.A.

Originally designated A-26 and redesignated B-26 when the U.S.A.F.'s designation system was changed after World War 2, the Invader flew in prototype form in July 1942, and 2,451 machines were produced. The initial production version was the A-26B with a battery of six 0.5-in. guns in a "solid" nose and two 2,000 h.p. Pratt & Whitney R-2800-27 or -79 radials. This was succeeded by the A-26C with a transparent nose and 2,100 h.p. R-2800-71 engines, and, as the B-26C, remains in service with the U.S.A.F. and the French Air Force. Two 0.5-in. guns are fitted in each of the dorsal and ventral turrets.
(B-26B): Max. speed, 355 m.p.h. at 15,000 ft.; cruising, 198 m.p.h. at 10,000 ft.; initial climb, 2,030 ft./min.; range (with 4,000 lb.), 1,360 miles; span, 70 ft.; length, 49 ft. 11 in.; height, 18 ft. 6 in.

DOUGLAS D.117 DOLPHIN   U.S.A.

The Dolphin twin-engined amphibian was first introduced in 1931, and several versions were produced. Initial models were powered by two 300 h.p. Pratt & Whitney Wasp Junior R-985-1 radials. These were later replaced by 350 h.p. R-985-3, -5, and -9 radials, and eventually with 420 h.p. Wasp Juniors. A number of rebuilt machines were fitted with stainless-steel wings in place of the wooden wings previously fitted in 1936, and at least two Dolphins are still flying. The Dolphin's cabin can be arranged to seat up to twelve passengers, and a crew of two is normally carried. The following refers to the 450 h.p. engined version.
Max. speed, 151 m.p.h.; cruising speed, 135 m.p.h.; initial climb rate, 850 ft./min.; service ceiling, 17,000 ft.; empty weight, 7,000 lb.; loaded, 9,500 lb.; span, 60 ft.; length, 45 ft. 1 in.; height, 14 ft.

DOUGLAS DC-4 (C-54 SKYMASTER)   U.S.A.

The most widely-used four-engined airliner in international service, the Douglas DC-4 was designed in co-operation with five U.S. airlines, the prototype first flying in June 1938. A redesigned and scaled-down version of the DC-4 was placed in production, but all commercial DC-4s were taken over by the U.S.A.A.F. as the C-54 Skymaster. Various versions of the Skymaster were produced, the last military transports being the C-54E and G. When production ceased in August 1947, a total of 1,163 Skymasters had been built, 1,084 of these as C-54 military transports. Some three hundred surplus C-54s were sold to U.S. and foreign air lines.

Specification: Commercial and military transport. Engines: Four 1,540 h.p. Pratt & Whitney R-2800-2SD13-G. Weights: Empty, 40,806 lb.; loaded, 73,000 lb. Performance: Max. speed, 280 m.p.h. at 14,000 ft.; cruising, 246 m.p.h.; range, 1,680 miles. Dimensions: Span, 117 ft. 6 in.; length, 93 ft. 11 in.; height, 27 ft. 6¼ in.

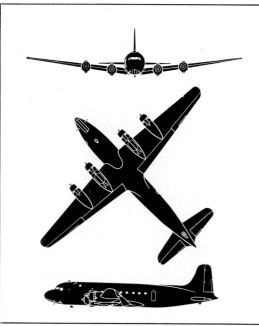

DOUGLAS DC-6A (R6D-1/C-118A)   U.S.A.

The DC-6A is a "stretched" freight-carrying version of the DC-6 which, in turn, is a more powerful and enlarged development of the DC-4. The DC-6A differs from the DC-6 primarily in having a 5-ft. increase in fuselage length, and can carry 28,500 lb. of freight. The DC-6B is a fifty-four/ninety-two passenger airliner version of the DC-6A, and the C-118A (*photo*) and R6D-1 are respectively U.S.A.F. and U.S. Navy variants. The C-118A can accommodate seventy-six troops or forty stretcher cases.

Specification: Military and commercial freighter. Engines: Four 2,500 h.p. Pratt & Whitney R-2800-CB17. Weights: Empty, 54,148 lb.; loaded, 106,000 lb. Performance: Max. speed, 370 m.p.h. at 20,500 ft., 318 m.p.h. at sea level; cruising speed, 316 m.p.h. at 23,100 ft.; initial climb rate, 1,020 ft./min. Dimensions: Span, 117 ft. 6 in.; length, 105 ft. 7 in.; height, 28 ft. 8 in.; wing area, 1,463 sq. ft.

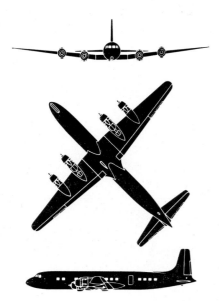

DOUGLAS DC-7 (DC-7C SEVEN SEAS)   U.S.A.

The DC-7 is a further development of the DC-4/DC-6 series of transports. The initial models of the DC-7 (*photo*) were 3 ft. 4 in. longer than the DC-6A and featured more powerful engines and increased fuel capacity. The DC-7 is designed for U.S. domestic services, and the DC-7B (weight increased to 125,000 lb.) is a long-range intercontinental version. The DC-7C (*silhouette*) is an enlarged version of the earlier models with a further increase in power, gross weight, etc. Figures in parentheses refer to the DC-7C.

Specification: Sixty-two/ninety-five-seat airliner. Engines: Four 3,250 (3,400) h.p. Wright R-3350. Weights: Empty, 71,025 (77,914) lb.; loaded, 126,000 (139,000) lb. Performance: Max. speed, 405 (398) m.p.h. at 22,500 ft.; max. cruising, 359 (343) m.p.h. at 24,000 ft.; service ceiling, 28,400 (26,000) ft.; initial climb rate, 1,673 (1,060) ft./min. Dimensions: Span, 117 ft. 6 in. (127 ft. 6 in.); length, 108 ft. 11 in. (112 ft. 3 in.); height, 28 ft. 7 in. (30 ft. 9 in.); wing area, 1,463 (1,637) sq. ft.

DOUGLAS F3D-2 SKYNIGHT U.S.A.

The prototype Skyknight, the XF3D-1, flew for the first time on March 22, 1948, and twenty-eight of the initial production model, the F3D-1 (two 3,000 lb.s.t. Westinghouse J34-WE-32), were produced, followed by seventy F3D-2 Skyknights. The F3D-2 was an improved model for the U.S. Marine Corps with the later APG-35 radar and larger turbojet housings. These housings were intended for the 4,800 lb. thrust Westinghouse J46-WE-3 turbojet, but development difficulties with the J46 led to the installation of J34-WE-36 turbojets.
Specification: Two-seat Naval all-weather and night fighter. Engines: Two 3,400 lb.s.t. Westinghouse J34-WE-36. Weights: Empty, 18,160 lb.; loaded, 27,000 lb. Approx. performance: Max. speed, 560 m.p.h. at sea level; initial climb rate, 2,500 ft./min.; combat radius, 600 miles. Armament: Four 20-mm. cannon. Dimensions: Span, 50 ft.; length, 45 ft. 6¼ in.; height, 16 ft. 6 in.

DOUGLAS F4D-1 SKYRAY U.S.A.

The Skyray interceptor fighter has been extensively modified since the first prototype, the XF4D-1, flew on January 23, 1951. The F4D-1 production model (*illustrated here*), flew for the first time on June 5, 1954, but this will be succeeded by the F4D-2N which has full all-weather radar and a radar fire control system. The Skyray's fixed armament of four 20-mm. cannon can be supplemented by six underwing pods, each housing seven 2.75-in. unguided rockets, four pods of nineteen rockets, or two 2,000-lb. bombs.
Specification: Single-seat Naval interceptor fighter. Engine: One 9,700 lb.s.t. (14,500 lb.s.t. with afterburning) Pratt & Whitney J57-P-2. Weights: Normal loaded, 20,000 lb. Approx. performance: Max speed, 730 m.p.h. at sea level, 660 m.p.h. at 36,000 ft.; initial climb rate, 16,000 ft./min.; endurance (internal fuel), 45 minutes (with two 250 imp. gall. underwing tanks), 1 hour 25 minutes. Dimensions: Span, 33 ft. 6 in.; length, 45 ft. 8¼ in.; height, 13 ft.; wing area, 557 sq. ft.

DOUGLAS X-3 U.S.A.

The X-3 was designed to explore the efficiency of turbojets and small-span, double-wedge aerofoils at speeds up to Mach 3.0 (1,960–2,280 m.p.h.), and it was intended to install two Westinghouse J46-WE-8 turbojets developing a total of 14,000 lb. thrust with afterburning. Increases in the overall diameter of this engine necessitated the installation of two J34-WE-17 developing a total thrust of only 8,400 lb. with afterburning. With the reduced power, the X-3 is incapable of attaining Mach 3.0. It was flown for the first time on October 20, 1952, and its tiny wing possesses a thickness/chord ratio of only 5 per cent and a loading of some 200 lb./sq. ft.
Designed speed, Mach 3.0; loaded weight, 27,000 lb.; span, 22 ft. 8 in.; length, 66 ft. 9 in.

DRUINE D-60 CONDOR FRANCE

The D-60 Condor side-by-side two-seat ultra-light cabin monoplane designed by Roger Druine is powered in its prototype form by a 60 h.p. C.N.A.D.4 engine, but proposed production models include the D-61 powered by a 65 h.p. Continental A65, and the D-62 powered by a 90 h.p. Continental C90. A variant of the latter, the D-620, is to be fitted with VHF radio and other equipment. The D-60 is of extremely simple construction, and complete aircraft will be built by Borea et Fils, while constructional kits may be made available for amateur groups.
Max. speed, 112 m.p.h.; cruising speed, 99 m.p.h.; initial climb rate, 689 ft./min.; ceiling, 13,779 ft.; range, 404 miles; empty weight, 665 lb.; loaded, 1,102 lb.; span, 30 ft. 2 in.; length, 21 ft. 4 in.

DRUINE D.3 TURBULENT & D.5 TURBI   FRANCE

The D.3 Turbulent and D.5 Turbi are respectively single-seat and two-seat ultra light monoplanes, designed for sale in kit form for assembly by private individuals or groups. The D.3 Turbulent (*silhouette*) may be fitted with a variety of small engines, but the majority built so far have the 25 h.p. Volkswagen. The D.5 Turbi is a two-seat development of the Turbulent. The Turbi (*photograph*) may be fitted with the 45 h.p. Beaussier, the 65 h.p. Walter, the 65 h.p. Continental, the 52 h.p. Zundapp, the 75 h.p. Minié, or the 75 h.p. Régnier. The following specification refers to the D.31 Turbulent (and the D.50 Turbi in parentheses).
Specification: Ultra-light monoplane. Engine: One 25 h.p. Volkswagen (45 h.p. Beaussier). Weights: Loaded, 507 (1,069) lb. Performance: Max. speed, 90 (99) m.p.h.; cruising, 74.5 (78) m.p.h.; range, 186 (404) miles. Dimensions: Span, 21 ft. 6 in. (28 ft. 6 in.); length, 15 ft. 9 in. (20 ft. 4 in.); wing area, 80.7 (145.2) sq. ft.

ENGLISH ELECTRIC CANBERRA B.6   G.B.

The English Electric Canberra first flew on May 13, 1949, and has since been produced in a variety of versions and currently serves the air forces of Venezuela, Ecuador, and the U.S.A., in addition to the R.A.F., and R.A.A.F. The first major production version was the Canberra B.2, followed by the P.R.3 (which had fuselage lengthened from 63 ft. 11½ in. to 66 ft. 8 in.), and the T.4 dual-control conversion trainer. The B.5 was an experimental "target marker" version, and the B.6 and P.R.7 differ from previous production versions in having the 6,500 lbs.t. Avon R.A.3s replaced by 7,500 lb.s.t. Avon R.A.7s. Some B.6s are in service as night intruders.
Specification: Three-seat light bomber. Engines: Two 7,500 lb.s.t. Rolls-Royce Avon R.A.7. Weights: Approx. loaded, 45,000 lb. Performance: Approx. max. speed, 620 m.p.h.; approx. range, 3,000 miles.; service ceiling in excess of 50,000 ft. Dimensions: Span, 63 ft. 11½ in.; length, 65 ft. 6 in.; height, 15 ft. 7 in.

ENGLISH ELECTRIC CANBERRA B.8   G.B.

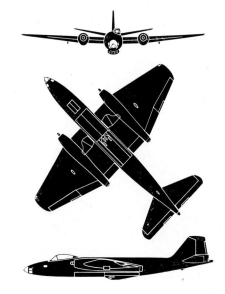

The Canberra B.8, which flew for the first time on July 23, 1954, is intended for the alternative roles of low-altitude night interdictor and high-altitude level bomber. It differs externally from all previous variants in having an offset fighter-type canopy and revised forward fuselage. The rear section of the bomb bay can house a gun pack containing four 20-mm. cannon, and additional offensive stores are carried on under-wing pylons. The Canberra P.R.9 differs from the B.8 in having a 4 ft. increase in wing span, an extension of the wing chord between the engine nacelles, and Avon 206s.
Specification: Night intruder and high-altitude bomber. Engines: Two 7,500 lb.s.t. Rolls-Royce Avon 109. Approx. weights: Empty, 26,000 lb.; loaded, 45,000 lb. Performance: Approx. max. speed, 640 m.p.h.; service ceiling, 50,000 ft.; approx. range, 3,000 miles. Dimensions: Span, 65 ft. 6 in.; length, 63 ft. 11½ in.; height, 15 ft. 7 in.; wing area, 960 sq. ft.

ENGLISH ELECTRIC P.1A — G.B.

The English Electric P.1 single-seat interceptor fighter has been designed to attain supersonic speeds in level flight. The first prototype flew on August 4, 1954, being followed on July 18, 1955 by a second prototype, and a pre-production batch of twenty P.1 fighters has been ordered for development trials. The first prototype P.1A is powered by two Armstrong Siddeley Sapphire turbojets without afterburner thrust augmentation, but foreign reports suggest that later machines will have late model Rolls-Royce Avons with afterburners. The wing of the P.1 is swept at approximately 60°, and an unusual feature of the design is the disposition of the ailerons across the wingtips.

Specification: Single-seat interceptor fighter. Engines: Two Armstrong Siddeley Sapphire. Weights: No details available for publication. Performance: Level speeds in the Mach 1.3-1.5 range. Dimensions: No details available for publication.

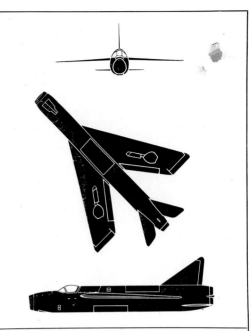

ERCOUPE MODEL 415-G CLUB-AIR — U.S.A.

The Ercoupe remained virtually unchanged from its first flight in October 1937 (then designated Erco 310 and powered by a 55 h.p. Erco IL-116) until production terminated in 1951. The first production version was the Model 415-C (75 h.p. Continental C75-12F) of 1940, but production was shelved with the U.S.A.'s entry into the war, being resumed in 1945. The Model 415-E and F (85 h.p. Continental C85-12 or 12J) were introduced in 1947, and were followed in 1949 by the 415-G and 415-H. The Ercoupe is unusual in dispensing with rudder pedals, being flown entirely by the control wheel.

Specification: Two-seat cabin monoplane. Engine: One 85 h.p. Continental C85. Weights: Empty, 838 lb.; loaded, 1,400 lb. Performance: Max. speed, 125 m.p.h.; cruising, 110 m.p.h.; range, 430 miles. Dimensions: Span, 30 ft.; length, 20 ft. 9 in.; height, 5 ft. 11 in.; wing area, 142.6 sq. ft.

EMIGH TROJAN A-2 — U.S.A.

The Trojan two-seat all-metal light cabin monoplane designed W. H. E. Emigh, was built in small numbers during 1948 and 1949 by the Emigh Trojan Aircraft Company. Some twenty-six Trojan A-2s are currently flying in the U.S.A. The Trojan A-2 is noteworthy for its extremely simple construction. The cabin seats two side-by-side with dual controls, and power is provided by a 90 h.p. Continental A90 engine.

Max. speed, 130 m.p.h.; cruising speed, 115 m.p.h.; service ceiling, 13,000 ft.; cruising range, 550 miles; loaded weight, 1,450 lb.; span, 31 ft. 7 in.; length, 20 ft. 5 in.; height, 6 ft. 5 in.

FAIRCHILD KR-21 — U.S.A.

Formerly the Kreider-Reisner Challenger C-6, the Fairchild KR-21 tandem two-seat training biplane was introduced in 1927, and was powered by 90 h.p. Kinner (KR-21), 125 h.p. Kinner (KR-21B), and 110 h.p. Warner Scarab engines. One example of the Kinner-powered KR-21 built in 1927 is active in the U.S.A., and one example of the 1931-built KR-21B. Both are of mixed construction with fabric covering, and have dual controls.

Max. speed, 113 m.p.h.; cruising, 90 m.p.h.; initial climb, 775 ft./min.; service ceiling, 15,000 ft.; range, 350 miles; empty weight, 1,015 lb.; loaded, 1,550 lb.; span, 27 ft.; length, 21 ft. 7 in.; height, 9 ft.; wing area, 193 sq. ft.

FAIRCHILD 22C-7-E   U.S.A.

The Model 22, built by the Kreider-Reisner Aircraft Company, appeared in 1931. A tandem two-seat parasol monoplane, it was one of the first successful light aircraft to be built in quantity. A variety of engines were installed during the five years in which the Model 22 was in production. Among those currently flying in the U.S.A. are the Model 22C-7-A with a 95 h.p. Cirrus, the C-7-D with a 90 h.p. Wright Gipsy, the C-7-E with a 125 h.p. Warner Scarab, and the C-7-F with a 145 h.p. Scarab. The specification refers to the Model 22C-7-E which is illustrated. The Model 22 is of mixed construction and has dual controls.
Max. speed, 128 m.p.h.; cruising, 110 m.p.h.; initial climb rate, 700 ft./min.; service ceiling, 18,000 ft.; range, 350 miles; empty weight, 1,102 lb.; loaded, 1,750 lb.; span, 32 ft. 10 in.; length, 22 ft.; height, 8 ft.

FAIRCHILD 24C-8-C   U.S.A.

The Model 24 first appeared in 1933, and progressive developments of the basic design remained in production for thirteen years. The 24C-8 was produced with a variety of engines until 1937 when it was supplanted in production by the Models 24G and 24H. The version of the Model 24C flying in largest numbers is the 24C-8-C illustrated here. This is powered by a 145 h.p. Warner Scarab radial engine, and the cabin provides accommodation for three persons. Others flying include the Ranger-powered 24C-8-D and the Wasp Junior-powered C-8-F.
Max. speed, 140 m.p.h.; cruising speed, 120 m.p.h.; initial climb rate, 750 ft./min.; service ceiling, 20,000 ft.; range, 550 miles; empty weight, 1,354 lb.; loaded, 2,150 lb.; span, 36 ft. 4 in.; length, 26 ft. 9 in.; height 7 ft.; wing area, 186 sq. ft.

FAIRCHILD 71-C   U.S.A.

The Fairchild Model 71 was first produced in 1928 as a refined version of the popular FC-2W2, and in 1929 Fairchild Aircraft Limited was established near Montreal, Canada, expressly to manufacture the Model 71. A considerable number of Model 71 aircraft were built in both the U.S.A. and Canada, and many are currently flying in Canada. Others are flying in the U.S.A. and Mexico. Two basic versions were produced in Canada; the 71-C and 71-CM, the latter having metal fuselage skinning in place of the normal fabric. The 71-C (*illustrated*), has a 420 h.p. Wasp radial and carries six passengers.
Max. speed, 132.5 m.p.h.; cruising, 106 m.p.h.; initial climb rate, 600 ft./min.; range 900 miles; empty weight, 3,158 lb.; loaded, 6,000 lb.; span, 50 ft.; length, 32 ft. 10¼ in.; height, 9 ft. 4 in.

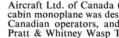

FAIRCHILD 82-B   CANADA

The second aircraft of original design to be produced by Fairchild Aircraft Ltd. of Canada (the first being the Super-71) the Model 82-B cabin monoplane was designed specifically to meet the unusual needs of Canadian operators, and appeared in 1935. Powered by a 500 h.p. Pratt & Whitney Wasp T1D1 radial engine, both landplane and float-plane versions of the Model 82-B were produced, and one or two examples of the latter are flying in Canada. The following specification refers to the floatplane. The Model 82-B carries ten passengers and is of mixed construction.
Max. speed, 152 m.p.h.; cruising speed, 127 m.p.h.; service ceiling, 17,000 ft.; range, 490 miles; empty weight, 3,890 lb.; loaded, 6,325 lb.; span, 51 ft.; length, 36 ft. 10¼ in.; wing area, 343 sq. ft.

FAIRCHILD F-45   U.S.A.

Introduced in 1936, the Fairchild F-45 five-seat cabin monoplane was designed as a high-performance personal transport for corporation executive use. The prototype was powered by a 220 h.p. Jacobs engine, but production machines received the 320 h.p. Wright R-760-E2 Whirlwind. Only a small number of F-45 monoplanes were produced and five of these are currently flying in the U.S.A. One of these (*illustrated*), has been re-engined with a 450 h.p. Pratt & Whitney Wasp Junior R-985-AN-3 engine, but the following specification refers to the standard Whirlwind-powered F-45.
Max. speed, 180 m.p.h.; cruising speed, 173 m.p.h.; initial climb rate, 1,100 ft./min.; range, 780 miles; empty weight, 2,474 lb.; loaded, 4,000 lb.; span, 39 ft. 6 in.; length, 30 ft. 3 in.; height, 8 ft.

FAIRCHILD F-11 HUSKY   CANADA

First flown in 1946 and subsequently produced in limited quantities for Canadian operators, the F-11 Husky can be considered as an outgrowth of the pre-war series of "bush-planes" such as the Model 82-B and Super-71. Carrying six to eight passengers and powered by a 450 h.p. Pratt & Whitney Wasp Junior R-985-SB3 radial engine, the Husky is of all-metal construction and may be fitted with skis, floats or wheels. For freight and passenger operations bench-type seats, which fold up against the fuselage sides, are used. A large freight-loading door is fitted in each side of the cabin.
Max. speed, 140 m.p.h. at 2,300 ft.; cruising, 116 m.p.h. at 2,000 ft.; initial climb rate, 775 ft./min.; empty weight, 4,200 lb.; loaded, 6,400 lb.; span, 54 ft. 9 in.; length, 37 ft. 5 in.; height, 17 ft. 9 in.

FAIRCHILD 24R/W   U.S.A.

In 1937, the three-seat Model 24 was supplanted in production by a four-seat version, the Model 24J. This was produced with both the 145 h.p. Warner Super-Scarab radial and the 165 h.p. Ranger R-690-D3 inline engine. In 1938, the similar Ranger-powered 24K and 24KS (de luxe model) appeared, to be followed in 1939 by the 24R-9 and 24R-9S with the Ranger engine, and the 24W-9 with the Warner. Nine hundred and ninety-five Warner- and Ranger-powered Model 24s were obtained by the U.S.A.A.F. as the UC-61. Production of the commercial models was resumed after World War 2 as the 24R-46 and 24W-46. Specification relates to Model 24W-46.

Specification: Four-seat cabin monoplane. Engine: One 165 h.p. Warner Super Scarab 175. Weights: Empty, 1,613 lb.; loaded, 2,562 lb. Performance: Max. speed, 132 m.p.h.; cruising, 117 m.p.h.; range, 639 miles; endurance, 5.75 hours. Dimensions: Span, 36 ft. 4 in.; length, 23 ft. 9 in.; height, 7 ft. 7½ in.; wing area, 193.3 sq. ft.

FAIRCHILD M-62A   U.S.A.

The Fairchild M-62, which first flew in March 1939, was widely used as a primary trainer during the war, and between February 1940 and May 1944, over eight thousand trainers of this type had been produced in the U.S.A., Canada and Brazil. The three production versions of the M-62 were the PT-19 and PT-26 (M-62A) with 200 h.p. Ranger L-440 engines, and the PT-23 with the 220 h.p. Continental R-670-4 radial. At least three thousand Ranger- and Continental-powered M-62 trainers are flying, and the photo depicts a Norwegian Air Force M-62A.

Specification: Two-seat primary trainer. Engine: One 200 h.p. Ranger L-440-7. Weights: Empty, 2,022 lb.; loaded, 2,741 lb. Performance: Max. speed, 126 m.p.h.; cruising, 114 m.p.h.; initial climb rate, 675 ft./min.; range, 450 miles. Dimensions: Span, 36 ft. 11¼ in.; length, 27 ft. 11¾ in.; height, 7 ft. 6 in.; wing area, 200 sq. ft.

FAIRCHILD C-119G PACKET   U.S.A.

The C-119 is an improved version of the earlier C-82, with increased power, a wider fuselage, repositioned flight deck, and other modifications. The C-119F Packet—frequently referred to by the unofficial name of Boxcar—is a progressive development of the earlier production models, the C-119B and C. The C-119G is similar to the C-119F but has Aeroproducts airscrews. The C-119B and G are designated R4Q-1 and -2 by the U.S. Marine Corps, and the C-119 is also employed by the R.C.A.F., and the Belgian, French and Italian Air Forces.

Specification: Military freight and troop transport. Engines: Two 3,500 h.p. Wright R-3350-32W. Weights: Empty, 39,751 lb.; normal loaded, 64,000 lb.; maximum, 72,800 lb. Performance: Max. speed, 296 m.p.h. at 17,000 ft., 258 m.p.h. at sea level; initial climb rate, 800 ft./min.; max. range, 3,480 miles. Dimensions: Span, 109 ft. 3 in.; length, 86 ft. 6 in.; height, 26 ft. 3 in.; wing area, 1,447 sq. ft.

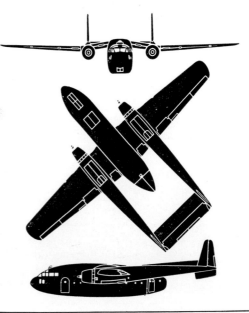

FAIRCHILD C-123B PROVIDER — U.S.A.

Originally developed by the Chase Aircraft Company as the Avitruc, the C-123B Provider has been taken over by the Fairchild company which concern now has total orders for 233 machines. A C-123B has been experimentally fitted with a 1,000 lb.s.t. Fairchild J44 turbojet at each wingtip for experimental jet augmentation studies, and the Stroukoff Aircraft Corporation has fitted one machine with boundary layer control as the XC-123D, and another with retractable hydroskis and a pontoon under each wing as the YC-123E. The C-123B can accommodate sixty troops.

Specification: Military transport. Engines: Two 2,500 h.p. Pratt & Whitney R-2800. Weights: Empty, 31,058 lb.; loaded, 54,000 lb.; maximum, 60,000 lb. Performance: Max. speed, 293 m.p.h. at 13,000 ft.; cruising, 188 m.p.h. at 5,000 ft.; initial climb rate, 1,380 ft./min.; service ceiling, 23,000 ft.; max. range, 3,450 miles. Dimensions: Span, 110 ft.; length, 76 ft. 4 in.; height, 34 ft. 1 in.; wing area, 1,223.22 sq. ft.

FAIRCHILD C-82A PACKET — U.S.A.

The prototype Packet, the XC-82, flew for the first time on September 10, 1944, and the type was placed in production by both Fairchild and North American, but the end of World War II led to the cancellation of the North American contract after only three C-82s had been completed. Fairchild produced 220 C-82A Packet transports for the U.S.A.F. before production was terminated in favour of the C-119. The C-82A has now been made surplus by the U.S.A.F., and the remaining ninety-three machines have been sold to civil operators.

Max. speed, 238 m.p.h. at 17,500 ft.; initial climb rate, 920 ft./min.; service ceiling, 22,000 ft.; range (with 13,000 lb. cargo), 500 miles; empty weight, 31,288 lb.; loaded, 50,000 lb.; span, 106 ft. 6 in.; length, 77 ft. 1 in.; height, 26 ft. 5 in.; wing area, 1,400 sq. ft.

FAIREY SWORDFISH — G.B.

The Swordfish torpedo-bomber was one of the last British biplanes to perform operational duties. It was in continuous production from 1935 until mid-1944, when the last of 2,387 aircraft of this type was delivered. Powered by a 690 h.p. Bristol Pegasus III radial engine, the Swordfish was produced in three versions, the Mk.2 differing from the initial Mk.1 in having special lower wings to enable R.P.s to be launched, and the Mk.3 was distinguished by a ventral radome. The Mk.4 was a conversion with enclosed cockpits for Canada. One Swordfish, powered by a 750 h.p. Pegasus 30, exists in the U.K. for demonstration purposes, and a second is used for sky-writing in South Africa.

Max. speed, 138 m.p.h. at 5,000 ft.; initial climb, 1,220 ft./min.; empty weight, 4,700 lb.; loaded, 7,510 lb.; span, 45 ft. 6 in.; length, 35 ft. 8 in.

FAIREY FULMAR 2 — G.B.

Developed from the P.4/34, the Fulmar general-purpose fleet fighter-bomber was first flown in 1939, and production deliveries of the Fulmar Mk.1 to the Fleet Air Arm commenced in 1940. The Fulmar Mk.1 was powered by a 1,080 h.p. Rolls-Royce Merlin 8, and this was succeeded in production by the Fulmar Mk.2 which was distinguished from the earlier version by a 1,300 h.p. Merlin 30 engine and tropical equipment. The sole remaining example of the Fulmar is powered by a 1,300 h.p. Merlin 30F engine and has been converted for use as a three-seat personnel transport. A total of 602 Fulmars was built.

Max. speed, 280 m.p.h.; cruising speed, 235 m.p.h.; initial climb rate, 1,200 ft./min.; loaded weight, 9,672 lb.; span, 46 ft. 4½ in.; length, 40 ft. 3 in.; height, 14 ft.

FAIREY FIREFLY F.R.1 — G.B.

The Firefly first flew on December 22, 1941, and 440 Firefly F.1s and 376 F.R.1s were subsequently produced as carrier-borne day fighter and fighter-reconnaissance aircraft for the R.N. In 1948 a number of Firefly Mk.1s converted for use as target-tugs were delivered to the Svensk Flygjänst, and nine are currently flying in Sweden. A number of reconditioned Mk.1 aircraft have also been supplied to the Imperial Ethiopian Air Force as fighters, and others are used by the Royal Danish Air Force as target-tugs. The Firefly Mk.1 has a 1,735 h.p. Rolls-Royce Griffon II engine.

Max. speed (F.1), 277 m.p.h.; (F.R.1), 266 m.p.h.; range, 740 miles at 220 m.p.h.; loaded weight (F.1), 12,250 lb.; (F.R.1), 12,540 lb.; span, 44 ft. 6 in.; length, 37 ft. 7 in.; height, 13 ft. 7 in.

FAIREY FIREFLY A.S.6   G.B.

The Firefly A.S.6 is structurally similar to the earlier Firefly Marks 4 and 5, but carries no defensive armament and has special submarine detection equipment under the wing and fuselage. The A.S.6 is representative in appearance of the majority of Fireflies currently serving with the Royal Navy, the Royal Australian Navy, and the Royal Netherlands Navy. These include the T.T.4 target tug with winch under centre section, the F.R.5 fighter-reconnaissance aircraft, the A.S.5 anti-submarine aircraft, and the similar A.S.6. These all possess the reduced-span wing and leading-edge radiators introduced on the Mk. 4.

Specification: Two-seat anti-submarine aircraft. Engine: One 2,020 h.p. Rolls-Royce Griffon 74. Weights: Empty, 9,948 lb.; normal loaded, 13,927 lb. Performance: Max. speed, 386 m.p.h. at 14,000 ft.; economical cruising, 209 m.p.h.; service ceiling, 33,500 ft.; range, 760 miles. Dimensions: Span, 41 ft. 2 in.; length, 38 ft.; height, 13 ft. 10½ in.

FAIREY FIREFLY T.7   G.B.

The Firefly T.7 is an anti-submarine training aircraft developed from the Firefly A.S.7. The T.7 and A.S.7 are indistinguishable externally, but differ considerably from earlier production Fireflies. A "chin" type radiator replaces the wing radiators employed by the Mks. 4, 5 and 6, and a blister-enclosed rear cockpit accommodates two crew members. The Firefly A.S.7 was produced as an interim anti-submarine aircraft. The Firefly Mk. 8 is a target drone for guided weapon testing, and externally similar to the A.S.7.

Specification: Three-seat anti-submarine trainer. Engine: One 1,965 h.p. Rolls-Royce Griffon 5901. Weights: Empty, 11,016 lb.; loaded, 13,970 lb. Performance: Max. speed, 300 m.p.h. at 10,750 ft.; cruising, 257 m.p.h.; initial climb rate, 1,550 ft./min.; typical range, 860 miles. Dimensions: Span, 44 ft. 6 in.; length, 38 ft. 3 in.; height, 13 ft. 3 in.; wing area, 342.5 sq. ft.

FAIREY GANNET A.S.1   G.B.

Flown for the first time on September 29, 1949, the prototype Gannet was originally a two-seater and was the world's first aircraft to fly on the power of the double air-screw turbine engine. Changes in naval requirements led to the provision of a third seat and, as the Gannet A.S.1, this aircraft is now in service with the Royal Navy, and forty Gannets have been ordered by the R.A.N. A trainer variant, the Gannet T.2, was flown for the first time on August 16, 1954, the instructor occupying the second cockpit which, in the A.S.1, accommodates the navigator.

Specification: Three-seat anti-submarine aircraft. Engine: One 2,920 s.h.p. (plus 535 lb. residual thrust) Armstrong Siddeley Double Mamba ASMD.3. Performance (according to French sources): Max. speed, 309 m.p.h.; endurance, 3 hours 12 minutes. Approx. weights: Empty, 12,500 lb.; loaded, 18,500 lb. Dimensions: Span, 54 ft. 4 in.; length, 43 ft.; height, 13 ft. 8½ in.

FAIREY F.D.2 — G.B.

Although designed initially to investigate flight problems at high sub-sonic speeds, during the course of design and development of the F.D.2 research aircraft it became apparent that considerably higher speeds would be attainable, and the first of two aircraft of this type is now engaged on a trans-sonic and supersonic research programme. The first F.D.2 flew on October 6, 1954, and a second machine is currently under construction. It is of extremely advanced design, and the fuselage incorporates the novel feature of a hinged forward section which enables the pilot to droop the nose ten degrees to improve view for landing.

Specification: Single-seat high-speed research aircraft. Engine: One 10,000 lb.s.t. (approx.) Rolls-Royce Avon. Weights: No details available for publication. Performance: Max. speeds in excess of Mach 1.0. Dimensions: Span, 26 ft. 10 in.; length, 51 ft. 7½ in.; height 11ft.

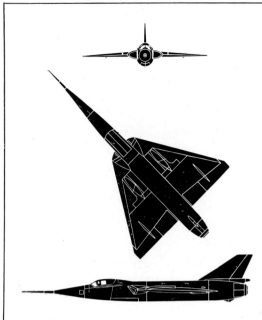

FARMAN F.192 — FRANCE

The Farman F.192 four-seat cabin monoplane is a variant of the original F.190 and powered by a 230 h.p. Salmson 9Ab engine. Various models ranging from F.190 to F.199 were produced, employing a variety of engines in the 230–300 h.p. class, and the type made several notable long-distance flights during 1929–30. The only remaining airworthy example is the French-registered F.192 illustrated.

Max. speed, 124 m.p.h.; cruising, 105 m.p.h.; climb to 3,280 ft., 6 minutes 5 seconds; ceiling, 18,040 ft.; empty weight, 2,271 lb.; loaded, 3,968 lb.; span, 46 ft. 2 in.; length, 32 ft. 9 in.; height, 9 ft. 10 in.; wing area, 431 sq. ft.

FARMAN F.402 — FRANCE

The Farman F.402 of 1933 was a three-seat cabin monoplane powered by a 110 h.p. Lorraine 5 Pb radial engine. Several variants of the basic type were produced with alternative engines, but only one of these, the F.404, remains flying. This is powered by a 140 h.p. Renault 4 Pei engine. One F.402 is currently active in France. Unlike most Farman cabin monoplanes, the wing of the F.402 is tapered with rounded tips. The wing is of wooden construction with plywood covering. The fuselage is a rectangular wooden structure also plywood covered.

Max. speed, 120.4 m.p.h.; cruising, 105.5 m.p.h.; climb to 1,181 ft., 2 minutes, 10 seconds; range, 621 miles; loaded weight, 2,420 lb.; span, 38 ft. 5 in.; length, 27 ft. 1 in.; height, 6 ft. 9 in.; wing area, 231 sq. ft.

FAWCETT 120 — AUSTRALIA

The Fawcett 120, designed by Luigi Pellerini, was flown for the first time on November 11, 1954. Powered by a 145 h.p. de Havilland Gipsy Major 10 Mk.2 engine, it is a four-seat cabin monoplane of all-metal construction intended for both training and touring roles. Designed as a four-seater to increase its appeal to Australian operators, the Fawcett 120 is intended primarily as a replacement for the Tiger Moth currently used by Australian flying clubs and now approaching the end of its useful life. An interesting feature of the design is the interchangeability of the flaps and ailerons.

Max. speed, 127 m.p.h.; cruising, 106 m.p.h.; initial climb rate, 550 ft./min.; range, 500 miles; span, 35 ft. 8 in.; length, 27 ft.; wing area, 185 sq. ft.

FIAT G.5bis — ITALY

The Fiat G.5 tandem two-seat touring and training monoplane was produced in 1933 in two versions, the G.5 with a 140 h.p. Fiat A.54 radial engine, and the G.5bis with a 205 h.p. Fiat A.70 radial. The prototype G.5 was powered by a 142 h.p. Fiat A.60 four-cylinder inverted inline engine. The G.5 was also produced as a three-seater. Dual controls are fitted and the aircraft is fully aerobatic. Mixed construction is employed; the wing structure being entirely of wood and the fuselage having a welded steel-tube structure. One example of the Fiat G.5bis is still flying in Italy.

Max. speed, 143 m.p.h.; cruising speed, 126 m.p.h.; ceiling, 18,900 ft.; range, 478 m.p.h.; empty weight, 1,280 lb.; loaded, 1,898 lb.; span, 34 ft. 1½ in.; length, 25 ft. 9 in.; height, 7 ft. 11¾ in.

FIAT G.49-2   ITALY

Specifically designed as a replacement for the North American T-6 basic trainers currently used by the majority of the N.A.T.O. air forces, the Fiat G.49 tandem two-seater trainer first flew at the end of September 1952, and two variants have been built in prototype form: the Fiat G.49-1 with a 570 h.p. Alvis Leonides 502/4 Mk. 24 engine, and the G.49-2 (*illustrated*) with a 600 h.p. Pratt & Whitney Wasp R-1340-S3H1 engine. The figures quoted in parentheses in the specification relate to the Leonides-powered G-49-1.

Max. speed, 230 m.p.h.; cruising speed, 196 (177) m.p.h.; time to 5,000 ft., 3 minutes 50 seconds (4 minutes 40 seconds); service ceiling, 22,300 (23,000) ft.; range, 1,180 (1,640) miles; empty weight, 4,940 lb.; loaded, 6,300 lb.; span, 42 ft. 8½ in.; length, 31 ft. 2 in.; height, 8 ft. 8¼ in.

FIAT G.55 (CENTAURO)   ITALY

The G.55A and G.55B single- and two-seat advanced trainers are derived from the wartime G.55 Centauro single-seat fighter which was first flown in 1942. Only one hundred Centauro fighters were produced, and these were employed by the Fascist Republican Air Force. Powered by a 1,310 h.p. Fiat R.A.1050 (version of the Daimler-Benz DB 605), the G.55 trainer is used by the air forces of Argentina (which purchased forty-five machines in 1949), Egypt and Syria. Both illustration and specification relate to the two-seat G.55B.

Max. speed, 385 m.p.h.; initial climb rate, 3,640 ft./min.; range, 765 miles; empty weight, 5,577 lb.; loaded, 6,820 lb.; span, 38 ft. 10¾ in.; length, 30 ft. 9 in.; height, 10 ft. 5 in.; wing area, 228 sq. ft.

FIAT G.12C-G.212CP   ITALY

The Fiat G.12 series of transports was introduced in 1939 for high-altitude alpine crossings, and has since appeared in a variety of versions. Versions currently in use include the G.12C (*photo*) with 770 h.p. Fiat A-74 RC.42 engines, the G.12LA with 860 h.p. Alfa 128RCs, and the G.12LP with 1,065 h.p. Pratt & Whitney R-1830s. The G.212, introduced in 1947, embodies much of the structural design of the earlier G.12 but is slightly larger. Versions include the G.212CP Monterosa (*silhouette*), the G.212TP Monviso freighter, and the G.212AV crew trainer for the Italian Air Force. Specification relates to the G.212CP.

Specification: Twenty-six/thirty-four seat transport. Engines: Three 1,215 h.p. Pratt & Whitney R-1830-S1C3-G. Weights: Empty, 24,640 lb.; loaded, 39,600 lb. Performance: Max. speed, 236 m.p.h. at 12,136 ft.; cruising speed, 199 m.p.h.; max. range, 1,710 miles. Dimensions: Span, 96 ft. 4 in.; length, 75 ft. 7 in.; height, 21 ft. 4 in.

FIAT G.46-5   ITALY

First flown in 1948, several hundred G.46 basic trainers have since been delivered to the air forces of Italy, Syria, and Argentina. Various versions have been produced, including the G.46-1 (205 h.p. Alfa 115bis), G.46-2 (250 h.p. D.H. Gipsy Queen 30), and the G.46-3, -4 and -5 (225 h.p. Alfa 115ter). These have been produced both in single-seat (*photo*) and two-seat (*silhouette*) versions. The following specification refers to the G.46-5B two-seat basic trainer.

Specification: Two-seat basic trainer. Engine: One 225 h.p. Alfa 115ter. Weights: Empty, 2,442 lb.; loaded, 3,102 lb. Performance: Max. speed, 196 m.p.h.; cruising, 178 m.p.h.; initial climb rate, 1,280 ft./min.; service ceiling, 19,850 ft.; range, 570 miles. Armament: One 7.7-mm. Breda-SAFAT gun. Dimensions: Span, 34 ft. 1¼ in.; length, 27 ft. 10 in.; height, 7 ft. 10 in.; wing area, 173 sq. ft.

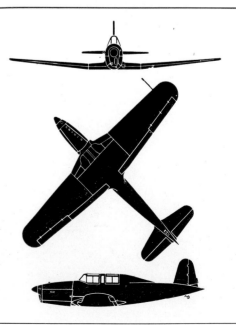

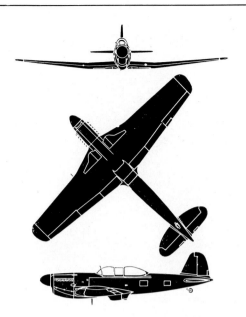

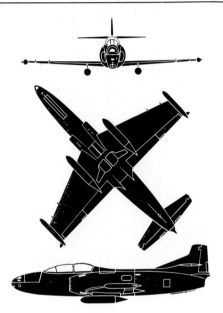

FIAT G.59-4   ITALY

The Fiat G.59 advanced trainer is a progressive development of the G.55, and the first production versions differed from the earlier type only in the power plant installed. Initially known as the G.55AM (single-seat) and G.55BM (two-seat), the designation was changed to G.59 in 1948 when production commenced, and the initial production versions were the G.59-1 and G.59-2 with the 1,610 h.p. Merlin 24 engine. The G.59-3 had the Merlin 500/20, and the latest version, the G.59-4, differs in having a "bubble" type all-round vision cockpit hood. The G.59 has been supplied to the air forces of Italy, Argentina and Syria.

Specification (G.59-4B): Two-seat advanced trainer. Engine: One 1,400 h.p. Rolls-Royce Merlin 500/20. Weights: Empty, 6,285 lb.; loaded, 7,465 lb. Performance: Max. speed, 380 m.p.h.; cruising, 286 m.p.h.; range, 780 miles. Dimensions: Span, 38 ft. 10½ in.; length, 31 ft. 1 in.; height, 12 ft. 1 in.; wing area, 228 sq. ft.

FIAT G.82   ITALY

The G.82 is the latest variant of Italy's first post-war jet aircraft, the G.80, and differs primarily in having a Nene R.N.2-21 engine in place of the 3,500 lb.s.t. Fiat-built Goblin 35. It is proposed that production machines will employ the 5,400 lb.s.t. Nene R.N.6. Ten G.80-3B armament trainers powered by the Goblin turbojet are currently under construction, and these are generally similar to the G.82 (*illustrated here*). Figures quoted in parentheses relate to the G.80-3B.

Specification: Two-seat advanced trainer. Engine: One 5,000 lb.s.t. Rolls-Royce Nene R.N.2-21. Weights: Empty, 9,724 (8,700) lb.; loaded, 13,483 (12,566) lb. Performance: 578 (534) m.p.h.; cruising, 339 m.p.h. at 34,800 ft.; initial climb rate, 5,510 ft./min.; range, 620 miles. Armament: Two 12.7-mm. Browning guns, eight 5-in. HVAR. Dimensions: Span, 38 ft. 1 in.; length, 42 ft. 5 in.; height, 13 ft. 4 in.; wing area, 270.6 sq. ft.

F.F.A. P-1604   SWITZERLAND

Produced by the Flug. und Fahrzeugwerke A.G., the P-1604 was flown for the first time on April 28, 1955. Intended as an attack fighter with the ability to operate from small, high-altitude alpine fields, the P-1604 is fitted with a new type of leading-edge flaps which substantially increase lift. The first prototype had a wing thickness/chord ratio of between 5 per cent and 6 per cent, but the second prototype will have this reduced to 4 per cent and, with a higher-powered turbojet, will be supersonic in level flight. Boundary-layer control may be applied to later prototypes, and a two-seat all-weather variant is being studied. The specification applies to the first prototype.

Specification: Single-seat attack fighter. Engine: One 7,900 lb.s.t. Armstrong Siddeley Sapphire A.S.Sa.6. Weights: Loaded, 17,857 lb. Performance: Approx. max. speed, 630 m.p.h. Armament: Two 30-mm. Oerlikon 302RK cannon, and various ordnance loads in fuselage bay. Dimensions: No details available.

FIESELER FI 156C-1 STORCH   GERMANY

The Fi 156 Storch (Stork) appeared in 1937, and was selected by the *Luftwaffe* for quantity production as an air observation post and liaison aircraft. The sub-variants produced in largest numbers were the Fi 156C-1 staff transport and C-2 air observation post. It was built during the war years in France by the German-controlled Morane-Saulnier plant (*see* Morane 502), and in Czechoslovakia where it became known as the Mraz Čáp. The Fi 156C is employed by the air forces of Spain, Switzerland (*see* photo), and Finland, as well as that of Czechoslovakia.
Specification: Three-seat general-purpose monoplane. Engine: One 240 h.p. Argus As 410C. Weights: Empty, 2,134 lb.; loaded, 3,267 lb. Performance: Max. speed, 109 m.p.h.; cruising speed, 89 m.p.h.; range, 240 miles. Dimensions: Span, 46 ft. 9 in.; length, 32 ft. 6 in.; height, 10 ft.; wing area, 279.7 sq. ft.

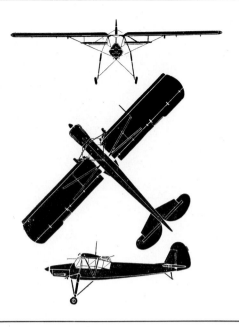

FLETCHER FD-25 DEFENDER   U.S.A.

The Fletcher Defender is a small, robust light aircraft intended for ground support, and able to carry two 40-gall. Napalm tanks, two 250-lb. anti-personnel bombs, or forty 2.75-in. rockets. A licence to manufacture the Defender has been acquired by the Japanese Toyo Aircraft Company, and Toyo-built Defenders have been delivered to the Cambodian Air Force. The single-seat version (*silhouette*) is designated FD-25B, and a two-seat variant with a longer fuselage to accommodate the second crew member is designated FD-25A (*photograph*).
Specification: Single-seat light ground support aircraft. Engine: One 225 h.p. Continental E-225-8. Weights: Empty, 1,428 lb.; loaded, 2,700 lb. Performance: Max. speed, 187 m.p.h.; cruising speed, 162 m.p.h.; initial climb rate, 1,725 ft./min.; range, 630 miles. Dimensions: Span, 30 ft.; length, 20 ft. 11 in.; height, 6 ft. 3 in.; wing area, 150 sq. ft.

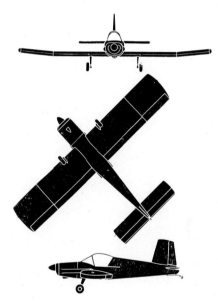

FLETCHER FU-24 UTILITY   U.S.A.

The FU-24 Utility has been designed specifically for agricultural purposes, and flew for the first time on June 14, 1954. One hundred FU-24 monoplanes have been ordered by the Cable-Price Corporation of New Zealand, eleven machines being delivered in fully assembled form, and the remainder being delivered in component form for assembly by James Aviation Limited in New Zealand. Of all-metal construction, the FU-24 can lift a useful load of 1,250 lb. from a short, rough-surfaced runway, and is treated with a special plastic paint to protect it from the corrosive effects of the chemicals that it carries for top-dressing operations.
Specification: Single-seat agricultural aircraft. Engine: One 225 h.p. Continental 0-470-E. Weights: Empty, 1,909 lb.; loaded, 3,500 lb. Performance: Max. speed, 124 m.p.h.; cruising, 108 m.p.h.; initial climb rate, 750 ft./min.; service ceiling, 15,700 ft.; range, 370 miles. Dimensions: Span, 42 ft.; length, 31 ft. 10 in.; height, 9 ft. 4 in.;

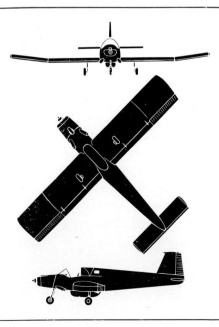

F

FLEET 16B FINCH II — CANADA

The Fleet 16B Finch II is a progressive development of the original Consolidated Fleet primary trainer, manufacture of which was commenced in Canada in 1930 by Fleet Aircraft Ltd. This concern was formed primarily to manufacture the Fleet trainer, and world rights in the type were later acquired from the Consolidated Aircraft Corp. A total of 606 Finch trainers were built for the R.C.A.F. between 1939 and 1941. The Finch is powered by a 125 h.p. Kinner B-5 radial engine. The earlier Consolidated Fleet Types 1, 2, 7, 9 and 10 are externally similar but have open cockpits and various engines.
Max. speed, 113 m.p.h.; cruising speed, 98 m.p.h.; initial climb rate, 990 ft./min.; cruising range, 320 miles; empty weight, 1,122 lb.; loaded, 1,860 lb.; span, 28 ft.; length, 21 ft. 8 in.; height, 7 ft. 9 in.; wing area, 194 sq. ft.

FLEET 80 CANUCK — CANADA

The Model 80 Canuck two-seat light cabin monoplane was produced in some numbers during 1946–47 by the Fleet Aircraft Limited, being designed primarily to meet the needs of the northern operator. Insufficient orders for the Canuck led to the temporary abandonment of light-plane manufacture by Fleet in 1947 after 210 Canucks had been built, some of these being assembled from components by Leavens Bros. The Canuck is powered by an 85 h.p. Continental C85-12J engine. A similarly-powered three-seat version, the Model 81 (*illustrated*), was produced in prototype form and is still flying in Canada, together with a substantial number of Model 80 Canucks.
Max. speed, 111 m.p.h.; cruising, 100 m.p.h.; initial climb, 550 ft./min.; empty weight, 858 lb.; loaded, 1,479 lb.; span, 46 ft. 9 in.; length, 32 ft. 6 in.

FLEETWINGS SEA BIRD — U.S.A.

Produced by Fleetwings Incorporated in 1936, which concern had been engaged for five years previously with design and research work in stainless-steel construction and had built a small quantity of stainless-steel wings for Douglas 0A-4C Dolphin amphibians, the Sea Bird four-seat amphibian was the first stainless-steel aeroplane in the U.S.A. to be awarded an Approved Type Certificate. Powered by a 285 h.p. Jacobs L-5 radial engine, the Sea Bird has a retractable wheel undercarriage, a two-step hull and fixed wingtip floats.
Max. speed, 150 m.p.h.; cruising speed, 133 m.p.h.; initial climb rate, 900 ft./min.; service ceiling, 15,000 ft.; empty weight, 2,320 lb.; loaded, 3,450 lb.; span, 40 ft. 6 in.; length, 31 ft. 5½ in.; height, 12 ft. 6 in.; wing area, 235 sq. ft.

FOCKE-WULF FW 44J STEIGLITZ — GERMANY

Developed by the Focke-Wulf Flugzeugbau A.G. in 1932, the Steiglitz tandem two-seat aerobatic training biplane was subsequently produced in large numbers and also built under licence in Sweden and Brazil. Forty Steiglitz trainers were built at the Fabrica do Galleao in Brazil, and a number of these are still in service with the Brazilian Air Force. Twenty-four Swedish-built ex-Flygvapnet Steiglitz trainers are privately owned or used by flying clubs in Sweden, and one Fw 44F Steiglitz is flying in Switzerland. The Fw 44J Steiglitz is powered by a 150 h.p. Siemens Sh 14a radial engine.
Max. speed, 115 m.p.h. at sea level; cruising, 107 m.p.h.; service ceiling, 12,792 ft.; cruising range, 420 miles; empty weight, 1,157 lb.; loaded, 1,914 lb.; span, 29 ft. 6 in.; height, 8 ft. 10 in.; length, 23 ft. 11 in.

FOCKE-WULF FW 58B-2 WEIHE — GERMANY

The Fw 58 Weihe twin-engined trainer and light transport was introduced in 1935 and was subsequently adopted by the *Luftwaffe*. Powered by two 240 h.p. Argus As 10C engines, the Fw 58B-2 was built under licence by the Fabrica do Galleao, and several of the twenty-five Brazilian-built aircraft (*photo*) are flying. In addition, two Fw 58C Weihe light transports are flying in Sweden. The Weihe is of metal construction with fabric covering, and can carry up to eight passengers.
Max. speed, 158 m.p.h. at sea level; cruising speed, 148 m.p.h.; service ceiling, 17,715 ft.; range, 208 miles; empty weight, 4,123 lb.; loaded, 6,394 lb.; span, 68 ft. 10 in.; length, 46 ft. 3 in.; height, 13 ft. 9 in.; wing area, 505.7 sq. ft.

FOKKER F.7A — HOLLAND

Produced in 1925, the Fokker F.7a eight-seat transport was a progressive development of the six-seat F.7 of 1924. The F.7a was produced with several engines, and the sole example remaining has a 500 h.p. Bristol Jupiter VI (*photo*). This has now been purchased for permanent preservation in Holland. A trimotor variant, the F.7a-3m, was also developed in 1929 with three 240 h.p. Wright Whirlwind radial engines. This was followed by the F.7b-3m which differed in having a slightly increased wing span. One F.7b-3m is currently flying in the Belgian Congo. Details quoted in parentheses refer to the latter.
Max. speed, 115 (128.5) m.p.h.; cruising speed, 93 (105) m.p.h.; range, 559 (528) miles; empty weight, 4,299 (6,724) lb.; loaded, 7,936 (11,464) lb.; span, 63 ft. 3¾ in. (71 ft. 2¼ in.); length, 47 ft. 10¾ in. (47 ft. 6¾ in.).

FOKKER F.11 UNIVERSAL HOLLAND

The F.11 Universal transport monoplane was first produced in 1928, being produced with both the 470 h.p. Lorraine 7A radial engine and the 480 h.p. Bristol Jupiter. One Lorraine-powered F.11 Universal is flying in Austria with a Swiss registration. The F.11 is of wooden construction and the cabin provides accommodation for five passengers. The F.11 is owned by the Société d'Aviation Suisse Alpar and is used primarily for passenger and freight charter duties.

Max. speed, 109 m.p.h.; cruising speed, 89 m.p.h.; ceiling, 14,435 ft.; cruising range, 497 miles; empty weight, 2,921 lb.; loaded, 4,189 lb.; span, 53 ft. 9½ in.; length, 36 ft. 5 in.; height, 10 ft.; wing area, 382.1 sq. ft.

FOKKER C.10 HOLLAND

The Fokker C.10 two-seat fighter-bomber biplane was first produced in 1936, and versions were produced with the 650 h.p. Rolls-Royce Kestrel and the 925 h.p. Hispano-Suiza 12Ycrs engines. A series of thirty-four Fokker C.10s powered by the 825 h.p. Bristol Pegasus XX radial engine (*photo*) were supplied to Finland. Several of these Fokker C.10s are still in service with the Finnish Air Force as target tugs. The C.10 is a single-bay, staggered sesquiplane of mixed construction, the wings of wood and the fuselage of welded steel-tube.

Max. speed, 212 m.p.h. at 10,000 ft.; cruising speed, 164.5 m.p.h.; service ceiling, 27,400 ft.; range, 520 miles; empty weight, 3,410 lb.; loaded, 5,500 lb.; span, 39 ft. 4 in.; length, 30 ft. 2 in.; height, 10 ft. 10 in.; wing area, 341 sq. ft.

FOKKER S.11 INSTRUCTOR HOLLAND

The S.11 Instructor first appeared in 1947, and licences for its manufacture have been granted to Italy and Brazil. A version of the Instructor fitted with a fixed nose-wheel undercarriage, the S.12, has also been developed. A total of 100 Instructors was built in Holland by the parent company, a further 150 have been built in Italy under the designation Macchi M.416, and both the S.11 and the S.12 will be built in Brazil by Fokker Industria SA do Brazil. Forty-one Instructors have been delivered to the Israeli Air Force (*photo*), and forty to the Royal Netherlands Air Force.
Specification: Two/three-seat primary trainer. Engine: One 190 h.p. Lycoming 0-435-A. Weights: Empty, 1,784 lb.; loaded, 2,426 lb. Performance: Max. speed, 130 m.p.h.; cruising, 102 m.p.h.; service ceiling, 12,600 ft. Dimensions: Span, 36 ft. 1 in.; length, 26 ft. 8 in.; height, 7 ft. 5 in.; wing area, 199 sq. ft.

FOKKER S.14 MACH-TRAINER HOLLAND

The first jet aircraft to be designed for the training role from the outset, the Mach-Trainer flew for the first time on May 20, 1951, and the first of an initial order for twenty Mach-Trainers for the Royal Netherlands Air Force flew on January 15, 1955. The Mach-Trainer is to be built in Brazil by Fokker Industria SA do Brazil, five being assembled from components supplied by the parent concern and forty-five being manufactured in Brazil. The experimental Mach-Trainer II is powered by a 5,100 lb.s.t. Nene 3, and figures relating to this version are quoted in parentheses.
Specification: Two-seat conversion trainer. Engine: One 3,470 lb.s.t. F.N.A.-built Rolls-Royce Derwent 8. Weights: Empty, 8,304 (8,745) lb.; loaded, 11,800 (12,230) lb. Performance: Max. speed, 445 (516) m.p.h.; cruising, 366 (386) m.p.h.; initial climb rate, 3,200 (5,400) ft./min.; range, 620 (565) miles. Armament: Two 20-mm. cannon. Dimensions: Span, 39 ft. 5 in.; length, 43 ft. 8 in.; height, 15 ft. 4 in.; wing area, 342 sq. ft.

FOKKER F.27 FRIENDSHIP   HOLLAND

Designed as a medium-size airliner suitable for short- and medium-range continental traffic, the F.27 Friendship can be powered by either Rolls-Royce Dart turboprops or Wright Cyclone piston engines. The first prototype Friendship is fitted with Dart 507s which provide 1,547 e.h.p., but the second prototype and production aircraft will have 1,780 e.h.p. Dart 511s. Two machines are currently on order for K.L.M., and a military freighter version is under consideration.

Specification: Twenty-eight/thirty-six seat commercial transport. Engines: Two 1,780 e.h.p. Rolls-Royce Dart 511 (R.Da.6). Weights: Empty, 20,610 lb.; normal loaded, 32,630 lb.; maximum, 34,200 lb. Estimated performance (32,630 lb.): Max. cruising speed, 280 m.p.h. at 20,000 ft.; economical cruising, 275 m.p.h. at 20,000 ft.; initial climb rate, 1,500 ft./min.; service ceiling, 35,000 ft.; normal stage distance, 300 miles; maximum, 830 miles. Dimensions: Span, 95 ft.; length, 73 ft.; height, 26 ft. 6 in.

FOKKER S.13   HOLLAND

The S.13 twin-engined crew trainer was flown for the first time in March 1950, being designed to replace the Airspeed Oxfords at that time employed by the Royal Netherlands Air Force for crew training purposes. However, no orders for the type were forthcoming and only one prototype was completed. This is powered by two 600 h.p. Pratt & Whitney Wasp S1H1-G radial engines and is of all-metal construction. The S.13 was intended for use as a bombardier, pilot, navigator and wireless operator trainer.

Max. speed, 220 m.p.h. at 8,000 ft.; cruising speed, 196 m.p.h. at 11,800 ft.; service ceiling, 21,300 ft.; empty weight, 9,225 lb.; loaded, 12,720 lb.; span, 63 ft.; length, 44 ft. 3 in.; height, 18 ft.; wing area, 495 sq. ft.

FORD 4-AT-E   U.S.A.

First produced in 1926 by the Ford Motor Company's Stout Metal Airplane Co. division, which first developed the type in 1926, the all-metal Ford 4-AT was produced with three 235 h.p. Wright Whirlwinds (4-AT-B), and three 330 h.p. Wright Whirlwind J-6s (4-AT-E). Two of the former and five of the latter are active in the U.S.A. Several of these are based in Montana where they are used for crop spraying and dusting, and for paradropping fire-fighters of the U.S. Forest Service. A number are also serving in Central America. The Ford 4-AT-E trimotor provides accommodation for twelve passengers.

Max. speed, 134 m.p.h.; cruising, 110 m.p.h.; ceiling, 18,600 ft.; range, 570 miles; empty weight, 6,500 lb.; loaded, 10,130 lb.; span, 74 ft.; length, 49 ft. 10 in.; height, 12 ft. 8 in.; wing area, 785 sq. ft.

FORD 5-AT-B   U.S.A.

Continuing Ford's line of all-metal transport trimotors, the Model 5-AT was introduced in August 1928 and was developed concurrently with the Model 4-AT-E of which it was a slightly enlarged and more powerful variant. Carrying fifteen passengers and a crew of two, the Ford 5-AT-B is powered by three 420 h.p. Pratt & Whitney Wasp or three 450 h.p. Wright Whirlwind engines, and five examples are registered in the U.S.A. The Hayden Aircraft Corporation has announced plans to build one hundred Wasp-powered Ford trimotors. These will be almost exact duplicates of the original transport and will be known as the Stout Bushmaster.

Max. speed, 152.5 m.p.h.; cruising, 122 m.p.h.; ceiling, 18,600 ft.; range, 570 miles; empty weight, 7,500 lb.; loaded, 13,250 lb.; span, 77 ft. 10 in.; length, 49 ft. 10 in.; wing area, 835 sq. ft.

FOSTER WIKNER WICKO G.M.1   G.B.

First produced in 1936 by the Foster Wikner Aircraft Company, the Wicko two-seat cabin monoplane was originally flown with an 85 h.p. Wicko "F" (Ford V-8 conversion) engine, but this was replaced in production aircraft by the 130 h.p. de Havilland Gypsy Major 1. A three-seat conversion of the Wicko was known as the Warferry. Only one example of the Wicko is known to be airworthy. The Wicko is of wooden construction and the cabin accommodates two persons side-by-side with dual controls.

Max. speed, 140 m.p.h.; cruising speed, 120 m.p.h.; service ceiling, 20,000 ft.; cruising range, 500 miles; empty weight, 1,255 lb.; loaded, 2,000 lb.; span, 31 ft. 6 in.; length, 23 ft. 3 in.; height, 6 ft. 1 in.; wing area, 153 sq. ft.

FOLLAND F.O.141 GNAT   G.B.

Flown for the first time on July 18, 1955, the Gnat lightweight fighter is powered by an Orpheus which provides 3,285 lb.st. as installed in the prototype, but will ultimately give 4,850 lb.s.t., and 6,000 lb.s.t. with afterburning. The figures quoted from foreign sources in the specification relate to the Gnat with the fully developed engine. The Fo 139 Midge was a low-powered development aircraft with a 1,640 lb.s.t. A.S. Viper 101. Six Gnats have been ordered by the M.o.S. for evaluation.
Specification: Single-seat fighter-bomber. Engine: One 4,850 lb.s.t. Bristol B.E.26 Orpheus BOr.3. Weights: Max. loaded, 8,223 lb. Performance: Approx. max. speed, 725 m.p.h.; initial climb rate, 15,000 ft./min.; time to 40,000 ft., 3 minutes; service ceiling, 57,000 ft. Armament: Two 30-mm. Aden cannon and (fighter-bomber) two 500-lb. bombs or twelve 3-in. rocket missiles. Dimensions: Span, 22 ft. 2 in.; length, 29 ft. 9 in.; height, 8 ft. 10 in.

FOUGA C.M.170R MAGISTER   FRANCE

The C.M.170R Magister flew for the first time on July 23, 1952, and has since been placed in production for French Air Force training units, pre-production and production series totalling 105 machines being on order. The C.M.170M is a navalised version for the French Navy, the C.M.160 is a less extensively equipped trainer, the C.M. 170RR high-speed version with redesigned wing and powered ailerons, the C.M.101 is a projected four-seat liaison version, and the C.M.171 is a test aircraft for the C.M. 195 swept-wing development with two Turboméca Gabizo jets.
Specification: Two-seat basic trainer. Engines: Two 836 lb.s.t. Turboméca Marboré II. Weights: Empty, 3,968 lb.; loaded, 5,952 lb. Performance: Max. speed, 435 m.p.h.; climb to 30,000 ft., 19 minutes; service ceiling, 38,000 ft. Armament: Two 7.5-mm. guns plus four 55-lb. rockets. Dimensions: Span, 37 ft. 1 in.; length, 32 ft. 2 in.; height, 9 ft. 2¼ in.; wing area, 186.1 sq. ft.

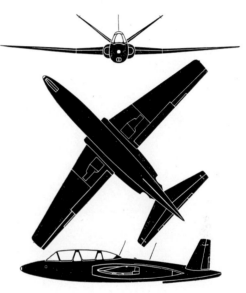

FOUGA C.M.8.R   FRANCE

The C.M.8.R series of light jet aircraft stem from the C.M.8 glider, the first model, the C.M.8.R-13 Sylph, being a C.M.8-13 sailplane with a 240 lb. thrust Turboméca Piméné turbojet. This was followed by the C.M.8.R-9.8 Cyclope which was a refined aerobatic version with reduced wing span. The Cyclope II (*photo*) and Cyclope III differed in having the 350 lb. thrust Turboméca Palas, and the C.M.8.R-8.3 Midjet was a competition aircraft derived from the Cyclope III with wing span reduced still further. Specification refers to Cyclope III (and Midjet).
Max. speed, 205 (217) m.p.h. at sea level, 217 m.p.h. at 13,120 ft.; initial climb rate, 1,575 (1,770) ft./min.; range, 186 (108) miles; empty weight, 902 (800) lb.; loaded, 1,255 (1,195) lb.; span, 28 ft. 9 in, (23 ft. 2 in.); length, 21 ft. 10 in. (21 ft. 11 in.); wing area, 105.4 (89.3) sq. ft.

FRATI F.8 FALCO   ITALY

The latest design by the Italian engineer Stelio Frati, the F.8 Falco flew for the first time on June 15, 1955. Powered by a 90 h.p. Continental C90 engine, the Falco has exceptionally clean lines which result in an unusually high performance. A side-by-side, two-seat monoplane, the Falco has primary blind-flying instruments, V.H.F. radio, etc., and is of wooden construction with plywood covering. The nosewheel member of the retractable tricycle-type undercarriage is steerable, and flaps are mechanically set to either 15° for take-off or 45° for landing.

Max. speed, 180 m.p.h. at sea level; ceiling, 15,500 ft.; loaded weight, 1,415 lb.; span, 25 ft. 8 in.; length, 21 ft.; height, 7 ft.; wing area, 107.5 sq. ft.

FUJI LM-1 NIKKO — JAPAN

The LM-1 Nikko is a four-seat liaison aircraft adapted from the design of the Beech T-34 Mentor which is being built under licence by Fuji Heavy Industries for the Japanese Self-Defence Force. Flown for the first time on June 6, 1955, and powered by a 225 h.p. Continental 0-70-13 engine, the LM-1 Nikko employs the wing, undercarriage and tail assembly of the Mentor, and a new centre fuselage. It is anticipated that this type will be ordered by the Japanese Land Self-Defence Board for liaison duties.

Max. speed, 185 m.p.h.; cruising speed, 157 m.p.h.; service ceiling, 17,388 ft.; empty weight, 2,234 lb.; loaded, 3,375 lb.; span, 32 ft. 9½ in.; length, 25 ft. 11 in.; height, 9 ft. 7 in.; wing area, 177.6 sq. ft.

FUNK MODEL B-75L — U.S.A.

The Funk Aircraft Company was formed in 1941 to replace Akron Aircraft Inc., and the new company continued production of the Model B side-by-side two-seat light cabin monoplane which had entered production in 1939 as the Akron Funk B. The initial Akron Funk was fitted with a Funk engine of 63 h.p., which was mainly made up of automobile engine parts, but this was replaced by the 75 h.p. Lycoming GO-145. After World War 2, the Model B-85C was introduced. This differed from the pre-war B-75L only in having an 85 h.p. Continental C85-12 and minor refinements. About one hundred and fifty B-75L and B-85C models are active in the U.S.A.

(B85C): Max. speed, 115 m.p.h. at sea level; cruising, 100 m.p.h.; initial climb rate, 800 ft./min.; cruising range, 350 miles; empty weight, 890 lb.; loaded, 1,350 lb.; span, 35 ft.; length, 20 ft. 1 in.; height, 6 ft. 1 in.

G.C.A.2 DUMBO — ITALY

The second design to emanate from the Gruppo Construzioni Aeronautiche of Milan, the G.C.A.2 Dumbo was designed by Dr. Ing. Emilio Bianchi and Ing. Giovanni Buzzachi. First flown in 1951, the Dumbo is a single-seat ultra-light monoplane, and an interesting feature of the design is the "butterfly-type" tail assembly. All-wood structure is employed with plywood and fabric covering, and power is provided by a 23 h.p. Ambrosini P.25 engine. Only one prototype has been built.

Max. speed, 93 m.p.h.; cruising speed, 74.5 m.p.h.; climb to 3,280 ft., 6 minutes, 30 seconds; ceiling, 13,120 ft.; range, 300 miles; empty weight, 264 lb.; loaded, 484 lb.; span, 24 ft. 3 in.; length, 16 ft. 5 in.; height, 5 ft. 7 in.; wing area, 85.249 sq. ft.

FULTON FA-2 AIRPHIBIAN — U.S.A.

Flown on November 7, 1946, the FA-2 Airphibian roadable monoplane became the first aircraft of its type to obtain an approved type certificate. Three FA-2 Airphibians were built for test and certification. A production version, the FA-3, appeared in 1954. This differs from the FA-2 (*illustrated*), in having a fully cantilever wing, and retractable wing-wheels (which are required when the wing is detached from the roadable portion). Powered by a 160 h.p. Franklin 6A4-150-B3 engine, the Airphibian seats two persons, and in three minutes the wing/rear fuselage unit can be detached from the roadable section.

(FA-2): Max. speed, 120 m.p.h.; cruising speed, 110 m.p.h.; landing speed, 48 m.p.h.; initial climb rate, 600 ft./min.; ceiling, 12,000 ft.; cruising range, 350 miles.

G.C.A.1 PEDRO — ITALY

Designed by Ing. Emilio Bianchi and built in 1953 by the Gruppo Costruzioni Aeronautiche, the G.C.A.1 is a side-by-side two-seat cabin monoplane powered by a 60 h.p. C.N.A. D4 air-cooled engine. The Gruppo Construzioni Aeronautiche is a group of aircraft enthusiasts which builds aircraft of its own design at the Instituto Industriale in Pisa. The G.C.A.1 Pedro is of all-wood construction with plywood covering. Dual controls are fitted.

Max. speed, 106 m.p.h.; cruising speed, 93 m.p.h.; climb to 3,280 ft., 6 minutes, 30 seconds; service ceiling, 14,100 ft.; absolute ceiling, 17,550 ft.; cruising range, 342 miles; empty weight, 748 lb.; loaded, 1,276 lb.; span, 32 ft. 1½ in.; length, 20 ft. 8 in.; height, 6 ft. 2½ in.; wing area, 140 sq. ft.

G.C.A.3 ETA BETA — ITALY

The G.C.A.3 Eta Beta is virtually a tandem two-seat scaled-up version of the earlier G.C.A.2 Dumbo, retaining the basic characteristics of the smaller machine, including the unusual "butterfly" or V-type tail assembly. Powered by a 60 h.p. C.N.A. D4S four-cylinder air-cooled engine, the Eta Beta appeared in 1952, and was designed for both training and touring roles. The fuselage is an all-wood stressed-skin structure and the wing is an all-wood monospar structure with a stressed plywood skin. Cantilever spring steel main undercarriage legs are fitted, and the enclosed cabin is provided with dual controls and HF radio.

Max. speed, 124 m.p.h. at sea level; cruising, 106 m.p.h.; initial climb rate, 984 ft./min.; range, 404 miles; empty weight, 710 lb.; loaded, 1,151 lb.; span, 27 ft. 10½ in.; length, 20 ft. 4 in.

GENERAL AIRCRAFT GENAIRCO AUSTRALIA

The Genairco biplane was introduced in 1930 by the General Aircraft Co. Ltd., and was produced in two versions: a three-seater with open cockpits (the front cockpit seating two persons side-by-side), and a four-passenger cabin biplane with an open cockpit for the pilot aft of the cabin (*illustrated*). Two examples of the former version (one with a D.H. Gipsy III and the other with a D.H. Gipsy II), and one example of the latter powered by a D.H. Gipsy Major remain.

Max. speed, 105 m.p.h.; cruising, 93 m.p.h.; initial climb, 650 ft./min.; empty weight, 1,000 lb.; loaded, 1,980 lb.; span, 30 ft. 4 in.; length, 22 ft. 6 in.; height, 9 ft.

GENERAL AIRCRAFT S.T.12 MONOSPAR   G.B.

Introduced in 1935 by General Aircraft Ltd., which had been formed in 1934 to take over the Monospar Co. Ltd., the S.T.12 four-seat general-purposes monoplane was a progressive development of the S.T.4 of 1931, differing primarily in having the two 90 h.p. Pobjoy Niagara engines of the earlier aircraft replaced by two 140 h.p. de Havilland Gipsy Majors. One example of each of these versions of the Monospar is flying: an S.T.4 is flying in Spain and an S.T.12 (*illustrated*) is flying in Australia. Thirty S.T.4s and ten S.T.12s were built. The following specification relates to the Pobjoy-powered S.T.4 Monospar.

Max. speed, 130 m.p.h.; cruising, 120 m.p.h.; initial climb rate, 850 ft./min.; range, 540 miles; empty weight, 1,480 lb.; loaded, 2,550 lb.; span, 40 ft. 2 in.; length, 26 ft. 4 in.; height, 7 ft.

GENERAL AIRCRAFT S.T.25 MONOSPAR   G.B.

The S.T.25 "Jubilee" Monospar was produced in 1935, and the type number "25" was adopted to mark the Silver Jubilee of H.M. King George V in that year. The most popular of the Monospar series, the S.T.25 was initially produced with a fixed undercarriage and single fin and rudder, being externally similar to the S.T.4 (*illustrated*), but in 1936 twin fins and rudders were fitted, and the final production version was the S.T.25 Universal. A total of sixty S.T.25s were built. Powered by two 90 h.p. Pobjoy Niagara III engines, one S.T.25 is flying in Spain, together with an S.T.4, and another in the Belgian Congo.

Max. speed, 135 m.p.h. at sea level; cruising, 123 m.p.h.; initial climb, 700 ft./min.; range, 496 miles; empty weight, 1,758 lb.; loaded, 2,875 lb.; span, 40 ft. 2 in.; length, 26 ft. 4 in.; height, 7 ft. 10 in.

GENERAL AIRCRAFT G.A.L.42 CYGNET II G.B.

Originally designed by C. W. Aircraft Ltd., the design of the Cygnet was acquired by General Aircraft in 1938. After extensive modification, including the replacement of the original single fin and rudder assembly with a twin assembly, and the application of a fixed nosewheel landing gear, the Cygnet entered production as the G.A.L.42, and two versions were produced; the Cygnet I with a 130 h.p. de Havilland Gipsy Major, and the Cygnet II with a 150 h.p. Cirrus Major. Three Cygnet IIs are currently registered in the U.K., and the specification relates to this version.

Max. speed, 135 m.p.h.; cruising, 115 m.p.h.; initial climb rate, 800 ft./min.; range, 445 miles; empty weight, 1,475 lb.; loaded, 2,200 lb.; span, 34 ft. 6 in.; length, 23 ft. 3 in.; height, 7 ft.

GENERAL AIRPLANE MODEL 11   U.S.A.

The General Airplane Model 11 agricultural aircraft employs the fuselage of a Piper J-3 with Piper PA-18 top cabin structure, wing and tail. The 200 h.p. Ranger engine and mounting are from a Fairchild M-62. To this combination has been added a special Whitaker tandem-wheel undercarriage designed for rough- or soft-ground operation. The Model 11 can be fitted with dust hoppers or spray tanks, and carries a 1,500 lb. payload.

Operating speeds, 40–100 m.p.h.; empty weight, 1,200 lb.; loaded, 3,000 lb.; span, 32 ft. 2½ in.; length, 24 ft.; height, 6 ft. 8 in.

GLOSTER GLADIATOR   G.B.

Originally produced in 1934 as a private venture to meet specification F.7/30, the Gladiator was re-engined with a Bristol Mercury IX of 840 h.p. and placed in production for the R.A.F. The Gladiator II differed in having a Mercury VIIIA driving a three-blade airscrew, and the Sea Gladiator I and II were carrier-borne fleet-fighter versions. A total of 527 Gladiators was built, and 216 of these were exported. The Gladiator was the last biplane to serve with R.A.F. fighter squadrons, and production was completed early in 1940. The sole remaining example has been rebuilt from components of several machines.

Max. speed, 250 m.p.h. at 15,500 ft.; cruising speed, 212 m.p.h.; service ceiling, 32,800 ft.; range, 425 miles; empty weight, 3,745 lb.; loaded, 5,420 lb.; span, 32 ft. 3 in.; length, 27 ft. 5 in.; height, 10 ft. 4 in.

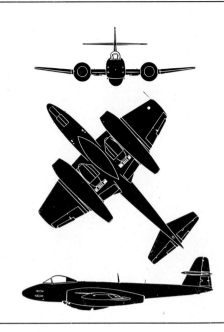

GLOSTER METEOR F.8   G.B.

First flown on March 5, 1943, the Meteor was produced in a number of versions, the most widely used being the F.8. It differs from its production predecessors primarily in having a lengthened fuselage, redesigned cockpit and tail assembly, and currently serves with the R.A.F., and the air forces of Belgium, Brazil, Denmark, Israel, the Netherlands and Syria. The F.R.9 and P.R.10 are respectively fighter-reconnaissance and unarmed photo-reconnaissance variants, the latter having a similar nose and cockpit to that of the F.R.9 but a 43 ft. span wing and an F.4 type tail.

Specification: Single-seat fighter. Engines: Two 3,600 lb.s.t. Rolls-Royce Derwent R.D.8. Weights: Empty, 10,626 lb.; max. loaded, 17,350 lb. Performance: Max. speed, 592 m.p.h. at sea level; initial climb rate, 7,700 ft./min.; service ceiling, 44,000 ft.; range, 767 miles at 40,000 ft. Armament: Four 20-mm. cannon. Dimensions: Span, 37 ft. 2 in.; length, 43 ft. 6 in.; height, 13 ft. 10 in.; wing area, 350 sq. ft.

GLOSTER (A.W.) METEOR N.F.14   G.B.

The Meteor N.F.14 is a progressive development of the earlier Meteor two-seat all-weather fighters built by Armstrong Whitworth Aircraft Ltd. The first Meteor all-weather fighter, the N.F.11, was virtually a new aircraft, and was succeeded by the Meteor N.F.12 which featured a lengthened nose. The N.F.13 is a tropicalised version of the N.F.11, but the final model, the N.F.14 is equipped with U.S. airborne interception radar, and a revised, clear-vision cockpit canopy. No details of the weights or performance of the Meteor N.F.14 have been revealed, but it may be assumed that they are generally similar to those quoted for the N.F.11.

Specification: Two-seat night and all-weather fighter. Engines: Two 3,600 lb.s.t. Rolls-Royce Derwent R.D.8. Weights: No details available. Performance: No details available. Armament: Four 20-mm. cannon. Dimensions: Span, 43 ft.; length, 49 ft. 11 in.; height, 13 ft. 10 in.; wing area, 374 sq. ft.

GLOSTER JAVELIN F.A.W.1   G.B.

The world's first twin-jet delta aircraft, the Javelin all-weather fighter will enter service with the R.A.F. during 1956. The F.A.W.2 is generally similar to the initial F.A.W.1 apart from internal equipment, and the F.A.W.4 and F.A.W.7 are progressive developments, the former introducing an 'all-flying' tail and the latter more powerful Sapphires. Cannon armament will be augmented by air-to-air missiles. Two flush-fitting, long-range, external drop-tanks can be fitted under the fuselage centre section.

Specification: Two-seat all-weather and night fighter. Engines: Two 8,000 lb.s.t. Armstrong Siddeley Sapphire A.S.Sa.6. Weights: Approx. loaded, 30,000–35,000 lb. Performance: Max. speed, 700 m.p.h. (plus) at sea level. Armament: Four 30-mm. Aden cannon and air-to-air missiles. Dimensions: Span, 52 ft.; length, 57 ft.; height, 16 ft. 3 in.; approx. wing area, 900 sq. ft.

GLOSTER METEOR T.7   G.B.

The Meteor T.7 is a tandem two-seat dual-control instructional version of the Meteor F.4. The front fuselage portion has been lengthened by thirty inches to permit seating an instructor, and the Meteor T.7 is powered by two 3,500 lb. thrust Rolls-Royce Derwent 5 turbojets. This Meteor variant has been delivered to the air forces of Denmark, France, Egypt, Brazil, Netherlands, Belgium and Israel, and the T.7s illustrated belong to the Israeli Air Force. Five hundred and thirty Meteor F.4s have been converted to T.7s. Other conversions have been made in Belgium and the Netherlands, and some machines have F.8-type tail assemblies.
Max. speed, 585 m.p.h. at sea level, 490 m.p.h. at 40,000 ft.; initial climb rate, 7,920 ft./min.; range, 250 miles at Sea level, 520 miles at 40,000 ft. empty weight, 10,290 lb.; loaded, 14,000 lb.; span, 37 ft. 2 in.; length, 43 ft. 6 in.

GOODYEAR GA-2B DUCK   U.S.A.

The GA-2B Duck all-metal three-seat experimental amphibian flying-boat was developed by the Goodyear Aircraft Corporation, and four machines were built in 1949 and loaned to selected operators in the U.S.A. to obtain operational experience and customer reaction. The GA-2B Duck is powered by a 145 h.p. Franklin engine. A further development, the GA-22, has a 225 h.p. Continental E-225 engine, an N.A.C.A. planing type hull, a four-seat cabin, and was generally re-designed. One GA-22 has been built and details are quoted in parentheses.
Max. speed, 125 (150) m.p.h.; cruising, 110 (135) m.p.h.; initial climb 650 (1,070) ft./min.; empty weight, 1,450 (1,900) lb.; loaded, 2,200 (3,000) lb.; span, 36 (34) ft.; length, 26 ft. (29 ft. 9 in.).

GOTHA GO 145   GERMANY

Introduced in 1935 by the Gothaer Waggonfabrik A.G., the Go 145 two-seat primary training biplane was the first type to be produced by this concern after it re-entered the aircraft industry—being famous during World War I as a producer of multi-engined bombers. The Go 145 was used by the *Luftwaffe* and a licence for the manufacture of the type was acquired by Construcciones Aeronauticas S.A., in Spain. Twenty-five Go 145 trainers were built in Spain under the designation C.A.S.A. 1145-L. Several of these, powered by the 240 h.p. Argus As 10c, are currently used by the Spanish Air Force as the ES.2.
Max. speed, 132 m.p.h.; cruising speed, 112 m.p.h.; range at cruising speed, 404 miles; empty weight, 1,918 lb.; loaded, 2,976 lb.; span, 29 ft. 6 in.; length, 28 ft. 5 in.; height, 9 ft. 6 in.; wing area, 234 sq. ft.

GLOSTER METEOR N.F.11   G.B.

A two-seat night fighter adaptation of the single-seat Meteor F.8, the Meteor N.F.11 was developed by Sir W. G. Armstrong Whitworth Aircraft Ltd. While many components are similar to, or even interchangeable with, those of other Meteors, the N.F.11 is virtually a new aircraft. The forward fuselage has been lengthened to accommodate A.I. radar, and the four 20-mm. Hispano cannon have been transferred to the wing. The Meteor N.F.11 has been supplied to the French, Danish and Belgian Air Forces, in addition to the R.A.F., and the photo depicts a Belgian A.F. aircraft. Performance and weight figures are quoted from French sources.
Max. speed, 579 m.p.h. at 9,842 ft.; initial climb rate, 5,797 ft./min.; max. range, 920 miles at 30,000 ft.; service ceiling, 43,000 ft.; empty weight, 13,906 lb.; loaded, 19,747 lb.; span, 43 ft.; length, 48 ft. 6 in.

GÖTAVERKEN GV-38   SWEDEN

The GV-38 is a licence-built version of the American Rearwin 9000-L Sportster two-seat light cabin monoplane produced in 1938–39 by the Götaverken concern of Göteborg. Eight GV-38 light planes are currently flying in Sweden, and there is also one flying in Norway. The GV-38 is powered by a 90 h.p. Le Blond air-cooled radial engine and is of mixed construction, the wing of spruce spars and ribs with fabric covering and the fuselage of welded steel-tube with metal and fabric covering.

Max. speed, 123 m.p.h.; cruising, 110 m.p.h.; initial climb rate, 1,000 ft./min.; range, 450 miles; empty weight, 830 lb.; loaded, 1,460 lb.; span, 35 ft.; length, 22 ft. 3½ in.; height, 6 ft. 9 in.; wing area, 166 sq. ft.

GREAT LAKES 2T-1A   U.S.A.

Produced by the Great Lakes Aircraft Corporation in substantial numbers and a variety of versions between 1929 and 1933, the 2T-1A Sports Trainer tandem two-seat light biplane was produced with a number of different engines in the 85–185 h.p. range. About a dozen 2T-1As are flying in the U.S.A., and many of these are re-built, non-standard machines such as that illustrated which was originally a float-plane and is fitted with a cut-down Ford Trimotor airscrew and a 145 h.p. Warner. Others are flying with the 90 h.p. A.C.E. Cirrus, 125 h.p. Continental, 150 h.p. Franklin, 160 h.p. Kinner, and 125 h.p. Menasco.
(Cirrus): Max. speed, 110 m.p.h.; cruising, 90 m.p.h.; initial climb rate, 600 ft./min.; service ceiling, 13,010 ft.; empty weight, 1,102 lb.; loaded, 1,580 lb.; span, 26 ft. 8 in.; length, 20 ft. 4 in.

GRUMMAN G-32A U.S.A.

After the completion of contracts for the Grumman F3F-1, -2, and -3 single-seat carrier-borne fighter biplanes for the U.S. Navy, the Grumman Aircraft Engineering Corporation built three further airframes: one single-seat and two two-seat. All three machines were powered by the 1,000 h.p. Wright Cyclone GR-1820-G engine, and the single-seat model was designated G-22 Gulfhawk. This now reposes in the Smithsonian Institute. The two two-seat models were completed in July 1938. One was destroyed, but one is still flying in the U.S.A. Designated G-32A, this was impressed in the U.S.A.A.F. as the UC-103 but is now privately owned.
Max. speed, 250 m.p.h. at 7,500 ft.; cruising, 215 m.p.h.; initial climb rate, 2,700 ft./min.; service ceiling, 32,000 ft.; loaded weight, 3,400 lb.; span, 32 ft.; length, 23 ft. 3 in.; height, 8 ft. 9 in.; wing area, 260 sq. ft.

GRUMMAN G-23 (GOBLIN) U.S.A.

The Grumman G-23 two-seat carrier-borne fighter biplane was first flown in 1932, and twenty-seven were delivered to the U.S. Navy as FF-1 fighters and a further thirty-four as SF-1 reconnaissance-fighters early in 1934. Powered by a 770 h.p. Wright Cyclone GR-1820-F radial, the Grumman FF-1 carried one fixed and two movable 0.30-in. Browning guns. A number of ex-U.S. Navy SF-1s were overhauled and rebuilt by the Canadian Car & Foundry in 1940 and were used by the R.C.A.F. as the Goblin I until May 1942. Several FF-1s found their way to Spain and were used in the Civil War. One remains airworthy (*photo*) and is known as the R-6 Delfin.
Max. speed, 216 m.p.h. at 5,300 ft.; initial climb rate, 1,600 ft./min.; service ceiling, 22,500 ft.; range, 647 miles; empty weight, 3,221 lb.; loaded, 4,800 lb.; span, 34 ft. 6 in.; length, 24 ft. 6 in.

GRUMMAN G-21 (GOOSE) U.S.A.

The G-21 was first flown in June 1937 as a commercial amphibian, but a number were purchased by the U.S.A.A.F. in 1938 as the 0A-9 and, with later series Wasp engines, as the 0A-13A. Between 1939 and 1943, the G-21 was delivered to the U.S. Navy as the JRF-1A, -4, -5 and -6, and the U.S. Coast Guard as the JRF-2, -3, and -5B. The photo depicts a French Navy JRF-5, and 275 of this version were delivered to the U.S.N. and U.S.C.G. It has two 450 h.p. Pratt & Whitney R-985-AN-6. Production was completed in September 1945. More than forty G-21As are registered in the U.S.A., and many JRFs remain in service.
Max. speed, 180 m.p.h. at 5,000 ft.; initial climb rate, 1,100 ft./min.; service ceiling, 21,000 ft.; max. range, 800 miles; empty weight, 5,425 lb.; loaded, 8,500 lb.; span, 49 ft.; length, 38 ft. 4 in.; height, 15 ft.

GRUMMAN J2F-6 DUCK U.S.A.

Nine series of Duck general utility amphibian were built for the U.S. Navy and Coast Guard between May 4, 1933, when the first prototype, the XFJ-1, flew, and 1945, when the last of 330 J2F-6 Ducks was delivered by the Columbia Aircraft Corporation. Initial production models JF-1, JF-2, and JF-3 were delivered to the U.S. Navy and Coast Guard during 1934–35, and a modified version with deck arrester gear, the J2F-1, flew on June 25, 1935. The J2F-1, -2, -3, and -4 models were delivered during 1936–39, and production was resumed in 1941 with the J2F-5. Subsequently, Columbia produced the J2F-6 with the 900 h.p. Wright R-1820-54.
Max. speed, 190 m.p.h.; cruising, 155 m.p.h.; service ceiling, 20,000 ft.; loaded weight, 7,700 lb.; span, 39 ft.; length, 34 ft.; height (on wheels), 13 ft. 11 in.; wing area, 409 sq. ft.

GRUMMAN (EASTERN) G-36 WILDCAT U.S.A.

In 1942 the manufacture of the Grumman F4F Wildcat single-seat carrier-borne fighter was transferred to the Eastern Aircraft Division of the General Motors Corporation. Designated FM-1, the initial Eastern-built models were virtually identical to the Grumman-built F4F-4, but the FM-2 which entered production in 1943 was powered by the 1,200 h.p. Wright Cyclone GR-1820, and featured redesigned tail surfaces. In addition the oil coolers were removed from under the fuselage to permit the installation of universal racks. Two or three FM-2 Wildcats are privately-owned in the U.S.A.
Max. speed, 318 m.p.h.; initial climb rate, 1,920 ft./min.; service ceiling, 34,800 ft.; range, 925 miles; loaded weight, 7,412 lb.; span, 38 ft.; length, 28 ft. 10 in.; height, 11 ft. 11 in.; wing area, 260 sq. ft.

GRUMMAN G-44 WIDGEON U.S.A.

The G-44 Widgeon commercial utility amphibian was first flown in July, 1940, and was ordered by the U.S.C.G. as the J4F-1, and by the U.S.A.A.F. as the 0A-14. In 1944, one hundred and thirty-five were delivered to the U.S. Navy as five-seat light utility transports under the designation J4F-2. Military production of the G-44 was completed in 1945, and approximately fifty post-war commercial versions were built under the designation G-44A. The G-44A is powered by two 200 h.p. Ranger 6-440C-5 engines. A French licence-built version was designated S.C.A.N.30 (*photo*), but the forty Widgeons built by the Société de Constructions Aéro-Navales have been sold to the U.S.A. and are being re-engined with 220 h.p. Continental W-670 radials.
Max. speed, 160 m.p.h.; cruising, 130 m.p.h.; range, 715 miles; empty weight, 3,240 lb.; loaded, 4,525 lb.; span, 40 ft.; length, 31 ft. 1 in.

GRUMMAN (EASTERN) TBM-3 AVENGER U.S.A.

A considerable number of modernised TBM-3 Avenger anti-submarine aircraft serve with the Royal Navy, the Canadian, Dutch and Japanese navies for anti-submarine duties. The majority of the 9,834 Avengers built were produced by the Eastern Aircraft Division of General Motors, and no Grumman-built Avengers remain in service. Serving Avengers are primarily of the TBM-3E, TBM-3S2 and TBM-3W2 (*photo*) versions for anti-submarine roles, but a few TBM-3U target tugs and TBM-3R seven-seat transports are still flying. The TBM-3W2 version carries a large radome under the fuselage, and the TBM-3S2 is a search and strike variant.

Max. speed, 261 m.p.h.; cruising, 215 m.p.h.; economical cruising, 151 m.p.h.; ceiling, 22,600 ft.; range, 1,130 miles; loaded weight, 16,761 lb.; span, 54 ft. 2 in.; length, 40 ft. 11½ in.; height, 16 ft. 5 in.

GRUMMAN F6F-5 HELLCAT U.S.A.

Designed in the spring of 1942 and first flown in August of that year, the Hellcat was immediately placed in large-scale production, and the first model, the F6F-3, was first reported in action on September 1, 1943. The F6F-3N was a night fighter variant with a radar scanner in a radome on the starboard wing, and the F6F-5 differed in having a redesigned engine cowling, improved windshield, additional armour, etc. Variants include the F6F-5N night fighter and F6F-5P photo-reconnaissance aircraft. A total of 12,272 Hellcats were produced by Grumman, and a few remain with U.S.N. reserve units and with the French Navy.

Max. speed, 371 m.p.h. at 17,200 ft., 331 m.p.h. at sea level; initial climb rate, 3,410 ft./min.; range, 1,040 miles at 159 m.p.h.; empty weight, 9,212 lb.; loaded, 12,727 lb.; span, 42 ft. 10 in.; length, 33 ft. 7 in.

GRUMMAN F7F-3N TIGERCAT U.S.A.

Originally designed as a carrier-borne aircraft, the Tigercat was never used from carriers but was operated from shore bases by the U.S. Marine Corps during the Pacific campaign. The initial production model, the F7F-1D, was a single-seat day fighter and was fitted with carrier gear, but subsequent production models, including the two-seat F7F-2N, -3N, and -4N night fighters, and the single-seat F7F-3D, carried no deck-arrester gear. A few two-seat Tigercat night fighters still exist, and the specification relates to the F7F-2N model powered by two 2,100 h.p. Pratt & Whitney R-2800-22Ws. Only 364 Tigercats were completed.

Max. speed, 424 m.p.h. at 19,200 ft., 391 m.p.h. at sea level; initial climb 4,260 ft./min.; max. range, 1,630 miles at 181 m.p.h.; empty weight, 16,190 lb.; loaded, 21,650 lb.; span, 51 ft. 6 in.; length, 45 ft. 5 in.

GRUMMAN F8F-1D BEARCAT U.S.A.

The Bearcat first appeared in 1945, and the initial production version, the F8F-1, was powered by a 2,100 h.p. Pratt & Whitney R-2800-32W engine and carried an armament of four 0.50-in. Browning guns. The F8F-1B (R-2800-34W) featured a redesigned engine installation and an armament of four 20-mm. cannon. The F8F-1D (R-2800-22W) illustrated here and described in the specification, reverts to the 0.05-in. gun armament, and the final production versions were the cannon-armed F8F-2 with taller fin and rudder assembly, and the F8F-2P photo-reconnaissance model with two 20-mm. cannon. The Bearcat serves U.S.N. reserve units and Thai Air Force.

Max. speed, 424 m.p.h. at 17,300 ft., 393 m.p.h. at sea level; cruising, 175 m.p.h.; initial climb, 4,800 ft./min.; max. range, 1,450 miles; empty weight, 6,733 lb.; loaded, 8,788 lb.; span, 35 ft. 6 in.; length, 28 ft.

GRUMMAN AF-2 GUARDIAN U.S.A.

Originally designed as a torpedo bomber, the Guardian was first flown as the XTB3F-1 with composite power consisting of a Pratt & Whitney R-2800-34W piston engine in the nose and a Westinghouse 19XB-2B turbojet in the tail. Changes in U.S. Navy policy led to the abandonment of the turbojet and the installation of suitable equipment for the anti-submarine role. Powered by the 2,400 h.p. Pratt & Whitney R-2800-48W, the Guardian was produced in small quantities as the AF-2S (Attack), illustrated, and the AF-2W (Search), the latter having a large radar housing under the fuselage, and the two versions forming a hunter-killer team. Sixty-two AF-2S and sixty-three AF-2W Guardians were built.

Max. speed, 318 m.p.h. at 16,000 ft.; range, 1,500 miles; empty weight, 14,580 lb.; loaded, 22,500 lb.; span, 60 ft. 8 in.; length, 43 ft. 4 in.

GRUMMAN G-73 MALLARD U.S.A.

The G-73 Mallard ten-passenger commercial amphibian was the first Grumman flying boat of post-war design, and the first production deliveries commenced in 1947. Only sixty-one Mallards had been produced when production was terminated in 1951, and some forty of these are currently registered in the U.S.A., the majority acting as corporation executive transports. The Mallard is powered by two 600 h.p. Pratt & Whitney Wasp R-1340-S3H1, and passenger accommodation is provided in two compartments, six in the forward and four in the rear compartment.

Max. speed, 215 m.p.h. at 6,000 ft.; cruising, 180 m.p.h. at 8,000 ft.; initial climb rate, 1,290 ft./min.; range, 1,380 miles; loaded weight, 12,750 lb.; span, 66 ft. 8 in.; length, 48 ft. 4 in.

GRUMMAN F9F-5 PANTHER
U.S.A.

The first production Panther, the F9F-2, was powered by a 5,000 lb.s.t. Pratt & Whitney J42-P-6, and later -2s had the 5,750 lb.s.t. J42-P-8. A total of 437 F9F-2s were delivered to the U.S.N. and U.S. Marine Corps. The F9F-3 was originally powered by the 4,600 lb.s.t. Allison J33-A-8, but the 54 F9F-3s ordered were later converted to F9F-2s. The F9F-4 features a 2-ft. increase in fuselage length, and a 6,350 lb.s.t. Allison J33-A-16A: seventy-three were ordered but eventually incorporated into F9F-5 orders. The F9F-5, of which 641 were built, had larger fuselage and tail.
Specification: Single-seat naval fighter-bomber. Engine: One 6,250 lb.s.t. (7,000 lb.s.t. with water injection) Pratt & Whitney J48-P-2, -4, or -6A. Weights: Empty, 8,660 lb.; loaded, 17,000 lb.; max. 18,500 lb. Performance: Max. speed, 623 m.p.h. at sea level, climb to 40,000 ft., 10 minutes; max. range, 1,200 miles. Armament: Four 20-mm. cannon. Dimensions: Span, 38 ft.; length, 42 ft.; height, 16 ft.

GRUMMAN F9F-8 COUGAR
U.S.A.

The F9F-8 Cougar is an improved version of the F9F-6 (*photo*), featuring cambered leading-edge wing sections, increased wing area and fuselage length, and increased fuel capacity. The cambered leading-edge of the wing and extensions increase the wing chord by fifteen per cent and improve the limiting Mach number. The leading edge slats of the earlier F9F-6 and F9F-7 have been deleted, providing space for an additional 25 imp. gall. of fuel in each wing. The F9F-6 and F9F-8 have similar power plants, but the F9F-7 has a 6,350 lb.s.t. Allison J33-A-16A.
Specification: Single-seat naval fighter-bomber. Engine: One 7,250 lb.s.t. Pratt & Whitney J48-P-8. Weights: Approx. loaded, 20,500 lb. Performance: Max. speed, 714 m.p.h.; normal range, 1,300 miles; climb to 40,000 ft., 7 minutes; service ceiling, 50,000 ft. Armament: Four 20-mm. cannon plus four 500-lb. bombs. Dimensions: Span, 34 ft. 6 in.; length, 41 ft. 7 in.; height, 12 ft. 3 in.

GRUMMAN F11F-1 TIGER
U.S.A.

The prototype Tiger flew for the first time on July 30, 1954, only fifteen months after the design had been accepted by the U.S. Navy. Intended primarily as an "air superiority" fighter, initial contracts for six pre-production and thirty-nine production F11F-1s were awarded in October 1954. The first pre-production aircraft are powered by the 7,500 lb.s.t. Wright J65-W-7, but production aircraft have the afterburning Wright J65-W-4. The F11F-1 has been simplified in design to save weight.
Specification: Single-seat naval interceptor fighter. Engine: One 7,800 lb.s.t. (11,000 lb.s.t. with afterburning) Wright J65-W-4. Weights: Normal loaded, 13,850 lb. Approx. performance: Max. speed, 762 m.p.h. at sea level; 660 m.p.h. at 36,000 ft.; initial climb rate, 18,000 ft./min.; range, 600 miles. Armament: Four 20-mm. cannon. Dimensions: Span, 31 ft. 7½ in.; length, 40 ft. 10 in.; height, 12 ft. 8½ in.

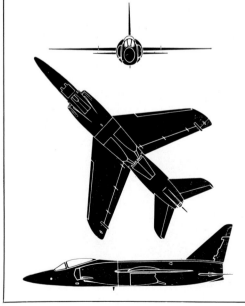

GRUMMAN S2F-1   U.S.A.

Combining the roles of *killer* and *hunter*, the S2F-1 is currently in production for the U.S. Navy and, as the CS2F-1, in Canada for the R.C.N. The S2F-1 carries a large offensive load, which can include torpedoes, depth-charges, or mines, in addition to a built-in armament of 20-mm. cannon. The fuselage houses search radar, magnetic airborne detection equipment, and a searchlight is carried under the starboard wing. Rocket projectiles can be carried outboard of the engine nacelles. Other versions in production include the TF-1 trainer/transport version carrying eight passengers or 1,600 lb. cargo, and the S2F-2 with a rotary-type bomb-bay.

Specification: Four-seat anti-submarine aircraft. Engines: Two 1,525 h.p. Wright R-1820-82. Armament: Four 20-mm. cannon plus 6,000 lb. offensive load. Performance: Approx. max. speed, 310 m.p.h.; cruising, 150 m.p.h.; range, 1,000 miles; endurance, 8 hours. Dimensions: Span, 69 ft. 8 in.; length, 42 ft. 3 in.; height, 16 ft. 3 in.

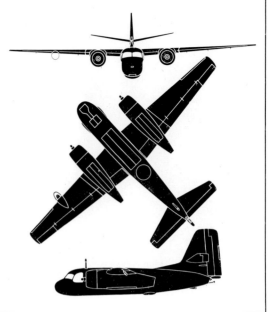

GRUMMAN SA-16A ALBATROSS   U.S.A.

The G-64, or XJR2F-1 Albatross, first flew on October 24, 1947, and the production model has been delivered to the U.S. Navy as the UF-1A utility amphibian and UF-1T trainer. A version for the U.S. Coast Guard is designated UF-1G, and the type has been adopted by the U.S.A.F. as a standard air/sea rescue aircraft under the designation SA-16A. SA-16As delivered since the beginning of 1952 are "triphibians", capable of operating from ice and snow. Three G-64s are employed by the U.S. Department of the Interior in the Trust Island Territory of the Pacific.

Specification: Air/sea rescue amphibian flying-boat. Engines: Two 1,425 h.p. Wright R-1820-76A. Weights: Empty, 24,000 lb.; loaded, 34,000 lb. Performance: Max. speed, 270 m.p.h. at 18,800 ft., 245 m.p.h. at sea level; initial climb rate, 1,400 ft./min.; range, 2,700 miles; endurance, 22.9 hours. Dimensions: Span, 80 ft.; length, 62 ft. 2 in.; height, 24 ft. 4 in.; wing area, 833 sq. ft.

GUERCHAIS ROCHE T.35/II   FRANCE

The T.35 produced by Roche Aviation was first flown in September 1944. After World War II, production of several variants of the T.35 was undertaken, and fifteen basically similar machines were built. These differ in the type of engine installed; two having the 140 h.p. Renault 4 Pei (T.35); one having the 100 h.p. Renault 4 Pei (T.35/I); six having the 140 h.p. Renault 4 P-03 (T.35/II); one having the 135 h.p. Regnier 4 L-00 (T.35/III); two having the 145 h.p. Mathis G 7R radial (T.39); two having the 175 h.p. Salmson 9 ND radial (T.39/II); and one having the 160 h.p. Walter Minor 6-III (T.55). The T.35s are two-seaters and the T.39s are three-seaters. Specification relates to T.35/II.

Max. speed, 149 m.p.h.; cruising, 134 m.p.h.; range, 497 miles; empty weight, 1,188 lb.; loaded, 1,867 lb.; span, 30 ft. 6 in.; length, 23 ft. 9½ in.

HANDLEY PAGE HALIFAX C.8   G.B.

The Halifax heavy bomber played a leading role in the British air offensive during World War II, and more than 6,000 Halifaxes had been built when production ceased in November 1946. A direct conversion of the bomber for freight carrying was designated Halifax C.8, and several machines of this type are used by commercial concerns. A large freight pannier is installed in the bomb-bay, and power is provided by four 1,650 h.p. Bristol Hercules 100 radial engines.

Max. speed, 320 m.p.h.; economical cruising, 210 m.p.h. at 15,000 ft.; range, with max. load, 1,860 miles; empty weight, 37,750 lb.; loaded, 68,000 lb.; span, 104 ft.; length, 73 ft. 7 in.; height, 21 ft. 7 in.; wing area, 1,275 sq. ft.

HANDLEY PAGE MARATHON T.11   G.B.

Originally developed by Miles Aircraft Ltd., and flown for the first time on May 19, 1946, the Marathon was acquired in 1948 by Handley Page (Reading) Ltd., and thirty-nine machines have been produced. Thirty of these have been delivered to the R.A.F. for use as navigational trainers under the designation Marathon T.11. The remaining nine aircraft were completed as 18/22-seat civil feeder liners under the designation Marathon 1A Series 103. A Marathon prototype is currently employed as an engine test-bed under the designation H.P.R.5; this is powered by two 850 h.p. Alvis Leonides Major radial engines.

Specification: Military navigational trainer. Engines: Four 340 h.p. de Havilland Gipsy Queen 70/3. Weights: Empty, 13,358 lb.; loaded, 17,535 lb. Performance: Max. speed, 232 m.p.h.; cruising, 155 m.p.h. at 5,000 ft.; initial climb rate, 595 ft./min.; range, 1,290 miles. Dimensions: Span, 65 ft.; length, 52 ft. 1½ in.; height, 14 ft. 1 in.

HANDLEY PAGE H.P.R.3 HERALD   G.B.

The H.P.R.3 Herald has been designed as a flexible medium-range civil transport, and the first of two prototypes flew on August 25, 1955, with production deliveries planned for 1957. Twenty-four Heralds have been ordered by Australian National Airways, and further machines have been ordered by Lloyd Aero Colombiano, Queensland Airlines, and Air Kruise. The Herald can be arranged as an airliner, seating thirty-six first-class passengers or forty-four tourist passengers, as a combined airliner-freighter, or solely as a freighter.

Specification: Commercial airliner and freighter. Engines: Four 870 h.p. Alvis Leonides Major. Weights: Empty, 21,136 lb.; loaded, 34,000 lb. Performance: Max. speed, 262 m.p.h. at 3,800 ft.; max. cruising speed, 231 m.p.h. at 13,500 ft.; range (with 10,705 lb.) 348 miles (6,929 lb.) 1,417 miles; initial climb rate, 1,820 ft./min.; service ceiling, 24,500 ft. Dimensions: Span, 95 ft.; length, 70 ft. 3 in.; height, 22 ft. 6 in.; wing area, 882 sq. ft.

HANDLEY PAGE VICTOR B.1   G.B.

The first of two H.P.80 Victor prototypes flew on December 24, 1952, being followed on September 11, 1954 by a second prototype. These were powered by Sapphire turbojets of the 8,000 lb.s.t. A.S.Sa.6 type, but the production Victor B.1 presumably utilises more powerful Sapphires (possibly of the 10,200 lb.s.t. A.S.Sa.7 series), and differs externally from the prototypes in having a lengthened forward fuselage and revised tail assembly. The Victor employs a wing planform described as being of "crescent" shape, a constant critical Mach number from root to tip being obtained by progressive reduction of both sweep angle and thickness/chord ratio.

Specification: Long-range medium bomber. Engines: Four 10,000 (approx.) lb.s.t. Armstrong Siddeley Sapphire. Weights: No details available. Performance: Cruising speeds in the vicinity of Mach .95 at 50,000–60,000 ft.; range, 3,000 (plus) miles. Dimensions: Span, 110 ft.; length, 114 ft. 11 in.; height, 26 ft. 9 in.

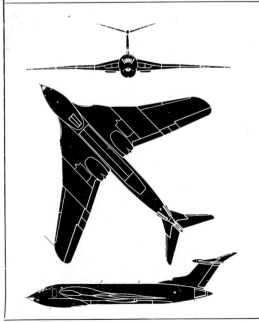

HANDLEY PAGE HASTINGS C.2   G.B.

The Hastings C.1 prototype flew for the first time on May 7, 1946. Several Hastings C.1 transports were converted to Hastings Met.1s for meteorological reconnaissance, and in 1950 production of the C.1 gave place to the improved C.2. This had Hercules 106 engines replacing the earlier Hercules 101s, the tailplane lowered to the centre line of the fuselage to correct a deficiency in longitudinal stability, increased fuel capacity, etc. The Hastings C.3 is basically the same as the C.2, apart from the installation of Hercules 737 engines, and four have been supplied to the R.N.Z.A.F., and the C.4 is a V.I.P. version of the Hastings C.2. The silhouette depicts the C.1.
Specification: Long-range military transport. Engines: Four 1,675 h.p. Bristol Hercules 106. Weights: Empty, 48,427 lb.; max. loaded, 80,000 lb. Performance: Max. speed, 348 m.p.h. at 22,000 ft.; cruising, 302 m.p.h. at 23,600 ft.; initial climb rate, 890 ft./min.; range (max. payload), 1,690 miles; maximum, 4,250 miles. Dimensions: Span, 113 ft.; length, 82 ft. 1 in.; height, 22 ft. 6 in.; wing area, 1,408 sq. ft.

HANDLEY PAGE H.P.81 HERMES 4A   G.B.

A commercial development of the Hastings military transport, the Hermes 4 was one of the first post-war British airliners to enter service. The initial versions, the H.P.68 Hermes I and IA, were externally similar to the Hastings, but the Hermes 2 had a 15-ft. increase in fuselage length, and the Hermes 4, the first production version, differed from its predecessor in having a nosewheel undercarriage, larger tail surfaces, etc. Twenty-five were built for B.O.A.C. as 40-74 passenger airliners powered by 2,200 h.p. Bristol Hercules 763 engines. The Hermes 4A serves with Airwork Ltd.
Max. speed, 355 m.p.h.; cruising, 266 m.p.h.; range (6,400 lb. payload), 3,080 miles; empty weight, 55,350 lb.; loaded, 86,000 lb.; span, 113 ft.; length, 96 ft. 10 in.; height, 30 ft.; wing area, 1,408 sq. ft.

HARLOW PJC-2   U.S.A.

The PJC-2 four-seat cabin touring monoplane was developed by the Harlow Engineering Corporation (later Harlow Aircraft Company) in 1938, and limited production was undertaken until December 1941, when the manufacturing facilities of the company were switched to military sub-contract work. Four PJC-2s were impressed into the U.S.A.A.F. under the designation UC-80, and a two-seat trainer development, the PC-5A, was produced in 1939. A small number of PJC-2s are still flying, powered by the 145 h.p. Warner Super Scarab R-500-1. The PJC-2 is of all-metal construction.
Max. speed, 150 m.p.h.; cruising speed, 135 m.p.h.; initial climb rate, 660 ft./min.; range, 500 miles; empty weight, 1,700 lb.; loaded, 2,600 lb.; span, 35 ft. 7½ in.; length, 23 ft. 3½ in.

HAWKER CYGNET   G.B.

Designed in 1923, the Cygnet ultra-light two-seat single-bay biplane was introduced in 1924 when two machines of this type were entered for the Light Aeroplane Competitions. During the following year, a Cygnet won the 100-mile International Handicap Race at 74 m.p.h., and in 1926 a pair of Cygnets participated in the *Daily Mail* competition for light two-seaters. Various engines were fitted, including the Anzani and the A.B.C. Scorpion, but the sole remaining example, which is one of the oldest aircraft on the British Register, is powered by a 32 h.p. Bristol Cherub 3.

Max. speed, 75 m.p.h.; cruising speed, 65 m.p.h.; empty weight, 373 lb.; loaded, 900 lb.; span, 28 ft.; length, 19 ft.

HAWKER HART   G.B.

The Hart two-seat day bomber was designed to meet a 1926 A.M. specification and was first flown in June 1928. With folding wings, the Hart became the carrier-borne Osprey, and with a Napier Dagger engine became the Hector. With a fully supercharged Kestrel V engine and other improvements it became the Hind and the Hartbees. Production of Harts and Hart variants totalled 2,201 aircraft, including two civil machines, one of which is still airworthy. This is powered by a 670 h.p. Rolls-Royce Kestrel 16 Special engine.
Max. speed, 184 m.p.h. at sea level, 172 m.p.h. at 10,000 ft.; climb to 10,000 ft., 8 minutes; ceiling, 21,320 ft.; range, 430 miles at 170 m.p.h.; empty weight, 2,530 lb.; loaded, 4,635 lb.; span, 37 ft. 4½ in.; length, 29 ft. 4 in.; height, 10 ft. 4 in.; wing area, 350 sq. ft.

HAWKER SEA HAWK F. (G.A.) 4   G.B.

Produced by Sir W. G. Armstrong Whitworth Aircraft Ltd. for the Royal Navy, the Sea Hawk F. (G.A.) 4 is a progressive development of the earlier Sea Hawks F.1, F.2 and F.B.3. The Sea Hawk F.2 differed from the initial production F.1 in having power-boosted ailerons, and the F.B.3 had a strengthened wing to enable it to carry heavier underwing offensive loads. The 5,000 lb.s.t. Nene 101 (R.N.2), originally installed, is being replaced retroactively by the 5,400 lb.s.t. Nene R.N.6. The Sea Hawk's range in "clean" condition is exceptional and can be further increased by the addition of two 45 imp. gall. or 90 imp. gall. underwing drop-tanks.

Specification: Single-seat naval fighter-bomber. Engine: One 5,400 lb.s.t. Rolls-Royce Nene R.N.6. Weights: No details available. Performance: Approx. max. speed, 630 m.p.h. at sea level; approx. initial climb rate, 9,000 ft./min. Armament: Four 20-mm. cannon. Dimensions: Span, 39 ft. 0 in.; length, 39 ft. 8 in.; height, 8 ft. 8 in.

HAWKER HUNTER F.4   G.B.

Designed to fulfil specification F.3/48, the first prototype Hunter flew on July 20, 1951, and several variants of the basic design have since been produced. The initial production versions were the Hunters F.1 and F.2, the latter being powered by the 8,000 lb.s.t. A.S. Sapphire A.S.Sa.6. These were succeeded by the Hunters F.4 and F.5 which are similar to the F.1 and F.2 apart from an increase in internal fuel capacity and provision for external underwing loads of drop-tanks, rockets or bombs. The latest production version is the Hunter F.6 (*photo*) which, according to foreign reports, has a 10,000 lb.s.t. Avon R.A.28.

Specification: Single-seat fighter. Engine: One 8,050 lb.s.t. Rolls-Royce Avon R.A.21 series. Weights: No details available. Performance: Max. speed exceeds 720 m.p.h. at sea level. Armament: Four 30-mm. Aden cannon. Dimensions: Span, 33 ft. 8 in.; length, 45 ft. 10½ in.; height, 10 ft.; wing area, 340 sq. ft.

HAWKER P.1101   G.B.

The P.1101 is a two-seat development of the standard Hunter F.4 single-seat fighter. Intended primarily for instructional purposes, the P.1101 was flown for the first time on July 8, 1955, and differs externally from the standard Hunter in having a 2 ft. 11½ in. increase in the length of the forward fuselage which is broadened to accommodate the side-by-side seats, and the semi-externally packaged armament. The manufacturers claim that the P.1101 can accommodate full all-weather radar equipment, suiting it for use as a night fighter.

Specification: Two-seat instructional aircraft. Engine: One 8,000 (approx.) lb.s.t. Rolls-Royce Avon. Weights: No details available for publication. Performance: Max. speed, 700 (plus) m.p.h. at sea level. Armament: Two 30-mm. Aden cannon. Dimensions: Span, 33 ft. 8 in.; length, 48 ft. 10½ in.; height, 13 ft. 2 in.; wing area, 340 sq. ft.

HAWKER TOMTIT   G.B.

The Tomtit was produced in 1929 to meet R.A.F. requirements. It could perform all the evolutions of the more powerful combat aircraft of its day, but only a few were supplied to the R.A.F., although the type was adopted as a standard trainer by the R.C.A.F. Various engines were installed, including the Cirrus Hermes and the Wolseley A.R.9, but the sole remaining example is powered by a 150 h.p. Armstrong Siddeley Mongoose IIIC. The Tomtit is an equispan, single-bay, tandem two-seat biplane.

Max. speed, 124 m.p.h.; initial climb rate, 1,000 ft./min.; service ceiling, 20,000 ft.; range, 350 miles; empty weight, 1,100 lb.; loaded, 1,750 lb.; span, 28 ft. 6 in.; length, 23 ft. 5 in.; wing area, 238 sq. ft.

HAWKER HURRICANE MK.2C   G.B.

The Hurricane prototype was first flown on November 6, 1935, and the last of some 15,000 machines built, a Mark 2C dubbed *The Last of the Many*, was delivered in September 1944. This particular aircraft remains airworthy as do several other examples of the type, and is powered by a 1,280 h.p. Rolls-Royce Merlin 24 engine. During its production life, the Hurricane was produced in a variety of versions with varying armament and for several different roles. A few Hurricane 2Cs are believed to be airworthy in Portugal.

Max. speed, 334 m.p.h. at 21,500 ft.; initial climb rate, 2,780 ft./min.; service ceiling, 36,000 ft.; loaded weight, 7,670 lb.; span, 40 ft.; length, 32 ft. 3 in.; height, 13 ft. 1½ in.; wing area, 257.5 sq. ft.

HAWKER TEMPEST F.B.2   G.B.

The Tempest was essentially a progressive development of the Typhoon single-seat fighter-bomber, the first version to fly, on September 2, 1942, being a Mark 5 with a Sabre 2 engine. The Tempest Mk.2 prototype followed on June 28, 1943, powered by a 2,520 h.p. Bristol Centaurus 5 radial engine. This was intended primarily for service in the Far East. During 1948–49, a number of Tempest F.B.2 fighter-bombers were supplied to the Royal Pakistani and Royal Indian Air Forces, and although no longer first-line equipment, a number remain as advanced trainers.

Max. speed, 440 m.p.h. at 15,900 ft., 406 m.p.h. at sea level; initial climb rate, 4,520 ft./min.; service ceiling, 37,000 ft.; normal range, 775 miles; max., 1,700 miles; empty weight, 9,300 lb.; loaded, 11,800 lb.; span, 41 ft.; length, 34 ft. 5 in.; height, 15 ft. 6 in.; wing area, 303.7 sq. ft.

HAWKER TEMPEST T.T.5   G.B.

The Tempest was designed to fulfil specification F.10/41, and two Sabre-powered production variants were produced in quantity, the F.5 with a 2,420 h.p. Sabre IIB, and the F.6 with the 2,700 h.p. Sabre 5. A number of both versions have been converted for the target-towing role under the designations Tempest T.T.5 and T.T.6 respectively. Simple towing gear is fitted, and outwardly the two marks can only be distinguished by the small intake ducts in the wing roots of the T.T.6. Specification relates to the T.T.5.

Max. speed, 435 m.p.h. at 17,000 ft., 392 m.p.h. at sea level; max. cruising, 391 m.p.h. at 18,800 ft.; normal range, 820 miles; initial climb rate, 4,700 ft./min.; empty weight, 9,250 lb.; loaded, 11,400 lb.; span, 41 ft.; length, 33 ft. 8 in.; height, 16 ft. 1 in.

HAWKER SEA FURY F.B.11   G.B.

The Sea Fury, the last piston-engined fighter-bomber to be built in quantity in the United Kingdom, is a navalised version of the land-based Fury which, externally similar, serves with the air forces of Egypt, India and Pakistan. The first production Sea Fury was the F.10, only fifty of which were built, and the major production model was the F.B.11 which was also built under licence in the Netherlands as the F.B.51. The Sea Fury F.B.11 is powered by a 2,480 h.p. Bristol Centaurus 18 engine.

Max. speed, 450 m.p.h. at 20,000 ft.; initial climb rate, 4,320 ft./min.; combat radius, 720 miles; empty weight, 9,240 lb.; loaded, 12,350 lb.; span, 38 ft. 4¾ in.; length, 34 ft. 8 in.; height, 14 ft. 9 in.; wing area, 280 sq. ft.

HEATH PARASOL   U.S.A.

The Heath Parasol was designed in the U.S.A. in the late 'twenties and was produced complete or in kit form by the International Aircraft Corporation of Niles, Michigan. A complete set of parts, minus engine, could be supplied for assembly by amateur constructors. A variety of engines in the 25–40 h.p. range could be installed, and two examples of this single-seat ultra-light aircraft are registered in the U.K., one powered by a 36 h.p. J.A.P. J.99 engine (*illustrated*), and the other powered by a 25 h.p. Blackburn Tomtit engine. Engines fitted to U.S.-built versions included the 25 h.p. Heath B-4 and the 37 h.p. Continental.

Max. speed (according to engine), 71–82 m.p.h.; cruising speed, 62–73 m.p.h.; initial climb rate, 300–450 ft./min.; loaded weight, 560–700 lb.; span, 23 ft.; length, 17 ft. 3 in.; height, 6 ft.

G

HEINKEL HE 70   GERMANY

The Heinkel He 70A *Blitz* seven-seat high-performance commercial monoplane introduced in 1932 was perhaps the first aerodynamically efficient, fast civil transport, establishing eight international records during its career. Produced by the Ernst Heinkel Flugzeugwerke G.m.b.H., the He 70 was designed primarily as a high-speed attack bomber, and the 7-G14 group was equipped with this type during the Spanish Civil War. At least one and possible two examples of the He 70 remain airworthy in Spain where it is designated R.2 Rayo. The He 70 carries a crew of two and is powered by a 630 h.p. B.M.W. VI engine.

Max. speed, 234 m.p.h.; cruising, 200 m.p.h.; range, 620 miles; empty weight, 5,647 lb.; loaded, 9,163 lb.; span, 48 ft. 6 in.; length, 37 ft. 8½ in.; height, 10 ft. 1 in.; wing area, 392.7 sq. ft.

HEINKEL HE 114   GERMANY

The He 114 two-seat reconnaissance seaplane appeared in 1937, and the first prototypes were powered by the liquid-cooled Junkers Jumo 210 engine. Later prototypes and production He 114s were powered by the 960 h.p. B.M.W.132K radial engine, and a limited number of machines were delivered to the German Navy. The only aircraft of this type still flying are owned by the Spanish Navy. The He 114 is of all-metal construction, and armament comprises one fixed forward-firing machine gun and one flexible gun mounted in the observer's cockpit.

Max. speed, 208 m.p.h. at 11,550 ft.; cruising speed, 192 m.p.h.; service ceiling, 22,960 ft.; normal range, 540 miles; max. range, 620 miles; empty weight, 5,148 lb.; loaded, 7,656 lb.; span, 44 ft. 6 in.; length, 39 ft.; wing area, 455 sq. ft.

HINDUSTAN HT-2   INDIA

The first powered aircraft to be designed and built completely in India, the HT-2 is in production for the Indian Air Force and for Indian flying clubs. One HT-2 has been presented to Indonesia by the Indian Government. The prototype HT-2 was first flown on August 13, 1951, powered by 145 h.p. de Havilland Gipsy Major 10. This engine was replaced in production aircraft by the Blackburn Cirrus Major III, and an initial production batch of one hundred machines is currently in hand. Hindustan Aircraft is also developing a jet basic trainer designated HJT-17.

Specification: Two-seat primary trainer. Engine: One 155 h.p. Blackburn Cirrus Major III. Weights: Empty, 1,560 lb.; loaded, 2,180 lb. Performance: Max. speed, 140 m.p.h.; cruising speed, 120 m.p.h.; initial climb rate, 700 ft./min.; service ceiling, 15,700 ft. Dimensions: Span, 35 ft. 2 in.; length, 24 ft. 8½ in.; height, 8 ft. 11 in.; wing area, 173.4 sq. ft.

HELIO H-391 COURIER   U.S.A.

The H-391 Courier is a production development of the two-seat Koppen-Bollinger Helioplane which first flew on April 8, 1949. With full-span automatic slats on the wing leading-edge, and 74 per cent span flaps, the Courier can fly under full control at less than 30 m.p.h. Powered by a 260 h.p. Lycoming engine, the Courier is a four-seater, and an initial production batch of six machines was completed early in 1954. Manufacture of the Courier is being undertaken by Fleet Manufacturing, Ltd., in Canada, which concern supplies major components to the Helio Aircraft Co. for final assembly, and will eventually manufacture the complete aircraft. Experimental U.S. Army liaison version was designated YL-24.

Cruising speed, 157 m.p.h. at 8,500 ft., 142 m.p.h. at sea level; range, 600 miles; empty weight, 1,880 lb.; loaded, 2,800 lb.; span, 39 ft.; length, 30 ft.

HIRSCH MAÉRCH 100   FRANCE

The MAÉRCH 100 is an experimental gust-absorption aircraft designed by M. Hirsch who has been experimenting with aerodynamic gust-alleviation since 1936. The MAÉRCH 100 was flown for the first time on June 15, 1954, and is powered by two 95 h.p. Regnier 4 EO engines. The fuselage is of wooden construction and exceptionally clean, and the engine nacelles are so designed that larger engines may be installed. The engines drive variable-pitch airscrew of M. Hirsch's own design. Accommodation is provided for a test crew of three persons.

Max. speed, 220 m.p.h.; cruising, 196 m.p.h.; initial climb rate, 1,338 ft./min.; range, 1,025 miles; ceiling, 19,685 ft.; empty weight, 1,995 lb.; loaded, 2,910 lb.; span, 28 ft. 2½ in.; length, 24 ft. 7¼ in.; height, 6 ft. 10½ in.

HIRTENBERG H.S.9A   AUSTRIA

The Hirtenberger Patronen-, Zündhutchen- und Metallwarenfabrik, A.G., began aircraft manufacture in 1935 by taking over the old Hopfner Company, and the H.S.9 tandem two-seat touring or training biplane appeared in 1936, powered by a 125 h.p. Siemens Sh.14a radial engine. The H.S.9A differed from the H.S.9 in having a 120 h.p. de Havilland Gipsy Major engine, and one example of this aircraft is currently registered in the United Kingdom. The specification relates to the H.S.9 but is generally similar to that for the H.S.9A.

Max. speed, 118 m.p.h.; cruising, 102 m.p.h.; normal range, 360 miles; empty weight, 1,254 lb.; loaded, 1,980 lb.; span, 36 ft.; length, 26 ft. 5 in.; height, 7 ft. 10 in.; wing area, 193.6 sq. ft.

HISPANO HA-132-L CHIRRI   SPAIN

The HA-132-L Chirri single-seat fighter biplane was built in quantity by Hispano Aviación S.A. during 1938–42 for the Spanish Air Force, and a number of Chirris are still employed as aerobatic trainers under the designation C.1. The Chirri is a licence-built version of the Fiat C.R.32 which, designed by Ing. Rosatelli, was first flown in 1933, and was subsequently built in quantity for the *Regia Aeronautica* in several versions, including the *bis, ter,* and *quater*. The Chirri is powered by a 600 h.p. Fiat A.30 R.A. engine.

Max. speed, 242 m.p.h.; cruising, 211 m.p.h. at 9,840 ft.; climb to 19,680 ft., 11 minutes; endurance, 2 hours, 30 minutes; empty weight, 2,805 lb.; loaded, 3,960 lb.; span, 28 ft. 11 in.; length, 22 ft. 8 in.; height, 9 ft.; wing area, 237.8 sq. ft.

HISPANO HA-43D-1   SPAIN

The HA-43 advanced trainer built by Hispano Aviacion is derived from the HS-42B (*silhouette*) from which it differs primarily in having a retractable undercarriage. The prototype HS-42 (430 h.p. Piaggio P.VIIC.16) appeared during World War 2, but the production version (A.S. Cheetah 25) was not delivered to the Spanish Air Force until March 1947. Both the HS-42B and the HA-43 are now serving in quantity with Spanish training units. The HA-43A, B, C, and D differ primarily in equipment, but the HA-43C differs from the HA-43D-1 (*photo*) to which the specification refers in having a 500 h.p. E.N.M.A. Sirio S-VIIA engine.

Specification: Two-seat advanced trainer. Engine: One 390 h.p. Armstrong Siddeley Cheetah 27. Weights: Empty, 3,309 lb.; loaded, 4,510 lb. Performance: Max. speed, 208 m.p.h.; cruising, 183 m.p.h.; initial climb rate, 1,410 ft./min. Dimensions: Span, 32 ft. 10 in.; length, 26 ft. 2 in.; height, 8 ft. 6 in.; wing area, 175.4 sq. ft.

HISPANO HA-1109/1110   SPAIN

In 1943, La Hispano Aviacion received a contract to produce under licence the Messerschmitt Me 109G for the Spanish Air Force. Inability to obtain the DB 605 engine from Germany led to the installation of the nationally-built Hispano-Suiza HS-12Z-89, and this version, designated HA-1109-J-1-L, first flew on March 2, 1945. In May 1951, an improved model, powered by the French HS-12Z-17 engine, was flown and designated HA-1109-K-1-L (*photo*). The similarly-powered HA-1110-K-1-L (*silhouette*) is a two-seat advanced trainer version, and the HA-1109-M-1-L Buchón and HA-1110-M-1-L are variants powered by the 1,600 h.p. Rolls-Royce Merlin 45.

Specification: Single-seat fighter. Engine: One 1,300 h.p. Hispano HS-12Z-17. Weights: Empty, 5,457 lb.; loaded, 6,834 lb. Performance: Max. speed, 404 m.p.h. at 20,670 ft.; range, 435 miles. Dimensions: Span, 32 ft. 6½ in.; length, 29 ft. 6 in.; height, 12 ft.; wing area, 173 sq. ft.

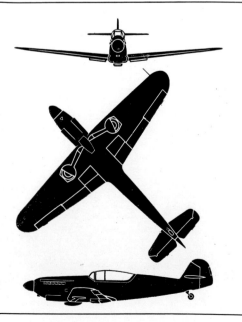

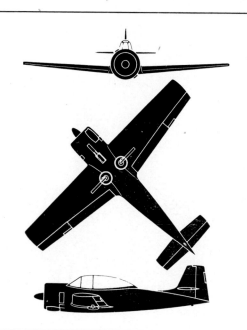

HISPANO HA-100-EI — SPAIN

The HA-100-E1 has been designed to replace the HS-42B and HA-43D series with advanced training elements of the Spanish Air Force. Flown for the first time on December 10, 1953, the HA-100-E1 is of all-metal construction, has a fixed armament of two 12.7-mm. guns, and can carry a 450-lb. underwing load of ordnance, such as 22-lb. Oerlikon rocket missiles, 110-lb. bombs, etc. A variant of the HA-100, designated HA-100-F1 (*photo*), is powered by a Wright Cyclone 7 engine. The HA-100 was designed by Professor W. Messerschmitt, and may be produced in Western Germany as the Me 100.

Specification: Two-seat operational trainer. Engine: One 750 h.p. E.N.M.A. E-9C Beta. Weights: Empty, 3,858 lb.; loaded, 6,012 lb. Performance: Max. speed, 289.5 m.p.h. at 9,514 ft.; cruising, 237 m.p.h.; range, 822 miles; endurance, 3 hours 28 minutes. Dimensions: Span, 34 ft.; length, 27 ft. 1 in.; height, 10 ft. 8 in.; wing area, 186.6 sq. ft.

HISPANO HA-200-RI SAETA — SPAIN

Designed under the supervision of Professor Messerschmitt, the HA-200-R1 Saeta (Arrow) is the first jet aircraft of Spanish construction. Flown for the first time on August 16, 1955, the prototype is designated XE-14 by the Spanish Air Force, and production Saetas will be designated E-14. The Saeta is of all-metal construction, and is intended primarily for use as a conversion trainer. Production of the Saeta is proposed in Germany under the designation Messerschmitt Me 200 Pfeil. Trainer role.

Specification: Two-seat conversion trainer. Engines: Two 880 lb.s.t. Turboméca Marboré II. Weights: Empty, 3,181 lb.; loaded, 7,066 lb. Performance: Max. speed, 405 m.p.h. at sea level, 441 m.p.h. at 29,520 ft.; initial climb rate, 2,676 ft./min.; service ceiling, 39,360 ft.; range, 1,056 miles at 32,800 ft. Dimensions: Span, 34 ft. 2 in.; length, 29 ft. 1½ in.; height, 9 ft. 4 in.; wing area, 187.2 sq. ft.

HOLSTE M.H.52-53 — FRANCE

The M.H.52 (*photo*) and the M.H.53 (*silhouette*) are generally similar apart from their undercarriage arrangements, the former having a fixed nosewheel and the latter having a tailwheel. Two versions of the M.H.52 have been produced: the M.H.52-G with a 120 h.p. de Havilland Gipsy Major 1 engine, and the M.H.52-R with a 140 h.p. Renault 4 P-01 engine. The M.H.53 Cadet is powered by a 135 h.p. de Havilland Gipsy Major 10. The following specification related to the M.H.52-E tourer and figures quoted in parentheses refer to the M.H.53 Cadet.

Specification: Two-seat cabin monoplane. Engine: One 150 h.p. Potez 4D. Weights: Empty, 1,411 (1,485) lb.; loaded, 1,918 (2,068) lb. Performance: Max. speed, 143 (137) m.p.h.; cruising, 130 (124) m.p.h.; initial climb rate, 679 (690) ft./min. Dimensions: Span, 32 ft. 1 in. (32 ft. 2 in.); length, 23 ft. 10¾ in. (23 ft. 9 in.); height, 7 ft. 1½ in. (6 ft. 11 in.); wing area, 150.5 sq. ft.

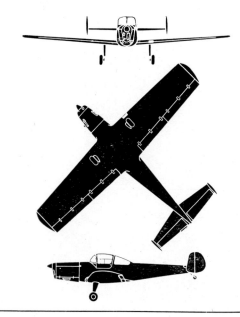

HOLSTE M.H.1521M BROUSSARD   FRANCE

The M.H.1521 Broussard was designed as a light colonial monoplane and derived from the experimental M.H.152 air observation post. Flown for the first time on November 17, 1952, the Broussard has since been ordered in quantity by the French Air Force as a general utility transport and liaison aircraft, and an initial production batch of two hundred machines is currently under construction. Several civil Broussards are registered in France. Particular attention has been paid in the design to interchangeability of components.

Specification: Six-seat utility transport. Engine: One 450 h.p. Pratt & Whitney Wasp R-985-AN. Weights: Empty, 3,212 lb.; loaded, 5,203 lb. Performance: Max. speed, 168 m.p.h.; cruising speed, 146 m.p.h.; range, 745 miles. Dimensions: Span, 51 ft. 7¾ in.; length, 28 ft. 2½ in.; height, 9 ft. 2 in.; wing area, 273.4 sq. ft.

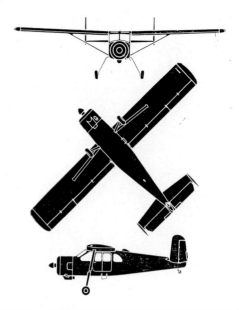

HK-1   FINLAND

The HK-1 single-seat ultra-light monoplane was designed by Juhani Heinonen of Helsinki and is powered by a 65 h.p. Walter Mikron III engine. The fuselage is a plywood-covered all-wood structure, as is also the wing, and the HK-1 is fully aerobatic. It was built in 1954 by the Jämi Soaring School, and was flown for the first time in August of that year. A rearward-sliding Perspex canopy is fitted, and a steel-tube crash pylon is mounted behind the pilot's head.

Max. speed, 135 m.p.h.; cruising speed, 115 m.p.h.; max. range at economical cruising speed, 430 miles; empty weight, 550 lb.; loaded (aerobatic), 795 lb. (normal), 880 lb.; span, 22 ft. 6 in.; wing area, 75 sq. ft.

HOLLEVILLE RH-1 BAMBI   FRANCE

Designed and built by Roger Holleville, the RH-1 Bambi side-by-side two-seat cabin monoplane was first flown in 1954. Powered by a 65 h.p. Continental E65 engine, the Bambi employs synthetic resins and sandwich construction, and will be made available in plan or kit form for construction by clubs or groups. Dual controls may be fitted, and the Bambi II will be fitted with Adam-type hydraulic brakes.

Max. speed, 124 m.p.h.; cruising speed, 105 m.p.h.; minimum speed, 34 m.p.h.; initial climb rate, 1,080 ft./min.; endurance, 4 hours, 30 minutes; empty weight, 637 lb.; loaded, 1,100 lb.; span, 27 ft. 6 in.; length, 22 ft.; height, 7 ft. 4½ in.; wing area, 107.639 sq. ft.

HÖNNINGSTAD FINNMARK 5A   NORWAY

The Finnmark 5A amphibian flying boat designed by Birger Hönningstad, and built by the Norsk Flyindustri A.S., of Fornebu, near Oslo, was produced to suit the special climatic conditions prevailing in Northern and Arctic regions. Powered by two 600 h.p. Pratt & Whitney Wasp R-1340-S1H1 radial engines, the Finnmark 5A can carry twelve passengers, and has a special wheel and ski undercarriage which retracts into the sponsons. It was originally proposed to produce an improved version designated Finnmark 5A-II, but only one prototype was eventually completed.

Max. speed, 190 m.p.h.; cruising, 156 m.p.h.; initial climb rate, 1,100 ft./min.; empty weight, 9,966 lb.; loaded, 13,100 lb.; span, 62 ft. 6 in.; length, 46 ft. 4 in.; wing area, 522 sq. ft.

HOWARD DGA-15P   U.S.A.

The DGA-15 five-seat cabin monoplane introduced by the Howard Aircraft Corp. in 1939 stemmed from the Bendix Trophy winner, the "Mr. Mulligan" of 1934. It was a progressive development of the externally similar DGA-8 (320 h.p. Whirlwind R-760-E2) and DGA-9 (285 h.p. Jacobs L-5) four-seaters of 1936, and the five-seat DGA-11 (450 h.p. Wasp Junior) and DGA-12 (330 h.p. Jacobs L-6). The DGA-15P is powered by a 450 h.p. Pratt & Whitney R-985-AN-12 Wasp Junior, and some 200 are currently flying in the U.S.A., together with a few DGA-8s, -11s, and -12s. U.S. Navy versions (DGA-16) included the GH-1 (transport), GH-2 (ambulance), and NH-1 (instrument trainer) Nightingale. Production terminated in mid-1944.

Max. speed, 175 m.p.h.; cruising, 154 m.p.h.; range, 984 miles; empty weight, 2,650 lb.; loaded, 4,350 lb.; span, 38 ft.; length, 25 ft. 8 in.

HOWARD DGA-18   U.S.A.

The DGA-18 two-seat primary trainer was produced in some numbers during 1940–42 by the Howard Aircraft Corporation for the Government-sponsored Civilian Pilot Training Programme. Two versions were produced: the DGA-18 powered by the 125 h.p. Warner Scarab 50, and the DGA-18K powered by the 160 h.p. Kinner R-5. A very few examples of both the DGA-18 and DGA-18K are flying in the U.S.A. The DGA-18 is of mixed construction, the wing of wood with plywood covering and the fuselage of welded steel-tube with metal and fabric covering. Figures in parentheses refer to the DGA-18K and the photograph depicts the DGA-18.

Max. speed, 115 (120) m.p.h.; cruising, 108 (109) m.p.h.; initial climb, 800 (900) ft./min.; range, 365 (300) miles; empty weight, 1,350 (1,525) lb.; loaded, 2,000 (2,200) lb.; span, 34 ft.; length, 26 ft. 6⅝ in.

HUREL-DUBOIS H.D.10   FRANCE

Designed by Maurice Hurel, the H.D.10 was produced to investigate the potentialities of the ultra high aspect ratio wing. Built by the Pierre Levasseur concern and initially powered by a 40 h.p. Mathis, the H.D.10 was first flown in 1948. The Mathis engine was later replaced by a 75 h.p. Praga D for further tests. The aspect ratio of the H.D.10's wing is only 32.5—probably the highest aspect ratio of any wing ever flown— and the wing area is only 48.3 sq. ft. Special aerofoil section struts contribute to the total lift.

Max. speed, 158 m.p.h.; economical cruising, 99 m.p.h.; service ceiling, 16,400 ft.; empty weight, 838 lb.; loaded, 1,151 lb.; span, 39 ft. 4½ in.; length, 18 ft. 0½ in.; wing area, 48.3 sq. ft.

HUREL-DUBOIS H.D.32   FRANCE

Derived from the H.D.31 which first flew on January 27, 1953, the H.D.32 employs an unusually high aspect ratio wing with high-lift bracing struts. Twenty-four H.D.32 transports have been ordered by Air France, and a further forty are likely to be delivered to the French Navy. The H.D.321 differs only in having 1,525 h.p. Wright Cyclone 9HE engines, and the projected H.D.33 and H.D.34 are respectively a freighter with rear loading doors and a photo survey aircraft for the French National Geographic Institute. The H.D.35 is an anti-submarine aircraft with similar power plants to the H.D.321, a MAD "stinger" tail, and ventral and wing radomes.

Specification: Forty-four seat transport or freighter. Engines: Two 1,200 h.p. Pratt and Whitney R-1830-92. Weights: Empty, 23,768 lb.; loaded, 39,960 lb. Performance: Max. speed, 210 m.p.h. at 10,000 ft.; cruising, 168 m.p.h.; range, 1,660 miles; initial climb rate, 710 ft./min. Dimensions: Span, 148 ft. 7½ in.; length, 76 ft. 4⅜ in.

HUNTING PERCIVAL SEA PRINCE T.1   G.B.

The Sea Prince is a naval crew trainer and staff transport variant of the commercial Prince Series III. The initial version of the Sea Prince, the C.1 (*photo*), was produced in small numbers as a naval staff transport, and is similar in most respects to the Prince Series II. The Sea Prince C.2 is an improved version with an increased disposable load, and the Sea Prince T.1 (*silhouette*) is employed for navigational and anti-submarine warfare instruction. The Prince Series III has 550 h.p. Leonides 502/4 engines replacing the 520 h.p. Leonides 501/4s of the Series I, and increased all-up weight.

Specification: Naval crew trainer. Engines: Two 550 h.p. Alvis Leonides 25. Weights: Empty, 8,850 lb.; loaded, 11,850 lb. Performance: Max. speed, 223 m.p.h. at 2,000 ft.; cruising, 183 m.p.h. at 11,000 ft.; initial climb rate, 1,400 ft./min.; service ceiling, 20,000 ft.; range, 400 miles at 160 m.p.h. at 10,000 ft. Dimensions: Span, 56 ft.; length, 46 ft. 4 in.; height, 16 ft. 1 in.; wing area, 365 sq. ft.

HUNTING PERCIVAL PROVOST T.1   G.B.

The P.56 Provost T.1 was selected as the standard R.A.F. basic trainer in 1951, having been designed to fulfil the requirements of specification T.16/48. Three prototypes were built, the first of these being fitted with an A.S. Cheetah 18 engine and flying on February 23, 1950. The Provost has also been selected for use by the Southern Rhodesian Air Force, the Eire Air Corps, and the Burmese Air Force. The latter air force's Provosts are designated T.53, and are armament training versions carrying two .303-in. guns and various underwing ordnance loads.
Specification: Two-seat basic trainer. Engine: One 550 h.p. Alvis Leonides 25. Weights: Empty, 3,321 lb.; loaded, 4,250 lb. Performance: Max. speed, 201 m.p.h. at sea level; max. economical cruising, 177 m.p.h.; initial climb rate, 2,100 ft./min.; service ceiling, 22,500 ft. Dimensions: Span, 35 ft. 2 in.; length, 28 ft. 8 in.; height, 12 ft. 2½ in.; wing area, 214 sq. ft.

HUNTING PERCIVAL JET PROVOST T.1   G.B.

The P.84 Jet Provost is virtually an adaptation of the P.56 Provost for the Viper 101 turbojet, the basic Provost fuselage being extended three feet and the cockpit moved forward to counteract the weight of the engine amidships. The basic Provost wing and tail assemblies are employed, although these have been suitably strengthened. Development of the Jet Provost was initiated as a private venture, but a production order was placed in March 1953, and the first prototype flew on June 26, 1954.
Specification: Two-seat basic trainer. Engine: One 1,640 lb.s.t. Armstrong Siddeley Viper 101 (ASV.5). Weights: Normal loaded, 5,950 lb.; max. loaded, 6,750 lb. Performance: Max. speed, 303 m.p.h. at sea level, 323 m.p.h. at 20,000 ft.; initial climb rate, 2,520 ft./min.; range, 268 miles at 186 m.p.h. at 10,000 ft., 397 miles with two 50 imp. gall. wing-tip tanks. Dimensions: Span, 35 ft. 5 in.; length, 31 ft. 11 in.; height, 12 ft. 8 in.; wing area, 213.7 sq. ft.

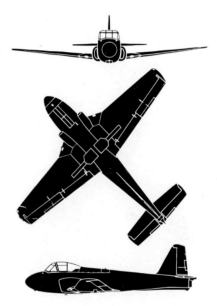

HUNTING PERCIVAL PEMBROKE C.1   G.B.

Developed from the P.50 Prince III, the P.66 Pembroke is a communications and light transport aircraft ordered by the R.A.F., and the air forces of Southern Rhodesia, Sweden and Belgium. Dual controls can be installed for twin-engine pilot conversion, and a flying classroom variant has been designed. The twelve Pembrokes delivered to the Royal Belgian Air Force have a perspex photographic sighting nose compartment and oblique camera apertures in the main fuselage. The twenty Pembrokes ordered by Sweden are designated Tp 83 and are used as radar trainers and light transports. A ten/twelve passenger civil version is known as the Prince V.
Specification: Eight/ten-seat military transport and crew trainer. Engines: Two 550 h.p. Alvis Leonides 127. Weights: Empty, 8,969 lb.; loaded, 13,000 lb. Performance: Max. speed, 220 m.p.h. at 2,000 ft.; cruising, 173 m.p.h. at 8,000 ft.; initial climb rate, 1,500 ft./min.; range, 575 miles. Dimensions: Span, 64 ft. 6 in.; length, 46 ft.; height, 16 ft.

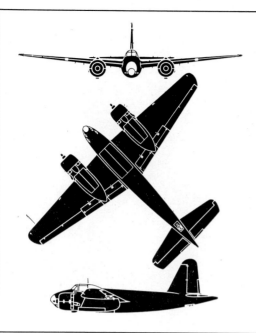

I.AÉ.24 CALQUIN   ARGENTINA

The Calquin (Royal Eagle) attack bomber flew for the first time in June 1946, and one hundred machines of this type were subsequently built for the Argentine Air Force. Similar in many respects to the de Havilland Mosquito, the Calquin was originally designed for Rolls-Royce Merlin engines and with these power plants a maximum speed of 404 m.p.h. would have been attained. Difficulties in obtaining supplies of Merlins led to the installation of lower-powered Pratt & Whitney radials in all production Calquins.

Specification: Two-seat attack bomber. Engines: Two 1,050 h.p. Pratt & Whitney R-1830-SC-G. Weights: Loaded, 15,793 lb. Performance: Max. speed, 273.4 m.p.h.; cruising speed, 236 m.p.h.; initial climb rate, 2,460 ft./min.; endurance, 3 hours. Armament: Four 20-mm. Hispano 804 cannon, plus 1,650-lb. bomb load. Dimensions: Span, 53 ft. 5¾ in.; length, 39 ft. 4½ in.; height, 11 ft. 4¼ in.; wing area, 409 sq. ft.

I.AÉ. D.L.22   ARGENTINA

Flown for the first time in May 1943, the I.Aé.D.L.22 was developed by the Fabrica Militar de Aviones (later renamed Instituto Aerotécnico), and two basic versions of this aircraft have been built: the D.L.22 (450 h.p. El Gaucho) and D.L.22-C (475 h.p. A.S. Cheetah 25). One hundred and twenty machines were delivered to the Argentine Air Force for reconnaissance and light attack duties. These have two fixed forward-firing .30-in. guns in the wings and underwing bomb racks. A further hundred machines were delivered as two-seat advanced trainers.

Specification: Two-seat advanced trainer. Engine: One 450 h.p. I.Aé.16 El Gaucho. Weights: Empty, 3,351 lb.; loaded, 4,994 lb. Performance: Max. speed, 180 m.p.h. at 1,475 ft.; cruising, 162 m.p.h.; ceiling, 17,060 ft.; range, 746 miles. Dimensions: Span, 41 ft. 4¾ in.; length, 30 ft. 2½ in.; height, 9 ft. 3 in.; wing area, 249.5 sq. ft.

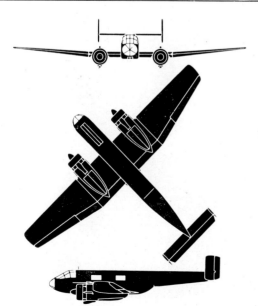

I.A.M.E.35   ARGENTINA

Produced by the Industrias Aeronauticas y Meccanicas del Estado, the I.A.M.E.35 is an all-metal multi-purpose aircraft with the roles of bombardier trainer, twin-engine pilot conversion trainer, radio/navigational trainer light transport, ambulance and photo-reconnaissance aircraft. As a light transport, it will carry a crew of three and eight passengers, and as an ambulance it will accommodate four stretcher cases and two medical attendants. First flown in 1953, the I.A.M.E.35 was to enter production towards the end of 1955 with an initial series of one hundred machines.

Specification: General utility aircraft. Engines: Two I.A.M.E. R-19C El Indio. Weights: Empty, 7,716 lb.; loaded, 12,566 lb. Performance: Max. speed, 225 m.p.h. at 5,000 ft.; max. cruising, 219 m.p.h.; econ. cruising, 215 m.p.h.; range, 930 miles; service ceiling, 21,300 ft. Dimensions: Span, 64 ft. 4 in.; length, 45 ft. 10 in.

I.AE.31 COLIBRI — ARGENTINA

The I.Aé.31 Colibri (Humming Bird) tandem two-seat primary training monoplane developed by the Institute Aérotecnico was first flown on September 15, 1947. The Colibri was designed for use both as a military trainer and for use by Argentine flying clubs in training and touring roles. The prototype was powered by a 155 h.p. Blackburn Cirrus Major III engine, but it was proposed to install the de Havilland Gipsy Major 10 in production machines. Plans to produce the Colibri in quantity for the flying clubs did not materialise.

Max. speed, 146 m.p.h.; cruising speed, 127 m.p.h.; landing speed, 37 m.p.h.; service ceiling, 21,320 ft.; empty weight, 1,397 lb.; loaded, 2,015 lb.; span, 34 ft.; length, 26 ft.; height, 6 ft. 3 in.

I.A.M.E.33 PULQÚI II — ARGENTINA

The I.A.M.E.33 Pulqúi II (Arrow) was first flown on June 27, 1950, and was designed by Prof. Dipl. Ing. Kurt Tank, former technical director of the German Focke-Wulf company. Six prototypes of the Pulqúi II were built, but several of these have been destroyed during the flight test programme. The Pulqúi II is powered by a 4,565 lb.s.t. Rolls-Royce Nene 2 turbojet and carries an armament of four 20-mm. cannon in the nose. No quantity production of this fighter is to be undertaken.

Max. speed, 652 m.p.h. at 16,400 ft.; initial climb rate, 5,850 ft./min.; absolute ceiling, 49,200 ft.; empty weight, 7,920 lb.; loaded, 12,210 lb.; span, 34 ft. 9 in.; length, 38 ft.; height, 10 ft. 10 in.; wing area, 270 sq. ft.

IKARUS TYPE 211 — YUGOSLAVIA

The Type 211 tandem two-seat primary training monoplane was one of Yugoslavia's first post-war aircraft and, designed by Kosta Sivcev, Sveta Popovic and Slobodan Zrnic, the prototype was produced by the Ikarus factory at Zemun, near Belgrade, in 1947. Intended to compete with the Aero 2, the Type 211 is primarily of wooden construction and is powered by a 160 h.p. Walter Minor 6-III engine. Alternatively, the 145 h.p. de Havilland Gipsy Major VII may be installed.

Estimated max. speed, 128 m.p.h.; cruising, 105 m.p.h.; approx. loaded weight, 1,980 lb. Dimensions: No details available for publication.

IRAKUS TYPE 212 — YUGOSLAVIA

The Type 212 tandem two-seat low-wing monoplane was developed in 1948 by Kosta Sivcev and Slobodan Zrnic, and was derived from the earlier Type 211 primary trainer. The decking of the rear fuselage has been raised, and into this is faired a long, glazed canopy which encloses both cockpits. A retractable undercarriage replaces the fixed landing gear employed by the Type 211, and power is provided by a 160 h.p. Walter Minor 6-III. The Type 212 was primarily intended as an advanced trainer but was not adopted by the Yugoslav Air Force.

Estimated max. speed, 140 m.p.h.; cruising speed, 125 m.p.h.; approx. loaded weight, 2,400 lb. Dimensions: No details available for publication.

IKARUS TYPE 214 — YUGOSLAVIA

Produced in 1951 to meet a Yugoslav Air Force specification for a combined crew trainer, light transport and ground support aircraft, the Type 214 was designed by Ing. Prof. Sima Milutinovic. The prototype (*illustrated*) is powered by two 480 h.p. Ranger SGV-770 engines, but the production version for the Yugoslav Air Force is powered by two 600 h.p. Pratt & Whitney R-1340 Wasp radial engines. Of all-wood construction, the Type 214 carries eight passengers as a light transport. As a crew trainer, it can provide simultaneous training for pilots, bombardiers, navigators and radio operators. The Type 214 has been ordered in quantity for the Yugoslav Air Force.
Specification: General-purpose crew trainer and light transport. Engines: Two 600 h.p. Pratt & Whitney R-1340 Wasp. Weights, performance and dimensions: No details available for publication.

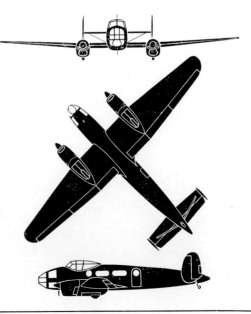

IKARUS TYPE 215   YUGOSLAVIA

The Type 215 advanced twin-engined trainer was designed by Professor Dusan Stankov and built in 1951 by the Ikarus factory. Powered by two 450 h.p. Ranger SVG-770-C-1B engines and employing a wooden structure, the Type 215 was designed for the training of pilots and air gunners, but was unsuccessful in competition with the Type 214 which is now in production for the Yugoslav Air Force. A crew of three is normally carried.

Max. speed, 238.5 m.p.h.; cruising speed, 176 m.p.h.; range, 650 miles; loaded weight, 10,077 lb.; span, 52 ft. 11¼ in.; length, 43 ft. 9½ in.

IKARUS PIONIR   YUGOSLAVIA

Designed by Major Dragoljub Besline and built by the Ikarus factory at Zemun, the Pionir was designed to participate in an extensive programme of prone-pilot research. Powered by two 55 h.p. Walter Mikron III engines, the Pionir weighs only 1,322 lb. loaded. Experience gained with this tiny machine resulted in the design and construction of the larger Type 451 which is of generally similar overall appearance. The Pionir was first flown in 1949 and is of all-wood construction. No details are available concerning the performance and dimensions of this experimental aircraft.

IKARUS TYPE 451   YUGOSLAVIA

The Type 451 is an experimental aircraft powered by two 160 h.p. Walter Minor 6-III engines and designed by Major Dragoljub Beslin of the Yugoslav Air Force. Built in 1951 by the Ikarus factory, the Type 451 is essentially a scaled-up development of the previously-described Pionir, and was designed to continue the research programme into prone-pilot positioning inaugurated with the earlier machine. The fuselage diameter is exceptionally small, allowing just sufficient room for the pilot to lie prone.

Max. speed, 208 m.p.h.; loaded weight, 2,665 lb.; span, 21 ft. 11¾ in.; length, 14 ft. 11 in.

IKARUS TYPE 451M   YUGOSLAVIA

The first jet-propelled aircraft of Yugoslav design, the Type 451M was designed by Major Dragoljub Beslin and can be considered as a development of the Type 451 with an orthodox pilot's cockpit and two 330 lb. thrust Turboméca Palas turbojets mounted under the wing. First flown late in 1952, the Type 451M was intended primarily to provide data for a lightweight ground attack aircraft, and a 12.7-mm. machine gun was mounted in a long fairing under the forward fuselage. A second prototype with a prone position for the pilot is reputedly under development.

Approx. max. speed, 360 m.p.h.; approx. loaded weight, 2,500 lb.; span, 22 ft.; length, 18 ft.

IKARUS TYPE 452M   YUGOSLAVIA

The Type 452M experimental single-seat jet-propelled aircraft is of extremely unorthodox conception. Of all-metal construction, the Type 452M is powered by two 330 lb. thrust Turboméca Palas turbojets superimposed one above the other in the rear of the fuselage nacelle. Each turbojet is fed by an individual pair of air intakes, those for the lower unit being disposed in the wing roots, and those for the upper unit being positioned above the rear fuselage. The wing surfaces are swept, and a swept tailplane is supported by a central fin and attached to vertical surfaces at the end of short tail booms. The first of two prototypes flew on July 24, 1953.

Max. speed, 484.6 m.p.h.; loaded weight, 2,337 lb.; span, 17 ft. 2½ in.; length, 19 ft. 7 in.

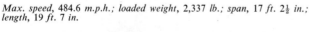

IKARUS S-49C   YUGOSLAVIA

Derived from the earlier S-49A, the S-49C is powered by a 1,500 h.p. Hispano-Suiza 12Z-17 engine, eighty of which were obtained from France with off-shore procurement funds. Differing from the S-49A primarily in being of all-metal construction, the S-49C carries an armament of one 20-mm. cannon and two 12.7-mm. machine guns, and was designed by Sivcev, Zrnic and Petkovie. The S-49C is a single-seat reconnaissance fighter, and has been built by the former Ikarus factory at Zemun.

Max. speed, 390 m.p.h. at 5,000 ft.; cruising speed, 240 m.p.h.; range, 480 miles; loaded weight, 7,646 lb.; span, 33 ft. 9½ in.; length, 29 ft. 8¾ in.

IKARUS TYPE 522   YUGOSLAVIA

The Type 522 has been adopted as the standard advanced trainer of the Yugoslav Air Force. Flown for the first time in February 1955, the Type 522 is basically an all-metal, re-engined version of the Type 213 Vihor (*photograph*) which, designed by Sostaric and Dabinovic, was built in prototype form in 1949 by the Ikarus factory. Two prototypes of the Vihor were built, the first having a rearward-retracting undercarriage and the second having an inward-retracting undercarriage. Both were powered by the 450 h.p. Ranger SGV-770-CB1 engine.

Specification: Tandem two-seat advanced trainer. Engine: One 600 h.p. Pratt & Whitney Wasp R-1340. Weights: Empty, 4,027 lb.; loaded, 5,384 lb. Performance: Max. speed, 227 m.p.h.; cruising, 171.5 m.p.h. Dimensions: Span, 36 ft. 1 in.; length, 27 ft. 3½ in.

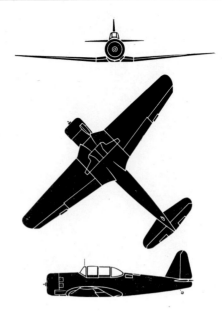

ILYUSHIN IL-10   U.S.S.R.

Designed by Sergei Ilyushin, the IL-10 (code-named *Beast* by N.A.T.O.) entered production towards the end of World War 2. Developed from the IL-2, the IL-10 is now considered to be obsolete by the Soviet Air Force but still serves in substantial numbers with the Sino-Communist, North Korean, Polish and Balkan Communist Air Forces. Some are still employed by the Yugoslav Air Force as trainers, the machines having been converted for dual-control by the Ikarus factory. Considerable use is made of 6-mm. and 13-mm. armour plate around engine and cockpit.
Specification: Two-seat close-support aircraft. Engine: One 2,000 h.p. AM-42. Weights: Not available. Performance: Max. speed, 335 m.p.h. at 7,000 ft.; cruising, 230 m.p.h.; approx. range, 400 miles. Armament: Two 7.62-mm. Sh-KAS, or two 23-mm. NS, or two 37-mm. N guns in wings, and one 12.7-mm. Beresin, plus four 500-lb. bombs. Dimensions: Span, 45 ft. 6 in.; length, 40 ft.; height, 11 ft. 6 in.

ILYUSHIN IL-12/IL-14   U.S.S.R.

Designed to replace the LI-2 (licence-built DC-3), the IL-12 (code-named *Coach*) is in service as a 27–32 passenger airliner with *Aeroflot*, and the Czech CSA and Polish LOT airlines. It also forms the backbone of the transport elements of the Soviet Air Force, and at least 3,000 machines of this type have been built. The IL-14 *Crate* (*silhouette*) is a progressive development of the IL-12 (*photo*) which appeared in 1953. It differs from its predecessor primarily in having more angular wingtips and vertical tail surfaces, and 2,600 h.p. ASh-82J engines with exhaust thrust augmentation.
Specification IL-12: Twenty-seven/thirty-two seat commercial transport. Engines: Two 1,850 h.p. ASh-82 FNV. Weights: Empty, 19,850 lb.; loaded, 38,000 lb. Performance: Max. speed, 226 m.p.h. at sea level, 252 m.p.h. at 8,220 ft.; cruising speed, 217 m.p.h.; range (32 passengers), 777 miles; (27 passengers), 1,240 miles. Dimensions: Span, 104 ft.; length, 69 ft. 11 in.; height, 26 ft. 6 in.

ILYUSHIN IL-28   U.S.S.R.

Russia's first service jet bomber, the Ilyushin IL-28 (code-named *Beagle* by N.A.T.O. forces) is in service with the air arms of Russia, China, Poland, and Czechoslovakia. The type is also built under licence in Poland and Czechoslovakia (*photo*). The production predecessor of the IL-28, the IL-26 (code-named *Butcher*) differs primarily in having axial-flow engines, and a freighter conversion, the IL-20, has been used experimentally by *Aeroflot*. The U-IL-28 (code-named *Mascot*) is a conversion trainer variant with a second cockpit ahead of the normal cockpit, and has the under-fuselage radome deleted.

Specification: Three-seat light bomber. Engines: Two 5,000 lb.s.t. RD-45FVK-1. Weights: No details available. Approx. performance: Max. speed, 570–600 m.p.h.; cruising, 460–490 m.p.h.; service ceiling, 45,000 ft.; range, 2,000 miles. Armament: Two forward-firing 23-mm. NS cannon and one 20-mm. cannon or two 12.7-mm. machine-guns in tail position. Approx. dimensions: Span, 68 ft.; length, 62 ft.; height, 22 ft.

ILYUSHIN (TYPE 39 BADGER)   U.S.S.R.

Designed by a team headed by Sergei Ilyushin, the Type 39 *Badger* medium bomber is in service with the Soviet Air Force in some numbers. Generally comparable to the Vickers Valiant, the *Badger* is powered by two large turbojets and its wing has a mean sweep angle of approximately 37°, the inboard sections being swept at some 42° at the leading edge. The main undercarriage members retract into fairings extending aft of the wing trailing edge, and defensive armament includes dorsal, ventral and tail gun positions.

Specification: Long-range medium bomber. Engines: Two turbojets (possibly of the 12,000–14,000 lb.s.t. Mikulin 209 type). Weights: Approx. loaded, 125,000–150,000 lb. Performance: Cruising speed, Mach 0.9–0.95 at 50,000 ft. (587–623 m.p.h.); range, 2,500–3,000 miles. Approx. dimensions: Span, 100 ft.; length, 105 ft.

ILYUSHIN (TYPE 37 BISON)   U.S.S.R.

The Type 37 *Bison* was first revealed publicly on May 1, 1954, when it participated in Russia's annual May Day celebrations. Like the Type 39 *Badger*, the *Bison* is the work of Sergei Ilyushin, and may be the bomber referred to as the IL-38. Comparable in size with the B-52B Stratofortress, the *Bison* has tandem main undercarriage members and outrigger-type stabilising wheels retracting into wingtip housings. It is believed that the *Bison* will form part of the operational strength of the Soviet Air Force's strategic bombing groups by the end of 1956.

Specification: Long-range heavy bomber. Engines: Four turbojets (possibly of the 12,000–14,000 lb.s.t. Mikulin 209 type). Weights: Approx. loaded, 250,000 lb. Performance: Approx. max. speed, 610 m.p.h.; range, 5,000–6,000 miles, (with max. bomb load) 3,000 miles. Approx. dimensions: Span, 170 ft.; length, 140 ft.; wing area, 3,000 sq. ft.

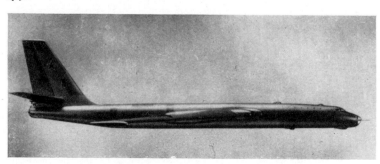

INLAND R-400 SPORTSTER   U.S.A.

The R-400 Sportster was one of three models introduced in 1930 by the Inland Aviation Corporation, the others being the S-300 Sport and the W-500 Super-Sport. The S-300 Sport and R-400 Sportster tandem two-seat parasol-wing monoplanes were identical apart from the engine installed, the former having a 65 h.p. Le Blond and the latter having a 90 h.p. Warner Scarab. Examples of both types are flying in the U.S.A.

Max. speed, 120 m.p.h.; cruising, 103 m.p.h.; loaded weight, 1,465 lb.; span, 30 ft.; length, 19 ft.; height, 7 ft. 10 in.; wing area, 144 sq. ft.

INLAND W-500 SUPER-SPORT   U.S.A.

The W-500 Super-Sport is a more powerful version of the R-400 Sportster tandem two-seat parasol-wing monoplane, featuring redesigned vertical tail surfaces and a 110 h.p. Warner Scarab radial engine. A small number of W-500 Super-Sport monoplanes were produced during 1930-31, and examples of these remain active in the U.S.A.

Max. speed, 136 m.p.h.; cruising, 122 m.p.h.; loaded weight, 1,495 lb.; span, 30 ft.; length, 19 ft.; height, 7 ft. 10 in.; wing area, 144 sq. ft.

INTERSTATE S-1B-1 CADET   U.S.A.

The Interstate Aircraft and Engineering Corporation first produced the Model S-1 Cadet in 1940, and during 1941-42 the Cadet was produced as the Model S-1A with the 65 h.p. Continental A65. Versions were also built with the 65 h.p. Franklin (S-1A-65F), 85 h.p. Franklin (S-1A-85F), 90 h.p. Continental (S-1A-90F), and 90 h.p. Franklin. The S-1B is a modified version with a 102 h.p. Franklin 0-200-5 and lengthened glazed canopy, and 250 aircraft of this type were supplied to the U.S. Army as the L-6. More than one hundred S-1A and S-1B Cadets are active in the U.S.A.

Max. speed, 114 m.p.h.; cruising speed, 105 m.p.h.; initial climb rate, 900 ft./min.; service ceiling, 16,500 ft.; range, 540 miles; empty weight, 1,103 lb.; loaded, 1,650 lb.; span, 35 ft. 6 in.; length, 23 ft. 5 in.; height, 7 ft.; wing area, 173.8 sq. ft.

JODEL D.112   FRANCE

Virtually a side-by-side two-seat development of the D.9 Bébé, the D.112 is one of several variants of the D.11 prototype which first flew on May 5, 1950, powered by a 45 h.p. Salmson 9 ADb engine. The D.111 (*illustrated*) has a 75 h.p. Minié 4 DC-32A, and the D.112 (*specification*) has a 65 h.p. Continental A65. Powered by a 60 h.p. Walter Mikron II, it is built under licence in Italy as the Pasotti J.P.1 Aviojeep, and the D.120 is a refined version with a 90 h.p. Continental C90-12F engine produced by the Wassmer company.

Max. speed, 112 m.p.h.; cruising speed, 94 m.p.h.; initial climb rate, 585 ft./min.; range, 290 miles; empty weight, 594 lb.; loaded, 1,100 lb.; span, 26 ft. 10 in.; length, 20 ft. 7 in.; wing area, 136.6 sq. ft.

JODEL D.92 BÉBÉ   FRANCE

The most popular of ultra-light single-seat aircraft in France is the Bébé-Jodel, designed by MM. Joly and Delemontez of Avions Jodel. The prototype, the D.9 Bébé, powered by a 25 h.p. Poinsard, flew on January 21, 1948, and as the D.92 with a 26 h.p. Volkswagen H12 engine, the Bébé-Jodel has since been built by amateur constructors in substantial numbers from kits supplied by the parent company. Variants include the D.93 (Poinsard), the D.94 (A.B.C. Scorpion), the D.95 (Echard-Lutetia 4-C.02) depicted by the photo, the D.97 (Sarolea Vautour), and the D.98 (AVA 4 A-00). The Bébé-Jodel is of all-wood construction with fabric covering.

Specification: Single-seat ultra-light monoplane. Engines: One 26 h.p. Volkswagen H12. Weights: Empty, 356 lb.; loaded, 598 lb. Performance: Max. speed, 93 m.p.h.; cruising speed, 81 m.p.h.; initial climb rate, 413 ft./min.; max. range, 276 miles. Dimensions: Span, 22 ft. 11½ in.; length, 17 ft. 10½ in.; wing area, 96.84 sq. ft.

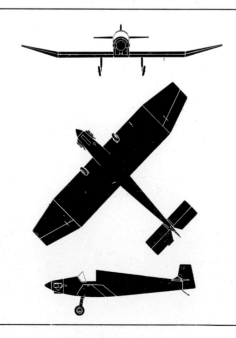

JOHNSON ROCKET 185   U.S.A.

Produced shortly after the war by the Johnson Aircraft Inc., the Rocket 185 is a high performance three-seat cabin monoplane powered by a 185 h.p. Lycoming engine. Designed by R. S. Johnson, the Rocket 185 possesses exceptionally clean lines which result in an unusually high performance for power. The Rocket was built under licence by the Aircraft Manufacturing Company which subsequently acquired design rights and produced a modified version known as the Texas Bullet 185.

Max. speed, 207 m.p.h.; cruising speed, 185 m.p.h.; initial climb rate, 2,000 ft./min.; service ceiling, 24,500 ft.; empty weight, 1,550 lb.; loaded, 2,450 lb.; span, 31 ft.; length, 21 ft. 7 in.; height, 7 ft.; wing area, 142 sq. ft.

JUNKERS W-33/W-34   GERMANY

In 1926 the Junkers concern produced a new single-engined transport derived from the original F-13 of 1919. The transport was produced in two versions: the W-33 with the 310 h.p. liquid-cooled inline Junkers L-5, and the W-34 with the 425 h.p. Gnôme-Rhône Jupiter radial or the Pratt & Whitney Hornet S4D-2 of 650 h.p. The jigs and tools used for the original F-13 were largely used for the W-33 and W-34 which were almost identical apart from the engine. Two W-33s are airworthy in Canada, and several W-34s are flying in North and South America and Finland. One W-34H with a Bristol Mercury 6 engine is flying in Sweden. Figures in parentheses refer to the W-34.

Max. speed, 121 (165) m.p.h.; cruising, 104 (135) m.p.h.; empty weight, 2,684 (3,670) lb.; loaded, 5,500 (7,050) lb.; span, 58 ft. 3 in.; length, 34 ft. 6 in. (34 ft.); height, 11 ft. 7 in.; wing area, 463 sq. ft.

JUNKERS A-50 JUNIOR   GERMANY

The A-50 Junior tandem two-seat light monoplane was introduced in 1929, and was one of the earliest all-metal light planes. Two examples are still flying: one registered in Finland and the other in Australia, both powered by the 80 h.p. Armstrong Siddeley Genet engine. The A-50 Junior achieved considerable popularity during the early 'thirties, and a number of aircraft of this type were exported abroad.

Max. speed, 109 m.p.h.; cruising, 87 m.p.h.; climb to 3,280 ft., 5.5 minutes; service ceiling, 12,500 ft.; range, 370 miles; empty weight, 770 lb.; loaded, 1,330 lb.; span, 32 ft. 10 in.; length, 23 ft. 6 in.; height, 7 ft. 11 in.; wing area, 148 sq. ft.

JUNKERS JU 86K-13 (B 3C-2)   SWEDEN

Introduced in 1935 in both commercial transport and bomber versions by the Junkers Flugzeug und Motorenwerke, A.-G., the Ju 86K-13 export model, powered by two 980 h.p. Bristol Mercury 24 radials, was built under licence in Sweden during 1938–41. The Swedish-built version was designated B 3D and was standard Swedish bomber equipment until 1943. Some of these have been converted as twelve-passenger transports under the designation B 3C-2, and one German-built commercial Ju 86Z-7 is also used by the Swedish Air Force as the Tp 3.

Max. speed, 232 m.p.h.; cruising speed, 178 m.p.h.; cruising range, 930 miles; empty weight, 12,980 lb.; loaded, 18,000 lb.; span, 73 ft. 9 in.; length, 58 ft. 8 in.; height, 15 ft. 8 in.; wing area, 882.3 sq. ft.

JUNKERS JU 52/3M   GERMANY

The Ju 52/3M first appeared in 1932, and 2,804 transports of this type were produced during the war for the *Luftwaffe*. During the occupation of France, production of the Ju 52/3M g7e was transferred to the Junkers-controlled Société Amiot, and production continued in France after the war, the type being designated A.A.C.1. The Ju 52/3M g7e has also been built under licence in Spain by Construcciones Aeronauticas S.A., and, powered by the 750 h.p. Elizalde-built BMW 132 engine, one hundred machines have been delivered to the *Ejercito del Aire* as the CASA-352-L.

Specification: Commercial and military transport. Engines: Three 830 h.p. BMW 132A or T. Weights: Empty, 14,325 lb.; loaded, 24,200 lb. Performance: Max. speed, 165 m.p.h.; cruising, 132 m.p.h.; service ceiling, 18,000 ft.; range, 800 miles. Dimensions: Span, 95 ft. 10 in.; length, 62 ft.; height, 14 ft. 10 in.; wing area, 1,190 sq. ft.

JUNKERS JU 88A-4/R GERMANY

The Ju 88A-4 was produced in larger numbers than any other sub-variant of this light bomber, the first prototype of which, the Ju 88V-1, flew on December 21, 1936. Introduced in 1940, the Ju 88A-4 differed from the initial production Ju 88A-1 in having increased wing span and 1,300 h.p. Junkers Jumo 211J engines. A small number of Ju 88A-4 bombers were supplied to the Spanish Air Force during 1941–42, and several of these remain in service under the designation B.6. The Ju 88A-4 carries a crew of four and a bomb load of 5,500 lb.

Max. speed, 274 m.p.h. at 18,040 ft.; range, 1,242 miles; service ceiling, 27,890 ft.; economical cruising speed, 249 m.p.h. at 15,900 ft.; loaded weight, 24,251 lb.; span, 65 ft. 10 in.; length, 47 ft.; height, 16 ft. 9 in.; wing area, 590 sq. ft.

JUNKERS JU 188F-1 GERMANY

Derived from the basic Ju 88, the Ju 188 was intended to replace the earlier aircraft in some of its numerous applications. As compared with the Ju 88, the Ju 188 had a redesigned nose and a wing of increased span. Limited production of the Ju 188F-1 (a photo-reconnaissance version of the Ju 188E bomber) was undertaken by the S.N.C.A. du Sud-Ouest in France and, powered by two 1,700 h.p. BMW 801G-2 radials, several machines of this type are still flying in France, being employed to test ramjet units and missiles.

Max. speed, 342 m.p.h. at 19,685 ft.; range with max. fuel, 1,553 miles; service ceiling, 23,620 ft.; loaded weight, 31,967 lb.; span, 72 ft. 2 in.; length, 49 ft.

JUNKERS JU 290A-6 GERMANY

Designed by Dipl. Ing. Zindel, the Ju 290 was a development of the Ju 90 of 1938, the first prototype actually commencing life as the Ju 90V-7. The pre-production Ju 290A-0 was originally built as a commercial airliner for *Lufthansa*, but these were taken over by the *Luftwaffe*, and subsequently both reconnaissance-bomber and transport variants were built. The sole remaining example of the type is a Ju 290A-6, a transport variant of the Ju 290A-5 maritime reconnaissance bomber, which is employed by the Spanish Air Force.

Max. speed, 280 m.p.h. at 18,000 ft.; range at max. economical cruising speed, 3,785 miles; loaded weight, 88,000 lb.; span, 138 ft.; length, 92 ft. 6 in.; wing area, 3,210 sq. ft.

KARHU 48B FINLAND

The Karhu 48B four-seat cabin monoplane was built by the Veljekset Karhumäki O/Y, and is generally similar to the earlier Karhu 48, one prototype of each model being built. Both the Karhu 48 and 48B are currently owned by the Karhumäki concern and are powered by 190 h.p. Lycoming O-435-A engines. Both provide accommodation for four persons with dual controls, and the interchangeable wheel or ski landing gear may be replaced by twin floats. The wing is a two spar wooden structure and the fuselage of welded steel-tube, the whole covered by fabric.

Max. speed, 142 m.p.h.; cruising, 109 m.p.h.; service ceiling, 13,780 ft.; cruising range, 404 miles; empty weight, 1,789 lb.; loaded, 2,882 lb.; span, 37 ft. 10 in.; length, 25 ft. 9 in.; wing area, 186.25 sq. ft.

KAWASAKI KAL-1 JAPAN

The Kawasaki KAL-1 was the first Japanese aircraft of post-war design to be built. Flown for the first time on July 21, 1953, the KAL-1 was built by the Kawasaki Gifu works and is powered by a 260 h.p. Lycoming GO-435-C-2 engine. Two prototypes have been completed. The KAL-1 was designed primarily as a four-seat liaison aircraft for the Japanese Air Self-Defence Force, but no production orders for the type have been placed to date. The KAT-1 tandem two-seat basic trainer employs a similar wing and tail assembly to that of the KAL-1.

Max. speed, 174 m.p.h.; cruising speed, 167.5 m.p.h.; service ceiling, 19,700 ft.; max. range, 1,000 miles; empty weight, 2,022 lb.; loaded, 3,230 lb.; span, 34 ft. 1½ in.; length, 29 ft. 6 in.; height, 8 ft. 2½ in.; wing area, 196 sq. ft.

KAWASAKI KAT-1 JAPAN

The first Japanese post-war military training monoplane of national design, the KAT-1 was designed as a competitor for the Fuji-built Beech Mentor trainer but no quantity production orders have yet been announced. The KAT-1 is a development of the KAL-1 liaison monoplane, from which it differs in having a new fuselage with tandem seating for the two crew members, and a tricycle undercarriage. The KAT-1 is powered by a 240 h.p. Lycoming GO-435-C-2 engine and is of all-metal construction.

Max. speed, 185 m.p.h.; cruising speed, 168 m.p.h.; initial climb rate, 1,122 ft./min.; service ceiling, 19,700 ft.; range, 765 miles; empty weight, 2,265 lb.; loaded, 2,977 lb.; span, 37 ft. 9 in.; length, 27 ft. 11 in.; height, 9 ft. 2¼ in.

KAWASAKI KAL-2   JAPAN

The KAL-2, designed and built by the Kawasaki-Gifu division of the Kawasaki Aircraft Company, was produced in 1955 as a development of the company's earlier KAL-1 four-seat cabin monoplane and KAT-1 tandem two-seat primary trainer. Of all-metal construction, the KAL-2 provides accommodation for four persons and is intended for the alternative roles of military liaison aircraft and cabin tourer. An initial order for two machines of this type has been placed by the Japanese Air Self-Defence Force.

Specification: Four-seat cabin monoplane. Engine: One 260 h.p. Lycoming GO-435-C2B. Weights: Empty, 2,315 lb.; loaded, 3,527 lb. Performance: Max. speed, 183 m.p.h., at 7,742 ft.; cruising speed, 112 m.p.h.; range, 994 miles. Dimensions: Span, 39 ft. 0½ in.; length, 28 ft. 8½ in.; height, 9 ft. 6 in.; wing area, 206.66 sq. ft.

KB-6 MATAJUR   YUGOSLAVIA

Designed by an amateur design group, the *Konstrukcijski Letalske Zveze Slovenije*, comprising students of the Ljubljana Technical High School, the KB-6 Matajur flew for the first time on June 4, 1952, and has since been produced in quantity by the Letov factory at Ljubljana. The first prototype Matajur was powered by a 136 h.p. Régnier 4 L00 engine, but the second prototype and production aircraft have been powered by the 160 h.p. Walter Minor engine.

Specification: Two-seat primary training monoplane. Engine: One 160 h.p. Walter Minor 6-III. Weights: Empty, 1,453 lb.; loaded, 2,185 lb. Performance: Max. speed, 138 m.p.h. at sea level; cruising speed, 114 m.p.h.; initial climb rate, 699 ft./min.; range, 441 miles. Dimensions: Span, 34 ft. 9 in.; length, 27 ft. 5 in.; height, 7 ft. 1 in., wing area, 150.7 sq. ft.

KINNER SPORTSTER   U.S.A.

The Sportster was introduced in 1932 by the Kinner Airplane and Motor Corporation as one of a range of four low-wing monoplanes employing Kinner radial engines. The Sportster is powered by a 100 h.p. Kinner K-5 radial engine, and accommodates two persons side-by-side in an open cockpit. The Sportwing was similar but employed a 125 h.p. radial and undercarriage spats, and the Playboy and Envoy were respectively two- and four-seat cabin versions with 160 h.p. and 300 h.p. engines. One or two examples of the Sportster remain airworthy in the U.S.A.

Max. speed, 104 m.p.h.; cruising speed, 90 m.p.h.; initial climb rate, 800 ft./min.; cruising range, 340 miles; empty weight, 1,218 lb.; loaded, 1,875 lb.; span, 39 ft.; length, 23 ft. 8 in.; height, 7 ft.; wing area, 202 sq. ft.

KLEMM KL 25D-7R   GERMANY

Produced during 1936-37, the Kl 25 tandem two-seat light monoplane achieved considerable international success and was produced under licence in several countries, including Sweden. A number of examples are flying with several different engines. The most widely used version is the Kl 25D-7R with the 70-80 h.p. Hirth HM 60R engine, two examples of which are flying in Sweden, a further two in Finland, and three in Switzerland. A Poinsard-powered version is also flying in Finland, and a Kl 25D-11 registered in Australia has a Siemens Sh 13B.

Max. speed, 99 m.p.h.; cruising speed, 87 m.p.h.; climb to 3,280 ft., 7.1 minutes; range, 404 miles; empty weight, 1,056 lb.; loaded, 1,544 lb.; span, 42 ft. 7½ in.; length, 24 ft. 7 in.; height, 6 ft. 8 in.; wing area, 215 sq. ft.

KLEMM KL 32B-VI   GERMANY

The Klemm Kl 32 three-seat cabin monoplane was introduced in 1935 and subsequently built in small numbers with the 150 h.p. Siemens Sh 14A radial engine. Providing two seats side-by-side in the front of the cabin and one seat to the rear, the Kl 32 is of mixed construction, and the sole remaining example of this type is currently registered in France.

Max. speed, 127 m.p.h.; cruising speed, 112 m.p.h.; climb to 3,280 ft., 6 minutes; service ceiling, 15,744 ft.; range, 466 miles; endurance, 4 hours; empty weight, 1,298 lb.; loaded, 2,090 lb.; span, 39 ft. 4 in.; length, 23 ft. 7 in.; height, 6 ft. 9 in.; wing area, 183 sq. ft.

KLEMM KL 35D   GERMANY

The Kl 35 was produced in considerable numbers prior to World War II by the Leichtflugzeugbau Klemm G.m.b.H., and was also built under licence in Sweden for the Swedish Air Force. Three Kl 35Bs powered by 100 h.p. Hirth HM 504A-2 engines, and thirty-three Kl 35Ds with 80 h.p. Hirth HM 60R engines are currently registered in Sweden, and three of the latter version are also flying in Switzerland. The Kl 35 is basically a tandem two-seat light touring, training and aerobatic monoplane. The following specification relates to the Kl 35D version.

Max. speed, 124 m.p.h.; cruising, 112 m.p.h.; range, 500 miles; climb to 3,280 ft., 5.6 minutes; absolute ceiling, 15,740 ft.; empty weight, 880 lb.; loaded, 1,551 lb.; span, 34 ft. 1 in.; length, 24 ft. 7 in.; height, 6 ft. 8 in.; wing area, 163.5 sq. ft.

KOOLHOVEN F.K.50 MK.II   HOLLAND

The Koolhoven F.K.50 was initially produced with a single fin and rudder tail assembly, but the sole remaining example of this type, serving with Alpar Air Service Ltd., of Berne, is of the later production model with twin fins and rudders. The F.K.50 Mk.II is powered by two 400 h.p. Pratt & Whitney Wasp Junior T1B radial engines, and provides accommodation for eight passengers and a crew of two. Construction is of welded steel-tube and wood, and the covering is primarily of fabric.

Max. speed, 183 m.p.h.; cruising, 158 m.p.h. at 8,200 ft.; initial climb rate, 1,280 ft./min.; service ceiling, 18,860 ft.; normal range, 682 miles; empty weight, 6,006 lb.; loaded, 9,350 lb.; span, 59 ft.; length, 45 ft. 11 in.; height, 12 ft. 1½ in.; wing area, 481 sq. ft.

LANGLEY 29-90   U.S.A.

The Langley monoplane was one of the first aircraft to employ plastic-bonded plywood mouldings for its construction. Basically a four-seat cabin monoplane, it was introduced in 1941 by the Langley Aircraft Corporation, and two prototypes were built, the Langley 29-65 with two 65 h.p. Franklin AC engines, and the Langley 29-90 (*photograph*) with two 90 h.p. Franklin 4AC-199-E3 engines, and the latter is still flying in the U.S.A. A manufacturing licence was sold to the Andover Kent Aviation Corp., in 1941, but owing to the war, production was abandoned.

Max. speed, 138 m.p.h.; cruising, 117 m.p.h.; range, 350 miles at 100 m.p.h.; initial climb rate, 695 ft./min.; empty weight, 1,738 lb.; loaded, 2,850 lb.; span, 35 ft.; length, 20 ft. 10 in.

LARSON DUSTER D-I   U.S.A.

The Duster D-1 has been developed and built by the Larson Aero Development concern and is intended as a replacement for the present modified types of ordinary aircraft currently used for agricultural purposes. The prototype (*illustrated*) is powered by a 200 h.p. Lycoming R-680, but it is ultimately intended to use the Continental R-670. Unusual in being an "inverted" sesquiplane, the Duster D-1 is of welded steel-tube construction with fabric covering, but the rear fuselage remains uncovered. A 27-cu. ft. hopper is situated in front of the pilot. In place of the conventional fin and rudder assembly are twin "all-flying" rudders.

Dusting speed, 60–80 m.p.h.; loaded weight, 3,500 lb.; span, 33 ft.

LASCURAIN   MEXICO

The Lascurain four-seat cabin monoplane was built in 1939 as a small charter aircraft or private owner type, but only one prototype was completed and this was employed by a small airline in South-east Mexico for several years. It is now privately owned. The Lascurain is powered by two 65 h.p. Continental C65 engines and is of all-wood construction with fabric and plywood covering. It is of unusual appearance with an exceptionally large wing span. The main undercarriage members are enclosed in "trouser" type fairings, and the fixed nosewheel is uncowled.

Max. speed, 130 m.p.h.; cruising speed, 112 m.p.h.; service ceiling, 19,685 ft.; weights and dimensions: No details available for publication.

H

LATÉCOÈRE 631 — FRANCE

The Latécoère 631 was originally designed in 1938 as a 40-passenger trans-Atlantic flying-boat, the prototype flying in November 1942. This was confiscated by the Germans and eventually destroyed by bombing, but production was resumed at the St. Nazaire works of the S.N.C.A. du Sud-Ouest after the war, seven machines being completed. Three of these are currently flying in French Equatorial Africa and are each powered by six 1,600 h.p. Wright Cyclone R-2600-20 radials.

Max. speed, 225 m.p.h. at sea level, 246 m.p.h. at 6,000 ft.; cruising, 200 m.p.h. at 1,640 ft.; cruising range, 3,670 miles; empty weight, 71,280 lb.; loaded, 157,300 lb.; span, 188 ft. 4 in.; length, 142 ft. 6 in.; height, 33 ft. 11 in.; wing area, 3,766 sq. ft.

LAVOCHKIN LA-7 — U.S.S.R.

The LA-7 (code-named *Fin*) single-seat fighter is virtually a re-engined LA-5, the 1,640 h.p. ASh-82F of the former being replaced by a 1,850 h.p. ASh-82FNV. The LA-7 was supplied to the Soviet "satellite" air arms in considerable numbers immediately after World War 2 and, although mostly relegated to the training role, serves as a second-line fighter with the Sino-Communist Air Force. A two-seat advanced trainer and liaison variant was also produced in limited numbers, having an extended cockpit and re-positioned air intake.

Max. speed, 373 m.p.h. at sea level; cruising speed, 280 m.p.h.; range, 466 miles; empty weight, 5,600 lb.; loaded, 7,482 lb.; span, 32 ft. 3 in.; length, 28 ft. 6 in.; wing area, 188 sq. ft.

LAVOCHKIN LA-9 — U.S.S.R.

The LA-9 (code-named *Fritz*) was developed during the closing stages of World War 2 but was too late to see combat service. Owing much to the earlier LA-5 and LA-7, the LA-9 was one of the first Russian fighters of all-metal construction to enter quantity production. Although no longer operational in the Soviet Air Force, many are used by operational training elements, and the LA-9 is employed as an escort fighter by the Sino-Communist Air Force playing a minor role in the air war over Korea. The LA-9 has a 1,850 h.p. ASh-82FNV radial.

Max. speed, 394 m.p.h. at 19,280 ft.; cruising speed, 302 m.p.h.; range, 780 miles at 286 m.p.h.; empty weight, 5,970 lb.; loaded, 8,230 lb.; max. overload, 9,100 lb.; span, 31 ft. 5 in.; length, 29 ft. 5 in.; wing area, 182.73 sq. ft.

LAVOCHKIN LA-11 — U.S.S.R.

The LA-11 escort fighter (code-named *Fang*) is basically a revised LA-9, differing externally primarily in having a shorter fuselage, increased wing area and no belly radiator. Armament was increased from one 20-mm. and two 12.7-mm. guns to three 20-mm. guns mounted asymmetrically in the engine cowling. Evidence of the existence of the LA-11 came in the summer of 1949 when an example of this aircraft was crash-landed near Tullinge, Sweden. It was probably the last piston-engined fighter to be produced in quantity in the Soviet Union.

Max. speed, 420 m.p.h. at 19,000 ft.; cruising speed, 335 m.p.h.; range, 750 miles; ceiling, 40,000 ft.; approx. loaded weight, 7,700 lb.; span, 32 ft. 6 in.; length, 28 ft. 5 in.

LAVOCHKIN (TYPE 21) — U.S.S.R.

Contemporary to the MIG-15, this single-seat fighter is known to have been designed by Semyon A. Lavochkin, and has been allocated the Type identification number "21" and code-name *Fantail* by N.A.T.O. forces. The original production version, which appeared in 1949, was designated "Type 15", but the improved "Type 21" (*illustrated here*), differs in having redesigned tail surfaces and a long ventral fin or "keel". Larger than the MIG-15 but presumably powered by the same type of turbo-jet, the "Type 21" is believed to be primarily intended for the tactical escort role.

Specification: Single-seat escort fighter. Engine: One 5,500 lb.s.t. RD-45F or 5,950 lb.s.t. VK-1. Weights: No details available. Approx. performance: Max. speed, 640 m.p.h.; tactical radius, 500 miles. Armament: Two 23-mm. NS cannon. Approx. dimensions: Span, 37 ft.; length, 40 ft.

LAVOCHKIN 'FLASHLIGHT' U.S.S.R.

This twin-engined combat aircraft was first publicly demonstrated over Tushino on July 3, 1955. Code-named *Flashlight*, it is believed to be the machine referred to by authoritative Soviet sources as the LA-14, and to be in service in both light attack bomber and night fighter/interdictor versions. The machine illustrated here appears to be of the latter type with large nose radome and under-fuselage gun pack. The *Flashlight* features marked anhedral on its shoulder-mounted swept wing and has tandem wheel main undercarriage members with wingtip-mounted stabilizing wheels. Presumably a two-seater, it is powered by two underslung axial-flow turbojets probably of 8,000–10,000 lb. thrust. Loaded weight is likely to be in the vicinity of 30,000 pounds, and the type is not likely to be capable of exceeding Mach unity.

LEDUC 010 FRANCE

The Leduc 010 was the first manned aircraft to be powered solely by a ramjet or athodyd. Originally designed in 1937 by M. René Leduc, the first of two Leduc 010 research aircraft was not completed until 1945. The first powered flight was effected on April 21, 1949, after launching from a "parent" S.O.161 Languedoc aircraft (*see photo*). The fuselage comprises inner and outer shells, the inner shell housing the pilot's cockpit which is surrounded by an annular duct forming the ramjet. The Leduc 010 is limited to Mach 0.84, at which speed the ramjet furnishes 4,400 lb. thrust, and this Mach number is maintained in the climb with a rate of 7,800 ft./min. at 29,000 ft. Normal loaded weight is 6,615 lb.

Span, 34 ft. 5½ in.; length, 33 ft. 7½ in.; wing area, 172.1 sq. ft.

LEDUC 016 FRANCE

The Leduc 016 is basically similar to the earlier Leduc 010s, and was completed in February 1951. As the ramjet has no static thrust, the combustible mixture being compressed by forward speed alone, the Leduc 010 was carried to altitude by a "parent" transport for launching, and all landings had to be made "dead stick". It was originally proposed to fit Turboméca Marboré II turbojets of 836 lb.s.t. at each wingtip of the more advanced Leduc 021 to provide standby power for landing. To provide experience with wingtip turbojet installations, it was planned to fit a 660 lb.s.t. Marboré I at each wingtip of the Leduc 016. However, this installation was eventually abandoned, the turbojets being supplanted by streamlined fairings. The general characteristics and performance of the Leduc 010 and 016 are similar.

LEDUC 021 FRANCE

Like the earlier 010 and 016, the Leduc 021 is a subsonic test vehicle for its ramjet power plant. The first of two Leduc 021s was completed early in 1953, and initial air tests commenced in May of that year. The first powered flight was made on August 7, 1953. The second machine flew under its own power for the first time on March 1, 1954. The Leduc 021 is limited to Mach 0.85, at which speed its ramjet develops 13,200 lb. thrust. The Leduc 021 is intended for research at altitudes between 33,000 ft. and 66,000 ft., and the initial climb rate is 39,420 ft./min., which falls off to 2,900 ft./min. at 49,000 ft. Flight endurance varies from 15 minutes to one hour according to the altitude.

Empty weight, 8,350 lb.; loaded, 13,200 lb.; span, 38 ft. 1 in.; length, 41 ft. 1 in.; height, 9 ft.; wing area, 238 sq. ft.

LEAR LEARSTAR U.S.A.

The Learstar is a conversion of the Lockheed Model 18-56 Lodestar, but the modifications are so extensive that this machine is virtually a new aircraft. Approximately four hundred Lodestars exist, and the conversion brings the performance and accommodation provided by this elderly design up to modern standards, meeting CAR Part 4b performance requirements. The Learstar has new engine nacelles, landing gear, modified wing and tailplane tips, new tail-cone and nose, and extensive detail refinements. The Learstar has been the subject of probably the most extensive and meticulous refinement programme ever carried out on an existing transport aircraft.

Specification: Twelve-passenger executive transport. Engines: Two 1,425 h.p. Wright R-1820-C-9HD. Weights: Empty, 15,300 lb.; loaded, 22,500 lb. Performance: Max. speed, 321 m.p.h.; cruising, 280 m.p.h.; initial climb rate, 1,710 ft./min.; max. range, 3,800 miles. Dimensions: Span, 65 ft. 6 in.; length, 51 ft.; height, 11 ft. 9 in.

LEDUC RL-16   FRANCE

The RL-16 two-seat monoplane, designed by Monsieur R. Leduc (not to be confused with the ramjet pioneer of the same name), gained the light plane altitude record on June 13, 1949, by attaining 25,551 ft. The RL-16 was designed specifically for high altitude flight and is powered by a 50 h.p. Zundapp engine. For long distance flying, the RL-16 can supplement its four wing fuel tanks with four fuselage tanks, raising total fuel capacity to 132 Imp. galls.

Max. speed, 110 m.p.h.; cruising, 90 m.p.h.; max. range, 4,163 miles; endurance, 47 hours, 30 minutes; ceiling, 28,871 ft.; empty weight, 562 lb.; loaded, 1,764 lb.; span, 41 ft. 11¾ in.; length, 42 ft.; wing area, 172.223 sq. ft.

LEOPOLDOFF L.3 COLIBRI   FRANCE

The L.3 Colibri two-seat light touring biplane was produced in 1937, and the type was revived after the war and a small series built for French flying clubs. Eight Colibris are currently flying in France: five of these are of the L.3 type (*illustrated*) which is powered by a 45 h.p. Salmson 9 Adb radial, and three are of the L.6 type, two of these being powered by the 74 h.p. Regnier 4D2 and one by the 65 h.p. Minié 4DF 28.

Max. speed, 77.6 m.p.h.; climb to 3,280 ft., 7 minutes, 20 seconds; range, 230 miles; empty weight, 540 lb.; loaded, 1,036 lb.; span, 28 ft. 6½ in.; length, 19 ft. 6½ in.; height, 7 ft. 9½ in.; wing area, 177.6 sq. ft.

LETOV KS-1C JANEZ   YUGOSLAVIA

The KS-1C Janez is a single-seat aerobatic training biplane, designed by Anton Kuhelj and built by the Letov factory at Ljubljana. The Letov concern had previously been devoted primarily to the development and construction of sailplanes and gliders, such as the Triglav and Zdral, and the Janez utilises glider-building techniques, all-wood construction with fabric covering being employed. The Janez is powered by a 75 h.p. Praga D engine, and only one example is known to have been built to date.

Max. speed, 123 m.p.h.; cruising speed, 108 m.p.h.; initial climb rate, 822 ft./min.; range, 210-270 miles; endurance, 2-3 hours; weights and dimensions: no details available.

LETOV S.218 SMOLIK   CZECHOSLOVAKIA

Derived from the S.18 and S.118, and designed by Ing. Alois Smolik, the S.218, sometimes known as the Letov Smolik, is a tandem two-seat training biplane, two examples of which are still airworthy in Finland. Produced during 1927-32, the S.218 differed from its predecessors, the S.18 (60 h.p. Walter) and S.118 (85 h.p. Walter), primarily in having a more powerful engine, a 120 h.p. Walter Castor. The S.218 was produced under licence in Finland by the Valtion Lentokonetehdas during the early 'thirties for Finnish Air Force training elements.

Max. speed, 93 m.p.h.; range, 233 miles; climb to 3,280 ft., 5 minutes, 30 seconds; empty weight, 1,124 lb.; loaded, 1,636 lb.; span, 32 ft. 9½ in.; length, 22 ft. 7½ in.; height, 7 ft. 10½ in.

LETOV LK-1   YUGOSLAVIA

Developed by the Letov factory at Ljubljana and designed by A. Kuhelj, the LK-1 is a four-seat cabin monoplane designed for use as a tourer or, with spray bars and chemical tanks, as an agricultural aircraft. The LK-1 is powered by a 160 h.p. Walter Minor 6-III, and is of mixed wood and steel-tube construction with fabric and plywood covering. Dual controls are fitted, and the LK-1 may be used as a training aircraft by the clubs of the Yugoslav Aero-Union.

Max. speed, 118 m.p.h.; cruising speed, 93 m.p.h.; ceiling, 8,530 ft.; range, 310 miles; empty weight, 1,521 lb.; loaded, 2,623 lb.; span, 37 ft. 0¾ in.; length, 24 ft. 7 in.; height, 7 ft. 2½ in.; wing area, 188.368 sq. ft.

LIGNEL 44 (TAUPIN)   FRANCE

The Lignel 44 is a development of the Peyret tandem monoplane of the late 'twenties. A licence for the manufacture of this single-seat ultra-light aircraft was acquired by the Société Française de Constructions Aéronautiques, and the type became known as the S.C.F.A. Taupin. A two-seat version appeared in 1937 as the "Cinq-demi Taupin", and it is this type that is now known as the Lignel 44. Powered by a 65 h.p. Régnier 4-J0 engine, the Lignel 44 has tandem wings attached to the upper fuselage longerons, the forward wing having an area of 140 sq. ft., and the rear wing being 75.3 sq. ft.

Max. speed, 84 m.p.h.; cruising, 74.5 m.p.h.; service ceiling, 13,776 ft.; range, 310 miles; empty weight, 543 lb.; loaded, 1,276 lb.; span, 28 ft. 7 in.; length, 19 ft. 10 in.; height, 8 ft. 11 in.

LIGNEL 46 COACH — FRANCE

The Lignel 46 Coach, produced by the Société Française de Constructions Aéronautiques, is a four-seat cabin monoplane powered by a 180 h.p. Mathis 8G-20 engine. Built only in prototype form, the Coach has taken first place in a number of European rallies. It employs a composite bonded material known as Brodeau-Lignel in its construction, and dual controls are provided. The Coach has exceptionally clean lines, and the cabin provides particularly good visibility for the four occupants. The sides of the canopy hinge forward for access and can be jettisoned in an emergency.
Max. speed, 168 m.p.h.; cruising speed, 152 m.p.h.; range, 620 miles; empty weight, 1,852 lb.; loaded, 2,943 lb.; span, 34 ft. 5 in.; length, 26 ft. 2¾ in.; height, 8 ft. 6¼ in.; wing area, 161.459 sq. ft.

LOCKHEED 5-C VEGA — U.S.A.

The Lockheed Vega was first produced in 1927, and progressive developments of this type continued in production until 1933, 131 being built. The Model 1 Vega, the first product of the newly-formed Lockheed Aircraft Company, flew on July 4, 1927, and in 1928 became the first aircraft to fly over the North Pole. The Model 2D Vega differed from the Model 1 in having the 220 h.p. Wright Whirlwind replaced by a 300 h.p. Wasp Junior, and the Models 5 and 5-C (*illustrated*) had the 450 h.p. Wasp Junior SC-1. These differed in having five and seven seats respectively, and at least three examples of the Model 5-C are currently active in the U.S.A.
Max. speed, 195 m.p.h. at 6,000 ft.; cruising, 170 m.p.h.; initial climb, 1,250 ft./min.; range, 550 miles; empty weight, 2,725 lb.; loaded, 4,750 lb.; span, 41 ft.; length, 27 ft. 6 in.; height, 9 ft.

LOCKHEED 9-C ORION — U.S.A.

The Orion was introduced by the Lockheed Aircraft Corporation in 1930, and employed a moulded-plywood type of monocoque construction. The early production Orions were powered by the 420 h.p. Pratt & Whitney Wasp C-1 or 5C-1, but the Model 9-D Orion was powered by the 550 h.p. Pratt & Whitney Wasp S1D1, and the specification refers to this variant. The sole remaining example of the ten Orions built is a Model 9-C (*illustrated*) which is now powered by a 735 h.p. Wright Cyclone engine. The Orion accommodates six passengers.
Max. speed, 225 m.p.h. at 5,000 ft.; cruising speed, 205 m.p.h. at 8,500 ft.; initial climb rate, 1,400 ft./min.; cruising range, 720 miles; empty weight, 3,640 lb.; loaded, 5,800 lb.; span, 42 ft. 10 in.; length, 28 ft. 4 in.; height, 9 ft. 8 in.

LOCKHEED 10-C ELECTRA — U.S.A.

The forerunner of the well-known line of Lockheed twin-engined transports, the Model 10 Electra was first produced in 1934, and subsequently built in substantial numbers. The Models 10 and 10-A had 400 h.p. Wasp Junior SB-2 engines, but the Model 10-B had 440 h.p. Wright Whirlwind R-975-E3s, and subsequent production versions such as the Model 10-C (*illustrated*), and 10-E, had 450 h.p. Wasp S3H-1s. Examples of the Models 10-A, -B, -C, and -E are currently registered in the U.S.A. and Canada, and a Model 10-B is flying in Australia. The Electra is an all-metal twelve-seat transport.
Max. speed, 210 m.p.h. at 5,000 ft.; range, 810 miles at 185 m.p.h.; initial climb rate, 1,140 ft./min.; empty weight, 6,325 lb.; loaded, 10,000 lb.; span, 55 ft.; length, 38 ft. 7 in.; height, 10 ft. 1 in.

LOCKHEED 12-A — U.S.A.

The Model 12 was first produced in 1936 as a smaller version of the Model 10 Electra, being an eight-seat monoplane. Versions included Models 12-A, -B, -F, and -M, and these were similar except for engine installations. The Model 12-A was produced in largest numbers, and is the most widely seen version today. This is powered by two 450 h.p. Pratt & Whitney Wasp Junior SB-2 engines, and more than thirty are active in the U.S.A., two in Australia and one in Sweden. Ten were delivered to the U.S.A.A.F. as the UC-40A, and ten commercial Model 12-As were impressed as the UC-40D.
Max. speed, 225 m.p.h.; range, 1,060 miles at 212 m.p.h. at 9,000 ft.; initial climb rate, 1,360 ft./min.; empty weight, 5,765 lb.; loaded, 8,650 lb.; span, 49 ft. 6 in.; length, 36 ft. 4 in.; height, 9 ft. 9 in.

LOCKHEED 14 SUPER ELECTRA — U.S.A.

First flown on July 29, 1937, the Model 14 Super Electra accommodates eleven passengers and three crew members. Three versions were produced, each differing from the others in motor installation only: Model 14-H2 (two 750 h.p. Pratt & Whitney Hornet S1E2-G), Model 14-F62 (two 760 h.p. Wright Cyclone GR-1820-F62), and Model 14-G3B (two 820 h.p. Wright Cyclone GR-1820-G3B). The Super Electra was the forerunner of the military Model 414 (Hudson), a contract for 250 of which was placed on behalf of the R.A.F. in 1938. Specification relates to the Model 14-F62.
Max. speed, 243 m.p.h.; range, 1,590 miles at 225 m.p.h. at 13,000 ft.; initial climb rate, 1,230 ft./min.; empty weight, 10,750 lb.; loaded, 17,500 lb.; span, 65 ft. 6 in.; length, 44 ft. 2½ in.; height, 11 ft. 10½ in.; wing area, 551 sq. ft.

LOCKHEED 18-56 LODESTAR — U.S.A.

The Model 18 Lodestar was produced as a successor to the Model 14, and a variety of engines were installed during the Lodestar's production life between 1940 and 1943. The version flying in largest numbers is the Model 18-56 with 1,200 h.p. or 1,350 h.p. Wright Cyclone radials, but other Models currently active are the 18-08 with 1,200 h.p. Pratt & Whitney Twin Wasps, the similarly powered 18-10 and 18-14, and the Cyclone-powered 18-40 and 18-50. Nearly two hundred Lodestars are flying in the U.S.A., and others are flying in many parts of the world. Specification relates to the Model 18-56.
Max. speed, 272 m.p.h. at 15,300 ft.; cruising, 248 m.p.h.; initial climb rate, 1,950 ft./min.; range, 1,890 miles; empty weight, 11,790 lb.; loaded, 17,500 lb.; max. 18,500 lb.; span, 65 ft. 6 in.; length, 49 ft. 10 in.

LOCKHEED 414 (HUDSON III) — U.S.A.

First flown on December 10, 1938, the Model 414 was a military reconnaissance bomber variant of the commercial Model 14, and a considerable number of aircraft of this type were supplied to the R.A.F. as the Hudson. Civil conversions of the Hudson III (*photo*) are flying in several parts of the world, including four in Australia, and others in Canada. These are powered by two 1,200 h.p. Wright Cyclone GR-1820-G205A radials. Three hundred Model 414s were supplied to the U.S.A.F. as target tugs and navigational trainers under the designations AT-18 and AT-18A, and two civil conversions of the AT-18 are active in the U.S.A.
Max. speed, 250 m.p.h.; cruising, 180 m.p.h.; initial climb rate, 2,215 ft./min.; range, 2,090 miles; empty weight, 12,929 lb.; loaded, 18,500 lb.; span, 65 ft. 6 in.; length, 44 ft. 4 in.; height, 11 ft. 10½ in.

LOCKHEED 237 (PV-1 VENTURA) — U.S.A.

The PV-1, or Vega 37 Ventura, bears the same relationship to the commercial Model 18 as the Hudson to the Model 14. The Vega 37 was supplied to the U.S.A.F. as the B-34 and B-37, and to the U.S. Navy as the PV-1. It was also supplied to the R.A.F. as the Ventura I (1,850 h.p. Pratt & Whitney R-2800-S1A4G), II, III, IV, and V (2,000 h.p. Wright R-2600-31). Some fifteen civil conversions of the PV-1 are currently active in the U.S.A., and the Ventura still serves with the S.A.A.F. and as a target tug with the R.C.A.F. Some are used for transport duties by the French Air Force, and civil conversions are flying in Canada.
Max. speed, 315 m.p.h.; economical cruising, 172 m.p.h.; max. range, 2,000 miles; empty weight, 19,373 lb.; normal loaded, 26,500 lb.; span, 65 ft. 6 in.; length, 51 ft. 7½ in.; height, 14 ft. 1⅛ in.

LOCKHEED 15 (PV-2 HARPOON) — U.S.A.

Derived from the PV-1 Ventura, the PV-2 Harpoon has greater wing span and new tail, and 535 patrol bombers of this type were supplied to the U.S. Navy. A number are still in service with U.S.N reserve elements, but the majority of the remaining PV-2 Harpoons have been supplied to the Japanese Self-Defence Force, while others have been supplied to the Royal Netherlands Navy under the M.D.A.P. The PV-2 is powered by two 2,000 h.p. Pratt & Whitney Double Wasp R-2800-31 engines.
Max. speed, 309 m.p.h. at 15,200 ft., 289 m.p.h. at sea level; econ. cruising, 157 m.p.h.; max. range, 2,895 miles; initial climb rate, 2,105 ft./min.; empty weight, 20,170 lb.; normal loaded, 29,305 lb.; span, 74 ft. 11⅞ in.; length, 52 ft. 1½ in.; height, 13 ft. 3 in.

LOCKHEED 422 (F-5G LIGHTNING) — U.S.A.

The F-5G is a photo-reconnaissance conversion of the P-38L Lightning single-seat fighter, and twelve are used in Canada for aerial survey and mapping by Spartan Air Services, while others are active in the U.S.A. The F-5G can carry three to five cameras in any one of four different installations, and is powered by two 1,475 h.p. Allison V-1710-111/113 engines. A number of P-38L Lightnings are also privately owned in the U.S.A. A total of 9,393 P-38/F-5 aircraft were produced during World War II.
Max. speed, 414 m.p.h. at 25,000 ft.; service ceiling, 35,000 ft.; normal range, 460 miles; empty weight, 12,700 lb.; loaded, 17,000 lb.; span, 52 ft. 0 in.; length, 37 ft. 10 in.; height, 12 ft. 10 in.; wing area, 327.5 sq. ft.

LOCKHEED 749A CONSTELLATION — U.S.A.

Although designed as a commercial transport, the Constellation first flew (January 9, 1943) as the C-69 military transport. Only twenty C-69s were delivered, the first commercial variant being the Model 49, seventy of which were assembled from C-69 components. The first Constellation built from the outset as a commercial transport was the Model 649, followed by the Model 749 with additional fuel capacity. Nine 749s for the U.S.A.F. are designated C-121A. This carries 44–64 passengers and has four 2,500 h.p. Wright Cyclone GR-3350-C18-BD1s.
Max. speed, 347 m.p.h.; cruising, 298 m.p.h. at 20,000 ft.; initial climb rate, 1,620 ft./min.; normal range, 3,000 miles; empty weight, 56,590–57,160 lb.; max. loaded, 107,000 lb.; span, 123 ft.; length, 95 ft. 1¼ in.; height, 23 ft.; wing area, 1,650 sq. ft.

LOCKHEED 1049G CONSTELLATION U.S.A.

The Model 1049 is a lengthened development of the Model 749. The Model 1049B is a cargo variant (the C-121C being a U.S.A.F. version), with 3,250 h.p. Wright Turbo Compound 972-TC-18DA1 engines, and the 1049C is a 47–99 passenger airliner with similar engines. The 1049E has its permissible take-off weight increased to 133,000 lb. from 130,000 lb., and the 1049G (*illustrated here*) has wingtip fuel tanks and TC-18DA3 engines developing an additional 100 h.p. each for climb. The 1049H is a version of the 1049G which can be adapted for either cargo or passengers.
Specification: Sixty-three/ninety-nine passenger airliner. Engines: Four 3,250 h.p. Wright 972-TC-18DA3. Weights: Empty, 73,016 lb.; loaded, 137,500 lb. Performance: Max. speed, 370 m.p.h. at 20,000 ft.; cruising, 355 m.p.h. at 22,600 ft.; max. range, 4,620 miles.; absolute, 5,840 miles. Dimensions: Span, 123 ft.; length, 113 ft. 7 in.; height, 24 ft. 9 in.; wing area, 1,650 sq. ft.

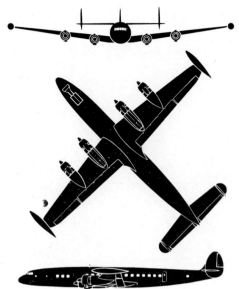

LOCKHEED RC-121C U.S.A.

Derived from the commercial Model 1049 Constellation which is employed by the U.S.A.F. as the C-121C, and by the U.S. Navy as the R7V-1, the RC-121C is a radar picket, or "flying radar station". Carrying nearly 15,000 lb. of radar equipment, the RC-121C is generally similar to the U.S. Navy's WV-2, and is used both for long range patrols and as an airborne control centre to guide interceptors. It carries ANAPS-20 search radar, and the nose houses APS-42 cloud-collision equipment. The 8-ft. vertical structure above the fuselage houses the height-finding antenna, and the belly radome contains a bearing antenna. A crew of thirty-one is carried. The RC-121D has wingtip tanks and increased internal fuel capacity.
Specification: Radar picket. Engines: Four 3,250 h.p. Wright R-3350-34. Weights: Approx. loaded, 120,000 lb. Performance: Approx. max. cruising speed, 335 m.p.h.; endurance: 24 hours. Dimensions: Span, 126 ft.; length, 116 ft. 2 in.; height, 30 ft.

LOCKHEED P2V-7 NEPTUNE U.S.A.

The P2V-7 is the current production version of the Neptune long-range patrol bomber, and it differs from its predecessors in several respects. Two versions of the P2V-7 are being produced: that for the U.S. Navy has a pair of turbojets which are employed during maximum-weight take-offs and during combat: and a dorsal turret housing two 0.50-in. machine guns (*silhouette*), and the version for the Royal Canadian Air Force (*photograph*) has no auxiliary turbojets or dorsal turret deleted. All P2V-7s are equipped with the "stinger" tail extension which houses search magneto-meter.
Specification: Seven-seat patrol bomber. Engines: Two 2,650 h.p. Wright R3350-30W Turbo Compound and two 3,800 lb.s.t. Westinghouse J34-WE-34 turbojets. Weights: Empty, 43,950 lb.; loaded, 72,000 lb. Performance: Max. speed, 344 m.p.h. (with turbojets), 411 m.p.h.; initial climb rate, 2,620 ft./min. (with turbojets), 3,100 ft./min.; range, 3,700 miles. Dimensions: Span, 103 ft. 10 in.; length, 91 ft. 8 in.; height, 29 ft. 4 in.

LOCKHEED T-33A   U.S.A.

Originally known as the TF-80C, the T-33A is a two-seat adaptation of the F-80C Shooting Star, with a lengthened fuselage to allow for the insertion of a second seat. The T-33A is used by the U.S. Navy as the TV-2 and, in addition to being used by the U.S.A.F., serves with numerous air forces. The T-33A is also built under licence in Canada by Canadair Limited. Powered by a 5,000 lb.s.t. Rolls-Royce Nene 10, a total of 576 Canadair-built T-33As are being built for the R.C.A.F. by which air arm they are known as Silver Stars.

Specification: Two-seat Advanced trainer. Engine: One 4,000 lb.s.t. (5,400 lb. with water-alcohol injection) Allison J33-A-35. Weights: Empty, 8,084 lb.; loaded, 11,965 lb.; max. 14,442 lb. Performance: Max. speed, 580 m.p.h.; initial climb rate, 5,525 ft./min.; range, 1,345 miles. Armament: Two 0.50-in. M-3 guns. Dimensions: Span, 38 ft. 10½ in.; length, 37 ft. 9 in.; height, 11 ft. 8 in.; wing area, 237 sq. ft.

LOCKHEED T2V-1   U.S.A.

The T2V-1 is basically an improved and more powerful version of the T-33A/TV-2 advanced trainer, and is in quantity production for the U.S. Navy. Originally developed as a private venture, the T2V-1 differs considerably from the earlier trainer. Leading-edge slats moving over a 17° arc are fitted to the wing, and the vertical surfaces are 20-in. taller and 12-in. wider. The rear seat is 6-in. higher than the front seat, and boundary-layer control is employed, compressed air being bled from the engine diffuser, ducted along the inside of the wing trailing edge, and then blown at high velocity over the ailerons and flaps. This increases the lift and reduces the stalling speed.

Specification: Two-seat Naval advanced trainer. Engine: One 6,100 lb.s.t. Allison J33-A-22. Weights: Loaded, 16,400 lb. Performance: Max. speed, 600 m.p.h.; max. range, 900 miles. Dimensions: Span, 42 ft.; length, 38 ft.; height, 13 ft.

LOCKHEED F-94C STARFIRE   U.S.A.

Developed from the F-94B, the F-94C features a thinner wing, lengthened, pointed nose, swept horizontal tail surfaces, larger vertical tail surfaces, and an all-rocket armament. Twenty-four 2.75-in. Mighty Mouse missiles are carried in a ring of firing tubes in the nose, and a further twenty-four missiles can be carried in wing leading-edge pods. An alternative armament of Hughes GAR-98 Falcon self-homing missiles may be carried by the DF-94C (the "D" signifying missile-director). A total of 279 F-94Cs had been built when production terminated in February 1954.

Specification: Two-seat all-weather fighter. Engine: One 6,250 lb.s.t. (8,300 lb. with afterburning) Pratt & Whitney J48-P-5. Weights: Empty, 9,557 lb.; loaded, 27,000 lb. Performance: Max. speed, 646 m.p.h. at sea level; initial climb rate, 9,250 ft./min.; max. range, 1,600 miles. Dimensions: Span, 37 ft. 4 in.; length, 41 ft. 5½ in.; height, 12 ft. 7 in.

LOCKHEED F-80C SHOOTING STAR   U.S.A.

The F-80 single-seat fighter was the first jet combat aircraft to be accepted for operational service with the U.S.A.F. The first prototype flew on January 8, 1944, and several production models were subsequently produced, including the F-80A (676 built), F-80B (240 built), and the F-80C (798 built). The F-80C was the final production version and is powered by an Allison J33-A-35 delivering 5,400 lb. thrust with water injection. The F-80C carries an armament of six 0.50-in. M-3 guns. It is no longer first-line equipment with the U.S.A.F.

Max. speed, 594 m.p.h. at 25,000 ft.; climb to 25,000 ft., 7 minutes; ceiling, 44,100 ft.; empty weight, 8,240 lb.; loaded, 15,336 lb.; span, 38 ft. 10½ in.; length, 34 ft. 6 in.; height, 11 ft. 4 in.; wing area, 237 sq. ft.

LOCKHEED XFV-1   U.S.A.

The XFV-1 was designed to meet U.S. Navy requirements for a vertical take-off fighter, and is powered by an Allison YT40-A-14 turboprop which provides 5,850 e.h.p., but 7,100 e.h.p. during the critical take-off period. Flight tests were commenced in March 1954 with a temporary undercarriage fitted to enable orthodox landings and take-offs to be made. The XFV-1 is designed to stand on small wheels at the tips of the cruciform tail assembly for take-off, and is lowered on to these when landing. The pilot's seat is mounted on gimbals, tilting forward 45° while the aircraft is in the vertical attitude. The XFV-1 is intended primarily as a development aircraft.

Approx. level speed, 500 m.p.h.; approx. dimensions: span, 24 ft.; length, 28 ft.; height (tail, top to bottom), 11 ft.

LOCKHEED C-130A HERCULES   U.S.A.

Flown for the first time on August 23, 1954, the prototype Hercules, the YC-130, was the first U.S. transport aircraft designed from the outset for turboprop power. Two YC-130 prototypes have been built, and the first production C-130A Hercules of a large number on order for the U.S.A.F.'s Tactical Air Command Troop Carrier Wings was completed on March 10, 1955. Termed a "medium combat transport", the Hercules is designed to operate from small, rough fields, and has a maximum payload of 40,000 lb. which can include a 155-mm. howitzer.

Specification: Medium assault transport. Engines: Four 3,750 e.s.h.p. Allison T56-A-1. Weights: Empty, 57,500 lb.; normal loaded, 108,000 lb.; max. 124,200 lb. Approx. performance: Max. speed, 405 m.p.h.; cruising, 380 m.p.h. at 30,000 ft.; range, 3,000 miles. Dimensions: Span, 132 ft.; length, 94 ft. 9½ in.; height, 38 ft. 3½ in.; wing area, 1,745 sq. ft.

LIORÉ-ET-OLIVIER LEO 455PH   FRANCE

The LeO 45 was one of the best French attack bombers designed before World War 2, and was built in quantity by the S.N.C.A. du Sud-Est. The LeO 45 was powered by two 1,015 h.p. Gnôme-Rhône 14N engines, and the LeO 451 had 1,300 h.p. Gnôme-Rhône 14Ns. After the war, a number of LeO 451s were employed for research purposes, some having the French engines replaced by 1,115 h.p. Pratt & Whitney R-1830-90C radials and being redesignated LeO 453P. Converted for transport duties and powered by 1,220 h.p. Gnôme-Rhône 14R-5, R-24, or R-201 engines, it is designated LeO 455PH (*photo*), and two LeO 453Ps and four LeO 455PHs are currently registered in France.

Max. speed, 311 m.p.h.; range, 1,510 miles at 247 m.p.h.; empty weight, 14,090 lb.; loaded, 26,455 lb.; span, 73 ft. 10 in.; length, 55 ft. 3 in.

LOMBARDI F.L.3   ITALY

The F.L.3 two-seat, all-wood training and sports monoplane was first produced in 1939 as the Avia F.L.3, and four hundred aircraft of this type were built by the A.V.I.A. concern between 1939 and 1942, some of these aircraft being delivered to the Croatian Air Force. In 1947, A.V.I.A. was taken over by Francis Lombardi and production of the F.L.3 was suspended; it has since been resumed by Meteor S.p.A. as the F.L.53. The F.L.3 was produced with both the 60 h.p. C.N.A. D-4 and the 85 h.p. Continental C-85, and with open and enclosed cockpits.

Max. speed, 121 m.p.h.; cruising speed, 105 m.p.h.; initial climb rate, 590 ft./min.; cruising range, 340 miles; empty weight, 748 lb.; loaded, 1,254 lb.; span, 32 ft. 3½ in.; length, 20 ft. 10¾ in.; height, 5 ft. 7¼ in.; wing area, 154.4 sq. ft.

LOMBARDI L.M.5 AVIASTAR   ITALY

Designed by Eng. P. Mortara and first produced in 1945 by the Azio-
naria Vercellese Industrie Aeronautiche (A.V.I.A.), the L.M.5 Aviastar
two-seat light cabin monoplane was taken over in 1947 by Francis
Lombardi & C. A small number of L.M.5 Aviastars are flying in
Italy, and one has been exported to Switzerland and is owned by the
well-known Swiss pilot, W. Spahni. The Aviastar is powered by a 60
h.p. C.N.A. D.4 engine, but an 85 h.p. Continental C85 may be installed.

*Max. speed, 118 m.p.h.; cruising speed, 102.5 m.p.h.; service ceiling,
16,400 ft.; range, 580 miles; empty weight, 726 lb.; loaded, 1,232 lb.;
span, 26 ft. 5 in.; length, 20 ft. 2 in.; height, 7 ft.*

LUSCOMBE 1 PHANTOM   U.S.A.

The Phantom side-by-side two-seat cabin monoplane first appeared
in 1934, and was the first product of the newly-formed Luscombe
Airplane Corporation. The Phantom is of all-metal construction and,
at the time of its appearance, employed a new system of construction,
the components being sub-contracted by specialist firms and the parent
company only undertaking the final assembly. The Phantom is powered
by a 145 h.p. Warner Super Scarab seven-cylinder radial engine, and a
few examples of the type remain active in the U.S.A.

*Max. speed, 168 m.p.h.; cruising speed, 144 m.p.h.; initial climb rate,
1,400 ft./min.; service ceiling, 19,000 ft.; range, 560 miles; empty weight,
1,300 lb.; loaded, 1,950 lb.; span, 31 ft.; length, 21 ft. 6 in.; height, 6 ft.
9 in.; wing area, 132 sq. ft.*

LUSCOMBE T8F SILVAIRE OBSERVER   U.S.A.

The Model T8F Observer introduced in 1947 was the first tandem two-
seater in the Silvaire series. Developed from the basic Model 8 Silvaire
design, it incorporates the general constructional features of all aircraft
in this series but possesses a totally redesigned cabin with exceptionally
large side-window area. The roof of the cabin is formed by a moulded
Plexiglas bubble, and power is provided by a 90 h.p. Continental C90
engine. Complete dual controls are provided and the Observer can be
used as a trainer.

*Max. speed, 125 m.p.h.; cruising speed, 112 m.p.h.; initial climb rate,
850 ft./min.; service ceiling, 17,000 ft.; range, 500 miles; empty weight,
820 lb.; loaded, 1,400 lb.; span, 35 ft.; length, 19 ft. 11 in.; height, 6 ft.
3 in.; wing area, 140 sq. ft.*

LOMBARDI L.M.7   ITALY

Derived from the L.M.5 Aviastar and designed by Pieraldo Mortara,
the L.M.7 is a three-seat cabin monoplane of all-wood construction,
the prototype of which was produced in 1949. No production of the
L.M.7 has been undertaken, as Francis Lombardi & C. abandoned
aircraft manufacture shortly after completion of the prototype. The
L.M.7 is powered by a 60 h.p. C.N.A. D.4 engine, and its cabin provides
accommodation for two persons side-by-side in front with a single seat
behind. Starboard front seat and rear seat are easily removable.

*Max. speed, 117 m.p.h.; cruising speed, 103 m.p.h.; climb to 3,280 ft.,
8 minutes, 21 seconds; service ceiling, 12,530 ft.; range, 550 miles; empty
weight, 770 lb.; loaded, 1,386 lb.; span, 38 ft. 6 in.; length, 20 ft. 10 in.;
height, 6 ft. 3 in.; wing area, 156.5 sq. ft.*

LUSCOMBE MODEL 8 SILVAIRE   U.S.A.

The Model 8 Silvaire was first produced in 1937, and during 1938–42
a total of 1,200 Silvaires of the Model 8 (50 h.p. Continental A-50),
8A (65 h.p. Continental A-65), 8B (65 h.p. Lycoming), 8C and 8D
(75 h.p. Continental A-75) were built. Production was resumed in
1946 with the generally similar models 8E and 8F with 85 h.p. and 90
h.p. Continental engines respectively. Production of the Silvaire was
discontinued in 1950, but several thousand Silvaires of all models are
currently active. A more angular fin and rudder assembly was introduced in 1949.

*Max. speed, 128 m.p.h.; cruising, 115 m.p.h.; initial climb, 850 ft./min.;
ceiling, 17,000 ft.; empty weight, 810 lb.; loaded, 1,400 lb.; span, 35 ft.;
length, 20 ft.; height, 6 ft. 3 in.; wing area. 140 sq. ft.*

LUSCOMBE 11A SILVAIRE SEDAN   U.S.A.

The Model 11A Silvaire Sedan introduced by the Luscombe Airplane
Corporation in 1948, is virtually a four-seat development of the two-
seat Model 8 Silvaire, with redesigned and deeper fuselage and a 165
h.p. Continental E165 engine. The Silvaire Sedan was produced in
limited numbers during 1948–50, and some fifty machines of this type
are currently active in the U.S.A. The Silvaire Sedan is of all-metal
construction, and dual controls are provided.

*Max. speed, 145 m.p.h.; cruising speed, 130 m.p.h.; initial climb rate,
900 ft./min.; service ceiling, 17,000 ft.; empty weight, 1,280 lb.; loaded,
2,280 lb.; span, 38 ft.; length, 23 ft. 6 in.; height, 6 ft. 10 in.; wing area,
165 sq. ft.*

L.W.D. JUNAK   POLAND

The Junak (Cadet) was developed by the Lotnicze Warsztaty Doswiadczaine (L.W.D.) as a primary trainer to replace the Polikarpov PO-2 biplane in service with the Polish Air Force. The prototype Junak was flown for the first time on February 22, 1948, but quantity production for the P.A.F. was not undertaken. Basically a tandem two-seat trainer powered by a 125 h.p. M-11G radial engine, the Junak is of mixed construction with a fabric-covered, welded steel-tube fuselage and wing centre section, and wooden outer wing sections.

Max. speed, 143 m.p.h.; cruising speed, 118 m.p.h.; initial climb rate, 690 ft./min.; service ceiling, 13,780 ft.; empty weight, 1,315 lb.; loaded, 2,030 lb.; span, 32 ft. 9½ in.; length, 24 ft. 7¼ in.; height, 6 ft. 8½ in.; wing area, 188.4 sq. ft.

L.W.D. ZUCH-1   POLAND

The Zuch-I (Dare-Devil) was produced in 1948 by the Lotnicze Warsztaty Doswiadzalme as a development of the previously described Junak. Employing the same basic wing and fuselage, the Zuch-I is powered by a 160 h.p. Walter Minor 6-III engine. Designed as a two-seat primary training monoplane, the Zuch-I is of mixed construction with a welded steel-tube fuselage and centre wing section, and wooden outer wing panels, the whole covered by plywood and fabric.

Max. speed, 155 m.p.h.; cruising speed, 130 m.p.h.; range, 930 miles; empty weight, 1,250 lb.; loaded, 2,200 lb.; span, 32 ft. 9½ in.; length, 29 ft. 6 in.; height, 6 ft. 8½ in.; wing area, 188.4 sq. ft.

L.W.D. SZPAK-4   POLAND

The Szpak-4 was developed from the Szpak-2 and -3 four-seat cabin monoplanes to which it bears a close resemblance. The Szpak-2 was designed in Lublin during the closing stages of the war, and later built by the Lotnicze Warsztaty Doswiadczalne (L.W.D.), first flying in November 1945. It bore the first post-war Polish civil registration, SP-AAA. The Szpak-3 was an experimental modification with a fixed nose-wheel undercarriage. Progressive development led to the Szpak-4A (*photograph*) two-seat advanced trainer, and the Szpak-4T (*silhouette*) four-seat tourer.
Specification: (Szpak-4T) four-seat cabin monoplane. Engine: One 160 h.p. PZL-built Bramo Sh.14. Weights: Empty, 1,433 lb.; loaded, 2,645 lb. Performance: Max. speed, 121 m.p.h.; cruising, 100 m.p.h.; initial climb rate, 450 ft./min.; range, 435 miles. Dimensions: Span, 37 ft.; length, 28 ft. 2 in.; height, 7 ft. 8 in.; wing area, 189.5 sq. ft.

L.W.D. ZAK 3   POLAND

Produced in larger quantities than any other Polish post-war light planes, the Zak series began with the Zak-1 which first flew in March 1947. The Zak-1 (CSS-built Walter Mikron 4-III) two-seat cabin monoplane was produced in small series, and was followed by the ZAK-2 (65 h.p. Continental C65) with an open cockpit, fifty of which were built for the flying clubs. The Zak-3 is actually a higher-powered two/three-seat development of the Zak-1 which has also been produced in quantity for the flying clubs. The Zak-4 is a trainer variant with open cockpits which reverts to the CSS-built Mikron.
Specification: Two/three-seat cabin monoplane. Engine: One 105 h.p. Walter Minor 4-III. Weights: Empty, 880 lb.; loaded, 1,375 lb. Performance: Max. speed, 100 m.p.h.; cruising, 81 m.p.h.; initial climb rate, 520 ft./min.; range, 248 miles. Dimensions: Span, 38 ft. 8½ in.; length, 23 ft. 11 in.; height, 6 ft. 5 in.; wing area, 183 sq. ft.

MACCHI M.B.308G   ITALY

The Macchi M.B.308 entered production in 1947, the initial version being a two-seater produced with both the 85 h.p. Continental C-85 and the 90 h.p. Continental C-90 engines. A twin-float seaplane variant with the latter engine was also produced. The two-seat model was replaced in production by the three-seat M.B.308G (*photo*), and a manufacturing licence for the type has been acquired by the German Siebel company. Eighty M.B.308s were purchased by the Italian Air Force, and the majority of these were subsequently leased to flying clubs. The silhouette depicts the two-seat M.B.308 without the additional side windows which distinguish the M.B.308G.
Specification: Three-seat light cabin monoplane. Engine: One 90 h.p. Continental C-90. Weights: Empty, 946 lb.; loaded, 1,520 lb. Performance: Max. speed, 124 m.p.h.; cruising speed, 103.7 m.p.h.; service ceiling, 12,460 ft.; range, 335 miles. Dimensions: Span, 32 ft. 9½ in.; length, 21 ft. 5 in.; height, 9 ft.; wing area, 147.6 sq. ft.

MACCHI M.B.320   ITALY

Introduced in 1949, the M.B.320 has since been produced in limited numbers by Aeronautica Macchi S.A. A manufacturing licence for the M.B.320 was acquired by the Société Francaise de Constructions Aéronautiques Lignel, which concern had planned to manufacture the type under the designation VEMA-51. This licence was not, however, taken up. In addition to being supplied to various Italian commercial concerns, three M.B.320s have been sold to East African Airways for use as feeder liners.
Specification: Six-seat cabin monoplane. Engines: Two 185 h.p. Continental E-185. Weights: Empty, 3,670 lb.; loaded, 5,511 lb. Performance: Max. speed, 186 m.p.h. at sea level; cruising speed, 156.6 m.p.h.; initial climb rate, 925 ft./min.; range, 665 miles. Dimensions: Span, 42 ft. 7 in.; length, 28 ft. 4 in.; height, 10 ft. 6 in.; wing area, 226 sq. ft.

MACCHI C.205V VELTRO   ITALY

The prototype C.205V Veltro flew on April 19, 1942, being a C.202 Folgore airframe with an imported German Daimler-Benz DB 605A engine of 1,250 h.p. The Veltro entered service with the *Regia Aeronautica* in 1943. Post-war assembled C.205V Veltro fighter-bombers have been exported to Egypt, and a number of machines of this type are still employed for second-line duties by the Italian Air Force. The Veltro is powered by a 1,475 h.p. Daimler-Benz DB 605A RC 58 engine, and carries an armament of two 20-mm. cannon and two 12.7-mm. guns.
Max. speed, 399 m.p.h. at 23,620 ft.; max. cruising, 310 m.p.h.; initial climb rate, 3,100 ft./min.; service ceiling, 36,100 ft.; empty weight, 5,691 lb.; loaded, 7,514 lb.; span, 34 ft. 8½ in.; length, 29 ft. 0½ in.; height, 9 ft. 11 in.; wing area, 180.8 sq. ft.

MACCHI M.B.323   ITALY

The M.B.323 was designed to meet an Italian Air Force specification for a two-seat basic trainer. The first prototype is powered by a 610 h.p. Pratt & Whitney Wasp, and the second prototype has an Alvis Leonides 502/5 Mk.24. A third version with a nosewheel undercarriage has been projected but no production orders have yet been announced. The M.B.323 is in a similar category to the Piaggio P.150 and the Fiat G.49.

Max. speed, 242 m.p.h. at 5,905 ft.; cruising, 199 m.p.h. at 9,842 ft.; initial climb rate, 1,436 ft./min.; service ceiling, 21,325 ft.; range, 808 miles; empty weight, 4,409 lb.; loaded, 5,575 lb.; span, 39 ft. 4½ in.; length, 29 ft. 11½ in.; height, 13 ft. 1½ in.; wing area, 217 sq. ft.

MARTIN MODEL 179 (B-26C MARAUDER) U.S.A.

The Martin Model 179, or B-26 Marauder, was first flown in 1940, and the first of 4,708 aircraft of this type for the U.S.A.A.F. was flown on February 25, 1941. Several production variants of the Marauder were produced, and a small number of civil conversions of the B-26C are currently flying. These have been converted extensively as high-speed executive transports, and are mostly powered by 2,000 h.p. Pratt & Whitney R-2800-41 radial engines. The specification relates to the military B-26C.

Max. speed, 287 m.p.h. at 5,000 ft.; cruising, 240 m.p.h.; range, 1,000 miles; empty weight, 25,300 lb.; loaded, 38,200 lb.; span, 71 ft.; length, 56 ft. 6 in.; height, 21 ft. 2 in.; wing area, 658 sq. ft.

MARTIN PBM-5A MARINER U.S.A.

An amphibious variant of the PBM-5 flying-boat, the PBM-5A has a modified forward hull. The XPBM-1, the first prototype, appeared in 1938, and three basic production versions, the PBM-1, -3 and -5, were built for the U.S. Navy, production being completed in 1947. Of the final production PBM-5, a total of 630 were acquired by the U.S. Navy. These were followed by thirty-six PBM-5A amphibians. The PBM-5A is powered by two 2,500 h.p. Pratt & Whitney R-2800-34 engines.

Max. speed, 200 m.p.h.; cruising, 143 m.p.h.; initial climb, 520 ft./min.; max. range, 2,900 miles; empty weight, 36,328 lb.; loaded, 60,300 lb.; span, 118 ft.; length, 79 ft. 10 in.; height, 27 ft. 6 in.; wing area, 1,408 sq. ft.

MARTIN JRM-1 MARS U.S.A.

The Martin Model 170, or JRM-1, Mars was originally built as an experimental patrol bomber with the designation XPB2M-1. It was subsequently modified as a cargo transport and redesignated XPB2M-1R. The JRM is the production development of this aircraft, and five machines have been delivered to the U.S. Naval Air Transport Service and four are currently operating in the Pacific, having flown 15,000 tons of freight and 195,000 passengers in their nine years of service. The JRM-1 has four 2,250 h.p. Wright R-3350-8 engines.

Max. speed, 220 m.p.h. at 13,900 ft.; economical cruising, 135 m.p.h.; initial climb, 570 ft./min.; max. range, 3,315 miles; empty weight, 77,920 lb.; loaded, 145,000 lb.; span, 200 ft.; length, 120 ft. 3 in.; height, 44 ft. 7 in.; wing area, 3,686 sq. ft.

MARTIN AM-1 MAULER U.S.A.

Developed during the closing stages of the war as the XBTM-1, the first production AM-1 Mauler flew on December 16, 1946, and a total of one hundred and forty-nine Maulers was built. These were retired from first-line service in 1949, and in 1950 the remaining Maulers were assigned to U.S. Navy Reserve units. The Mauler is powered by a 3,000 h.p. Pratt & Whitney R-4360-4 Wasp Major, and can carry three 2,000-lb. torpedoes and twelve 5-in. rocket missiles.

Max. speed, 350 m.p.h.; max. range, 1,300 miles; empty weight, 14,900 lb.; loaded, 22,166 lb.; max. 25,000 lb.; span, 50 ft. 1 in.; length, 41 ft. 8 in.; height, 17 ft.

MARTIN P4M-1 MERCATOR U.S.A.

The Mercator long-range naval patrol aircraft is actually four-engined, being powered by two 3,250 h.p. Pratt & Whitney R-4360-20 piston-engines plus two 4,600 lb.s.t. Allison J33-A-10 turbojets. Ordered under the 1947–48 Naval Appropriations Bill, the production contract for nineteen Mercators was completed in 1950. The Mercator carries a defensive armament of two 20-mm. cannon in nose and tail positions, plus two 0.50-in. guns in a dorsal turret.

Max. speed, 356 m.p.h. at 16,400 ft.; range, 3,000 miles; loaded weight, 80,000 lb.; span, 114 ft.; length, 85 ft. 3 in.; height, 29 ft. 9 in.; wing area, 1,311 sq. ft.

MARTIN XB-51 U.S.A.

The Martin Model 234, or XB-51, was designed specifically for the low- and medium-altitude assault bombing role, and the first of two machines of this type was flown on October 28, 1949. Powered by three 5,200 lb.s.t. General Electric J47-GE-9 turbojets, the XB-51 has a variable-incidence wing, pivoting on the rear spar, and lateral control is effected by spoilers. The two double-wheel main undercarriage members retract into the fuselage, and a crew of two is carried. No production orders for the XB-51 have been placed.

Max. speed, 620 m.p.h. at sea level; max. bomb load, 12,000 lb.; approx. loaded weight, 80,000 lb.; span, 53 ft.; length, 80 ft.; height, 17 ft.

MARTIN 4-0-4   U.S.A.

Derived from the Martin 2-0-2, the 4-0-4 differs externally in having a 39-in. increase in fuselage length. The Martin 2-0-2 flew on November 22, 1946, but only thirty-one aircraft were built. These were followed by twelve 2-0-2As for T.W.A. which had the same engines as the later 4-0-4, increased all-up weight and fuel capacity, but were otherwise similar to the standard 2-0-2. One hundred and three 4-0-4s were built (sixty-one for T.W.A., and forty for Eastern Air Lines) and two are in service with the U.S. Coast Guard under the designation RM-1.

Specification: Forty-seat commercial airliner. Engines: Two 2,400 h.p. Pratt & Whitney R-2800-CB-16. Weights: Empty, 27,799 lb.; loaded, 42,750 lb. Performance: Max. speed, 312 m.p.h. at 14,500 ft.; cruising speed, 280 m.p.h. at 18,000 ft.; initial climb rate, 1,790 ft./min.; service ceiling, 27,300 ft.; range, 800 miles. Dimensions: Span, 93 ft. 3 in.; length, 74 ft. 7 in.; height, 28 ft. 5 in.; wing area, 864 sq. ft.

MARTIN B-57B   U.S.A.

Known as the Model 272, the B-57 is a redesigned version of the Canberra, numerous internal changes having been made. The initial version, the RB-57A, was externally similar to the Canberra B.2, but the B-57B has tandem seating, and a rotary bomb-bay is installed. The B-57C is a dual-control trainer variant, the B-57D has Pratt and Whitney J57 engines which increase top speed to 675 m.p.h., and the B-57E is a target-tug.

Specification: Two-seat night intruder. Engines: Two 7,220 lb.s.t. Wright J65-W-3 or W-5. Weights: Empty, 30,000 lb.; loaded, 49,000 lb. Performance: Approx. max. speed, 620 m.p.h.; service ceiling, 45,000–50,000 ft.; max. range, 3,000 miles. Armament: Eight 0.5-in. machine guns and various internal and external ordnance loads. Dimensions: Span, 64 ft.; length, 65 ft. 6 in.; height, 15 ft. 7 in.; wing area, 960 sq. ft.

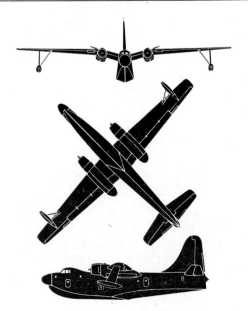

MARTIN P5M-2 MARLIN   U.S.A.

The Martin Model 237 Marlin has been produced in two basic versions, the P5M-1 (*silhouette*) and the P5M-2 (*photograph*), the latter differing primarily in having a T-type tailplane, and increased fuel capacity. Design of the Model 237 was initiated in July 1946, and the XP5M-1 flew on May 4, 1948. The first P5M-1 flew on June 22, 1951, and was delivered to the U.S. Navy in December 1951, and the first P5M-2 flew on April 29, 1954, and was delivered to the U.S. Navy in June 1954.

Specification: Anti-submarine patrol flying-boat. Engines: Two 3,450 h.p. (3,700 h.p. with water injection) Wright R-3350-32W. Weights: Empty, 46,933 lb.; normal loaded, 73,055 lb.; max. 85,000 lb. Performance: Max. speed, 262 m.p.h.; ceiling, 22,400 ft.; range, 3,600 miles; patrol duration, 20 hours. Armament: Two torpedoes or two 2,000-lb. bombs in each engine nacelle, and external racks carrying eight 1,000-lb. bombs. Dimensions: Span, 118 ft.; length, 98 ft. 11 in.; height, 33 ft.; wing area, 1,406.33 sq. ft.

MARTIN XP6M-1 SEAMASTER U.S.A.

The Model 275 Seamaster, or XP6M-1, is radically different in its concept and design from any other type of sea-going aircraft. Its primary tasks are those of minelaying and photo-reconnaissance, and its hull contains a watertight rotary mine door in which mines or a camera pod may be housed. The first of two XP6M-1 Seamaster prototypes flew on July 14, 1955, and it is proposed that production P6M-1s shall be powered by Wright J67 turbojets. A crew of five is carried, and sole defensive armament comprises a radar-controlled tail turret housing two 20-mm. cannon.
Specification: Long-range minelaying and reconnaissance flying-boat. Engines: Four 9,700 lb.s.t. (14,000 lb. with afterburning) Allison J71-A-4. Weights: Approx. loaded, 150,000 lb. Performance: Max. speed, 633 m.p.h. at 40,000 ft.; cruising altitude, 40,000 ft. Dimensions: Span, 100 ft.; length, 134 ft.; height, 31 ft.

MAUBOUSSIN M.129-48 CORSAIRE FRANCE

The M.129-48 Corsaire is a post-war production version of the pre-war M.123, fifty of which, powered by the 60 h.p. Salmson 9 Adr, were built by Avions Mauboussin in 1937–38. Eleven M.123s are still active in France, and single examples of the M.124 (80 h.p. Salmson 5AP-01), M.125 (65 h.p. Regnier 4J-0), and M.127 (95 h.p. Regnier 4-E0), and two pre-war examples of the M.129 (Minié Horus 4D of 70 h.p.), are currently airworthy. Twenty M.129-48 Corsaire two-seat primary trainers were produced in 1948 by Fouga et Cie, the first flying on March 20, 1948 (70 h.p. Minié 4 DA-28), and seventeen remain active.
Max. speed, 102 m.p.h.; cruising, 87 m.p.h.; range, 390 miles; empty weight, 876 lb.; loaded, 1,382 lb.; span, 38 ft. 6 in.; length, 22 ft. 7½ in.; height, 8 ft. 6 in.; wing area, 146.3 sq. ft.

MAX PLAN PF.204 FRANCE

The PF.204 single-seat racing and sport monoplane, designed by M. Max Plan, was flown for the first time on June 5, 1952, and is currently powered by a 75 h.p. Minié 4 DC 32 engine, but plans exist to replace this power plant with an 85 h.p. unit. The PF.204 is of all-wood construction with plywood skin, and has a fixed cantilever undercarriage enclosed by light alloy fairings. Only one prototype has so far been constructed.

Max. speed, 130 m.p.h.; cruising, 99 m.p.h.; initial climb rate, 394 ft./min.; endurance at full power, 2 hours, 30 minutes; normal loaded weight, 792 lb.; max., 1,100 lb.; span, 18 ft.; length, 17 ft. 6 in.

MCDONNELL FH-1 PHANTOM U.S.A.

The first U.S. jet-propelled aircraft designed from the outset for ship-board operations, the prototype Phantom, the XFD-1, flew on January 25, 1945, and the last of sixty production FH-1s was delivered to the U.S. Navy on May 27, 1948. A few examples remain. The FH-1 is powered by two 1,600 lb.s.t. Westinghouse J30-WE-20 turbojets. The Phantom was the first U.S. jet aircraft to operate from a carrier at sea, flying from the U.S.S. *Franklin D. Roosevelt* on July 21, 1946.

Max. speed, 505 m.p.h. at 40,000 ft.; normal range, 690 miles; max. range, 1,400 miles; empty weight, 6,683 lb.; loaded, 10,035 lb.; span, 40 ft. 9 in.; length, 38 ft. 9 in.; height, 13 ft. 2 in.; wing area, 276 sq. ft.

MCDONNELL F2H-2 BANSHEE U.S.A.

The F2H-2 is representative of the production versions of the Banshee carrier-borne single-seat fighter produced prior to the appearance of the lengthened F2H-3 model. The prototype, the XF2H-1, flew on January 11, 1947, and was followed by fifty-six F2H-1s and 392 F2H-2s (including fourteen F2H-2N night fighters and fifty-eight F2H-2P photo-reconnaissance aircraft). The F2H-2 is powered by two 3,250 lb.s.t. Westinghouse J34-WE-34 turbojets which replaced the 3,000 lb.s.t. J34-WE-22s of the F2H-1.
Max. speed, 630 m.p.h.; initial climb, 9,000 ft./min.; ceiling, 56,000 ft.; combat radius, 600 miles; combat weight, 14,000 lb.; max. 17,000 lb.; span, 44 ft. 11 in.; length, 40 ft. 1 in.; height, 14 ft. 5½ in.

MCDONNELL F2H-4 BANSHEE   U.S.A.

A progressive development of the F2H-3 which, in turn, was a long-range all-weather development of the F3H-2 with a 2 ft. 7 in. increase in fuselage length, the F2H-4 Banshee was the final production version of this carrier-borne fighter. The F2H-4 differs from the earlier F2H-3 primarily in having the improved J34-WE-38 turbojets replacing the J34-WE-34s. A total of 175 F2H-3s was delivered to the U.S. Navy, being followed by fifty-five externally-similar F2H-4s, the last of which was delivered on October 30, 1953.

Specification: Single-seat naval all-weather fighter. Engines: Two 3,250 lb.s.t. Westinghouse J34-WE-38. Weights: Approx. loaded, 19,000 lb. Performance: Max. speed, 610 m.p.h. at sea level; initial climb rate, 9,000 ft./min.; service ceiling, 56,000 ft.; range, 2,000 miles. Armament: Four 20-mm. cannon. Dimensions: Span, 44 ft. 11 in.; length, 47 ft. 6 in.; height, 14 ft. 5½ in.

MCDONNELL F3H-2N DEMON   U.S.A.

The first of two XF3H-1 Demon prototypes flew on August 7, 1951, and the fifty-six initial production machines, designated F3H-1N, were powered by the 7,200 lb.s.t. Westinghouse J40-WE-22 turbojet. This version has been succeeded by the extensively modified F3H-2N, the first of 220 machines of this type ordered by the U.S. Navy being delivered in June 1955. The F3H-2N has an increase of some fifteen per cent in wing area, this being effected by the extension of the root chord.

Specification: Single-seat naval fighter-bomber. Engine: One 9,700 lb.s.t. (14,250 lb. with afterburning) Allison J71-A-2. Weights: Approx. loaded, 24,000 lb. Performance: Approx. max. speed, 750 m.p.h. at sea level; 630 m.p.h. at 40,000 ft.; initial climb rate, 12,000 ft./min.; range, 2,000 miles. Armament: Four 20-mm. cannon and various underwing ordnance loads. Dimensions: Span, 35 ft. 4 in.; length, 58 ft. 4 in.; height, 13 ft. 11 in.; approx. wing area, 500 sq. ft.

MCDONNELL F-101A VOODOO   U.S.A.

The F-101A Voodoo long-range escort fighter is the heaviest and most powerful single-seat combat aircraft extant. First flown on September 28, 1954, the Voodoo is in production in two forms for the U.S. Strategic Air Command: the F-101A escort fighter, and the RF-101A photo-reconnaissance aircraft, the latter flying for the first time in 1955. An enlarged and more powerful variant of the Voodoo, the F-101B, has been ordered by the U.S. Air Defence Command. The F-101B will be powered by Pratt & Whitney J75s, and is intended for the long-range interceptor rôle.

Specification: Single-seat escort fighter. Engines: Two 9,700 lb.s.t. (14,250 lb. with afterburning) Pratt & Whitney J57-P-13. Weights: Approx. loaded, 40,000 lb. Performance: Approx. max. speed, 980 m.p.h. at 36,000 ft.; initial climb rate, 16,000 ft./min. Armament: Four 20-mm. M.39 cannon and air-to-air missiles. Dimensions: Span, 39 ft. 8 in.; length, 67 ft. 4¾ in.; height, 18 ft.

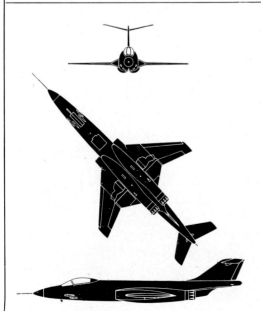

MESSERSCHMITT BF 108 TAIFUN   GERMANY

The Bf 108 Taifun, first produced by the Bayerische Flugzeugwerke (later Messerschmitt A.G.) in 1934, was used for communications by the *Luftwaffe*, and a number of examples are flying in various countries, particularly Switzerland. During the war, production was transferred to the S.N.C.A. du Nord in Occupied France, and production was continued after the war, the Bf 108 being redesignated Nord 1000. The Nord 1001 Pingouin I has the Argus engine replaced by the 240 h.p. Renault 6Q 10, and the Nord 1002 Pingouin II (*photo*) has a Renault 6Q 11. A total of 285 Pingouins were built in France.

Specification: Four-seat cabin monoplane. Engine: One 240 h.p. Argus As 10C. Weights: Empty, 1,773 lb.; loaded, 2,970 lb. Performance: Max. speed, 189 m.p.h.; cruising, 161 m.p.h.; ceiling, 20,340 ft.; range, 620 miles. Dimensions: Span, 34 ft. 5 in.; length, 27 ft. 2 in.; height, 7 ft. 6½ in.; wing area, 172.16 sq. ft.

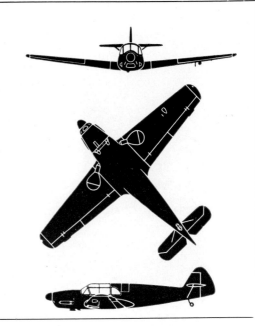
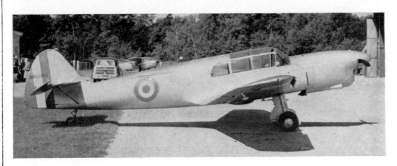

METEOR F.L.53-54   ITALY

The Meteor F.L.53 is an improved version of the Lombardi F.L.3 built by Meteor S.p.A. of Trieste under licence. The F.L.53 differs from the earlier F.L.3 in several respects, most noticeable of which is the all-round vision cockpit canopy and the cut-down rear fuselage. Various power plants may be installed, including the 75 h.p. Praga D (*silhouette*), the 65 h.p. Continental A-65 (*photo*), or the 60 h.p. CNA D-4. The F.L.54 is a three-seat model which can be powered by the 85 h.p. Continental C-85 or the 90 h.p. Continental C-90. The F.L.53 is of mixed construction, and the undercarriage is identical to that of the standard Piper Cub.

Specification: Two-seat cabin monoplane. Engine: One 65 h.p. Continental A-65. Weights: Empty, 772 lb.; normal loaded, 1,157 lb.; maximum, 1,378 lb. Performance: Max. speed, 112 m.p.h.; cruising speed, 97 m.p.h.; cruising altitude, 13,120–18,700 ft. Dimensions: Span, 33 ft. 9 in.; length, 21 ft. 7¾ in.; wing area, 152.85 sq. ft.

McKINNIE 165   U.S.A.

Produced by the McKinnie Aircraft Company and flown for the first time on August 10, 1952, the McKinnie 165 all-metal side-by-side two-seat cabin monoplane embodies a new and simplified method of airframe design and construction. All structural airframe components are of full cantilever construction and are fabricated from aluminium-clad sheet. The McKinnie 165 is fully aerobatic and dual controls are provided. Power is provided by a 165 h.p. Franklin 6A4-165-B3 engine.

Max. speed, 175 m.p.h. at sea level; cruising, 160 m.p.h.; initial climb rate, 1,550 ft./min.; range, 720 miles at 170 m.p.h. at 8,000 ft.; 1,050 miles at 150 m.p.h.; empty weight, 1,200 lb.; loaded, 1,840 lb.; span, 23 ft. 6 in.; length, 18 ft. 3 in.; height, 7 ft.

MEYERS OTW 160   U.S.A.

The Meyers OTW 160 two-seat primary training biplane is derived from the OTW 125 biplane of 1939 and the OTW 145 of 1940. The three models are externally similar, differing in the type of engine installed. The OTW 125 has a 125 h.p. Warner Scarab; the OTW 145 has a 145 h.p. Warner Scarab; and the OTW 160 has a 160 h.p. Kinner R-56. A considerable number of OTW biplanes were produced for schools operating under the C.A.A. War Training service during 1940–44, and some twenty-five of the three models remain active.

Max. speed, 120 m.p.h.; cruising, 105 m.p.h.; initial climb rate, 1,200 ft./min.; service ceiling, 17,500 ft.; range, 400 miles; empty weight, 1,340 lb.; loaded, 1,910 lb.; span, 30 ft.; length, 22 ft. 8 in.; height, 8 ft. 6 in.; wing area, 262 sq. ft.

MEYERS MAC 145   U.S.A.

The MAC 145, introduced in 1948, is a higher-powered development of the MAC 125-C, the first post-war design of the Meyers Aircraft Company. The MAC 145 differs from the earlier model in having a 145 h.p. Continental C145-2H in place of the 125 h.p. Continental C125. Both models are side-by-side two-seat cabin monoplanes of all-metal construction. Only a small series of MAC 145 aircraft was produced, and some nine aircraft of this type are currently active in the U.S.A.

Max. speed, 166 m.p.h.; cruising speed, 145 m.p.h.; initial climb rate, 950 ft./min.; service ceiling, 18,000 ft.; range, 600 miles; empty weight, 1,135 lb.; loaded, 1,735 lb.; span, 30 ft.; length, 21 ft. 4 in.; height, 8 ft. 6 in.; wing area, 149 sq. ft.

MEYERS MAC 200   U.S.A.

The MAC 200 is virtually a more powerful, four-seat development of the previously described two-seat MAC 145, with a lengthened fuselage and a fully-retractable nosewheel undercarriage. The MAC 200 is powered by a 225 h.p. Continental 0-470-E engine, and provides accommodation for four persons in two pairs. Dual controls are provided and the fuselage is an all-metal monocoque structure with stressed skin.

Max. speed, 196 m.p.h.; cruising speed, 182 m.p.h.; initial climb rate, 1,050 ft./min.; service ceiling, 18,000 ft.; max. range, 700 miles; empty weight, 1,625 lb.; loaded, 2,600 lb.; span, 30 ft. 4 in.; length, 23 ft. 8½ in.; height, 8 ft.; wing area, 160 sq. ft.

M.D.G. LD-261 MIDGY-CLUB   FRANCE

The LD-261 Midgy-Club is a progressive development of the single-seat LD-45 and two-seat LD-46 of 1946–47, and a few machines of this type were produced by Instruments de Precision M.D.G. A sole example of a slightly modified version, known as the Indraéro CB-10, was also built. Two Midgy-Clubs are currently registered in France; these are powered by 65 h.p. Continental A65 engines and are tandem two-seaters of mixed construction.

Max. speed, 112 m.p.h.; cruising, 98 m.p.h.; initial climb rate, 560 ft./min.; absolute ceiling, 22,200 ft.; empty weight, 704 lb.; loaded, 1,190 lb.; span, 22 ft. 11½ in.; length, 17 ft. 10½ in.; height, 6 ft. 5 in.; wing area, 114 sq. ft.

MIG-9   U.S.S.R.

The MIG-9 (code-named *Fargo*) is one of the earliest examples of Russian jet fighter design, and the first twin-jet aircraft to be employed by the Soviet Air Force. First flown early in 1946 and powered by two Russian derivatives of the Junkers Jumo 004B, the MIG-9 is no longer a first-line combat aircraft, but it is probably used as an advanced trainer. The two turbojets are disposed side-by-side below the wing centre section, heavy gauge metal shroud plates protecting the rear fuselage from the exhaust stream. The MIG-9 also possesses the distinction of being the first Soviet combat aircraft to employ a nosewheel undercarriage.

Estimated max. speed, 595 m.p.h.; approx. loaded weight, 14,000 lb.; approx. span, 34 ft.; length, 32 ft. 9 in.

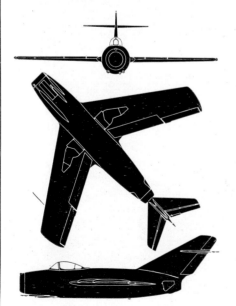

MIG-15   U.S.S.R.

The prototype MIG-15 flew for the first time on July 2, 1947, powered by an imported 4,850 lb.s.t. Rolls-Royce Nene. The initial production version was powered by the 5,500 lb.s.t. Klimov VK-1 (or RD-45F), but later production machines have the VK-2 and armament increased by the addition of a 37-mm. N cannon to the two 23-mm. NS cannon. Code-named *Fagot*, the MIG-15 serves with the Russian, Czech, Polish, Sino-Communist and Balkan "satellite" Air Forces. A two-seat trainer variant, the U-MIG-15 (code-named *Midget*) is depicted by the photo.

Specification: Single-seat fighter. Engine: One 5,953 lb.s.t. (6,750 lb. with water injection) Klimov VK-2. Weights: Empty, 8,320 lb.; combat, 11,268 lb.; maximum, 14,238 lb. Performance: Max. speed, 683 m.p.h.; initial climb rate, 10,400 ft./min.; ceiling, 51,000 ft. Dimensions: Span, 33 ft. 1¾ in.; length, 36 ft. 4 in.; height, 11 ft. 2 in.; wing area, 185.677 sq. ft.

MIG-17   U.S.S.R.

The MIG-17 single-seat interceptor fighter (code-named *Fresco*), is a progressive development of the MIG-15, and is used in considerable numbers by the Soviet Air Force. The wing has a mean sweep angle of 42° and differs from that of the MIG-15 in having extended inboard leading-edge sections, larger trailing-edge root fairings, modified flaps, and rounded tips. The wing modifications improve the MIG-17s critical Mach number as compared to that of the MIG-15, and it is believed that the VK-2 turbojet of the earlier fighter has been replaced by the VK-2Ja.
Specification: Single-seat fighter. Engine: One 6,850 lb.s.t. (7,700 lb. with afterburning) Klimov VK-2Ja. Approx. weights: Empty, 8,500 lb.; max. loaded, 15,000 lb. Approx. performance: Max. speed, 710 m.p.h.; initial climb rate, 14,000 ft./min.; service ceiling, 51,000 ft. Armament: Two 23-mm. NS and one 37-mm. N cannon. Dimensions: Span, 33 ft.; length, 36 ft. 9 in.; height, 11 ft. 2 in.

MILES M.2 HAWK MAJOR   G.B.

Derived from the Hawk primary trainer of 1933, the Hawk Major appeared in 1934. It differed from its predecessor in having the 90 h.p. Cirrus III replaced by a 130 h.p. Gipsy Major I and the braced undercarriage replaced by a trousered cantilever unit. Variants flying in the U.K. include the M.2F, the M.2H (with Miles split trailing-edge flaps), and M.2W with detail improvements. One M.2F is currently active in Australia. A development known as the Hawk Trainer appeared in 1935, a progressive development being the M.14 Hawk Trainer III.
Max. speed, 150 m.p.h.; cruising, 129 m.p.h. at 1,000 ft.; initial climb rate, 1,000 ft./min.; range, 560 miles; empty weight, 1,210 lb.; loaded, 1,720 lb.; span, 34 ft.; length, 24 ft.; height, 6 ft. 8 in.; wing area, 172 sq. ft.

MILES M.2L HAWK SPEED SIX   G.B.

Another variant of the versatile Hawk series was the Speed Six, produced in 1935 and flown in the King's Cup Race. Powered by a 200 h.p. de Havilland Gipsy Six engine, the Speed Six is a single-seat racing monoplane, and the sole surviving example (*illustrated*) has been fitted with a "bubble" type cockpit canopy. Construction and overall dimensions are similar to those of the standard Hawk Major. The structure is of wood with fabric and plywood covering.

Max. speed, 185 m.p.h.; cruising speed, 160 m.p.h.; initial climb rate, 1,450 ft./min.; empty weight, 1,200 lb.; loaded, 1,650 lb.; span, 24 ft.; length, 24 ft.; height, 6 ft.; wing area, 172 sq. ft.

MILES M.3B FALCON SIX   G.B.

The Falcon four-seat cabin monoplane appeared in 1934, and participated in the race to Australia in October of that year. The M.3 and M.3A Falcons were powered by the 130 h.p. D.H. Gipsy Major I engine, but the M.3B (*illustrated*), M.3C and M.3D Falcon Six models had the 200 h.p. D.H. Gipsy Six. Two M.3Bs are currently flying in the United Kingdom, an M.3B and an M.3D are flying in Sweden and Australia respectively, and an M.3A and an M.3B are flying in France. In pre-war years, the Falcon Six established a number of international records.
Max. speed, 180 m.p.h. at 1,000 ft.; cruising, 160 m.p.h.; initial climb, 1,125 ft./min.; normal range, 560 miles; max. 880 miles; empty weight, 1,550 lb.; loaded, 2,500 lb.; span, 35 ft.; length, 25 ft.; height, 6 ft. 6 in.; wing area, 174.3 sq. ft.

MILES M.7A NIGHTHAWK   G.B.

The M.7 Nighthawk two-seat cabin monoplane was produced in 1936 as a night- and blind-flying trainer which could also be used for radio and navigational instruction. The M.7A Nighthawk was a four-seater variant, one example of which is still active in the U.K. Limited production of a developed version of the Nighthawk, the M.16 Mentor, was undertaken for the Air Ministry. The Nighthawk could have either stick or wheel control and, for blind flying instruction, a black canvas hood was devised to fit over the pupil pilot. The M.7A Nighthawk is powered by a 200 h.p. de Havilland Gipsy Six engine.

Max. speed, 170 m.p.h.; cruising, 150 m.p.h. at 1,000 ft.; empty weight, 1,600 lb.; loaded, 2,450 lb.; span, 35 ft.; length, 25 ft.; height, 6 ft. 6 in.; wing area, 174.3 sq. ft.

MILES M.11A WHITNEY STRAIGHT   G.B.

The prototype M.11, which flew early in 1936, was designed by Phillips and Powis Aircraft Limited to meet the requirements of Whitney Straight, by which name it became known. The standard M.11A is powered by a 130 h.p. Gipsy Major III engine, but variants included the M.11B with the 135 h.p. Amherst Villiers Maya engine, and the M.11C with a 140 h.p. Gipsy Major II. A number of M.11As remain, including six in the U.K., two in Switzerland, one in New Zealand and one in France.

Max. speed, 145 m.p.h.; cruising, 130 m.p.h.; initial climb, 850 ft./min.; range, 570 miles; empty weight, 1,275 lb.; loaded, 1,896 lb.; span, 35 ft. 8 in.; length, 25 ft. 10 in.; height, 6 ft. 8 in.

MILES M.17 MONARCH   G.B.

The popularity achieved by the M.11A Whitney Straight resulted in the improved M.17 Monarch of 1938. A three-seater powered by a 130 h.p. de Havilland Gipsy Major I engine, the Monarch had identical wings to those of the M.14 trainer which was then in full production for the R.A.F. as the Magister. The Monarch could also be fitted as a two-seater with enlarged fuel tanks which increased cruising range to 900 miles. Two Monarchs currently appear on the British register.

Max. speed, 145 m.p.h.; cruising speed, 130 m.p.h.; initial climb rate, 850 ft./min.; service ceiling, 17,400 ft.; range, 600 miles; empty weight, 1,360 lb.; loaded, 2,000 lb.; span, 35 ft. 7 in.; height, 6 ft. 8 in.

MILES M.14 HAWK TRAINER III   G.B.

Fundamentally, the Hawk Trainer III is the same as the original Hawk Major of 1934, which, in turn, was one of no less than twenty-four variants of the Miles M.2 Hawk. Modified for military training, the Hawk Major became known as the M.14 Magister, and was adopted by the R.A.F. as a standard primary trainer in 1936. Many Magisters were sold as war surplus, and in civil guise the type is known as the Hawk Trainer III. It has been built by the *Turk Hava Kurumu Ucak Fabrikasi* in Turkey. Four examples of an improved version, the M.18 Magister II, powered by a 150 h.p. Gipsy Major III, were built, and at least one of these remains flying.

Specification: Two-seat primary trainer. Engine: One 130 h.p. de Havilland Gipsy Major I. Weights: Empty, 1,250 lb.; loaded, 1,863 lb. Performance: Max. speed, 145 m.p.h.; cruising, 123 m.p.h.; initial climb rate, 1,000 ft./min. Dimensions: Span, 33 ft. 10 in.; length, 25 ft. 3 in.; height, 6 ft. 8 in.; wing area, 176 sq. ft.

MILES M.25 MARTINET   G.B.

The M.25 Martinet was the first glider tug to be designed specifically for its task. Flown for the first time on April 24, 1942, the M.25 Martinet used many M.19 Master components, and 1,724 machines of this type were produced. In addition, sixty-five radio controlled pilotless M.50 Queen Martinets were built. The Martinet is powered by an 840 h.p. Bristol Mercury 30 radial engine, and the sole remaining example (*illustrated*) serves with the Irish Air Corps.

Max. speed, 232 m.p.h. at sea level; cruising speed, 225 m.p.h.; empty weight, 4,600 lb.; loaded, 6,600 lb.; span, 39 ft.; length, 30 ft. 11 in.; height, 11 ft. 7 in.; wing area, 238 sq. ft.

MILES M.28 MERCURY 6   G.B.

The M.28 Mercury cabin monoplane was a pre-war project, and construction of the prototype was suspended in 1939 but recommenced in 1941, the prototype flying on July 11, 1941. Three prototypes were produced during the war: the Mk.1 two-seat dual-control trainer, the Mk.2 three-seater with hydraulic undercarriage retraction, and the Mk.3 triple-control trainer. Three additional machines were produced after the war: one Mk.4 with a 145 h.p. Gipsy Major IIA, and two Mk.6s with 155 h.p. Blackburn Cirrus Major III. The Mercury 4 and one Mk.6 are flying in Australia, and the other Mk.6 in the U.K.

Max. speed, 157 m.p.h.; cruising, 139 m.p.h.; initial climb, 890 ft./min.; range, 410 miles; empty weight, 1,460 lb.; loaded, 2,427 lb.; span, 30 ft. 8 in.; length, 24 ft.; height, 8 ft. 4 in.

MILES M.38 MESSENGER 2A G.B.

The M.38 Messenger was a development of the M.28 Mercury, and the prototype—which also served as the prototype M.28—flew for the first time on September 12, 1942. Used in small numbers for liaison duties by the R.A.F. during the war, these machines were later converted for civil use as Messenger 4As. Production was terminated in January 1948 after sixty machines had been completed, the majority of these being the civil Messenger 2A with a 155 h.p. Blackburn Cirrus Major III.

Max. speed, 135 m.p.h.; cruising, 124 m.p.h.; initial climb, 950 ft./min.; range, 460 miles; empty weight, 1,450 lb.; loaded, 2,400 lb.; span, 36 ft. 2 in.; length, 24 ft.; height, 7 ft. 6 in.; wing area, 191 sq. ft.

MILES M.57 AEROVAN 4 G.B.

The M.57 Aerovan was first flown in 1945, the prototype being known as the Aerovan Mk.1. Only one Aerovan Mk.2, and very few Aerovan Mk.3s were produced, the major production version being the Mk.4. A total of forty-six Aerovans had been produced when production was terminated. Aerovans are currently flying in the United Kingdom and France, and one machine is being fitted with a special high aspect ratio wing with which it will be known as the Miles-Hurel-Dubois H.D.M.105. The Aerovan 4 has two 155 h.p. Cirrus Major engines.

Max. speed, 127 m.p.h.; cruising, 112 m.p.h.; initial climb, 575 ft./min.; range, 400 miles; empty weight, 3,000 lb.; loaded, 5,400 lb.; span, 50 ft.; length, 34 ft. 4 in.; height, 13 ft. 6 in.

MILES M.65 GEMINI 1A G.B.

The prototype Gemini was first flown on October 26, 1945, with a fixed undercarriage, and some 140 Geminis were built. Of these, fifty-six Gemini 1As, thirteen Gemini 3As, one Gemini 3 and one 3B are flying in the U.K., ten Gemini 1As are flying in Australia, and others are active in Canada, France, Switzerland, and other countries. The Gemini 1As has two 100 h.p. Cirrus Minor II engines, and the Gemini 3 has D.H. Gipsy Major 10s. The Gemini 7 is a rebuilt machine with some Aries refinements (Gipsy Major 10s) and the Gemini 8 has Cirrus Major IIIs.

Max. speed, 145 m.p.h.; cruising, 135 m.p.h.; initial climb, 650 ft./min.; empty weight, 1,910 lb.; loaded, 3,000 lb.; span, 36 ft. 2 in.; length, 22 ft. 3 in.; height, 7 ft. 6 in.

MILES M.75 ARIES G.B.

The M.75 Aries is an improved form of Gemini with more power, increased all-up weight and improved cabin comfort. In comparison with the Gemini, the Aries has been strengthened to meet the improved performance, and the redesigned tail surfaces provide increased stability and improved single-engine operation. The sole prototype Aries is powered by two 155 h.p. Blackburn Cirrus Major III engines, and is flying in Australia.

Max. speed, 172 m.p.h.; cruising, 150 m.p.h.; initial climb, 1,300 ft./min.; service ceiling, 20,000 ft.; max. range, 675 miles; empty weight, 2,350 lb.; loaded, 3,475 lb.; span, 36 ft. 2 in.; length, 22 ft. 3 in.; height, 7 ft. 6 in.

MILES M.77 SPARROWJET G.B.

The M.77 Sparrowjet is an extensively rebuilt M.5 Sparrowhawk airframe of 1935 vintage. The outer wings have been used in their original form, but an entirely new nose section and cockpit have been fitted, and metal engine bays containing two 330 lb.s.t. Turboméca Palas have been inserted between the fuselage and the original wing roots. The rebuilt aircraft bears little resemblance to the original Sparrowhawk, and was first flown in December 1953, being intended as a light racing monoplane.

Max. cruising speed, 220 m.p.h. at 10,000 ft.; initial climb, 2,100 ft./min.; empty weight, 1,578 lb.; loaded, 2,400 lb.; span, 28 ft. 7 in.; length, 30 ft. 10 in.; height, 7 ft. 2 in.; wing area, 156 sq. ft.

M.K.E.K. 4 UĞUR TURKEY

The M.K.E.K.4 Uğur (Luck) two-seat primary training monoplane has been designed as a replacement for the Miles M.14 Hawk Trainer III which was built under licence in Turkey. Powered by a 145 h.p. de Havilland Gipsy Major 10 Mk.1 engine, the Uğur is of all-wood construction with plywood covering. Dual flying controls are provided, and the main undercarriage members have levered-suspension cantilever legs. The Uğur is in quantity production for Turkish Air Force training schools, and some machines have been delivered to the Jordanian government.

Max, speed, 135 m.p.h.; cruising, 110 m.p.h.; initial climb rate, 800 ft./min.; service ceiling, 16,000 ft.; range, 300 miles; empty weight, 1,465 lb.; loaded, 2,045 lb.; span, 31 ft. 2½ in.; length, 24 ft. 7¼ in.; wing area, 171 sq. ft.

M.K.E.K.5A — TURKEY

The M.K.E.K.5A, originally known as the T.H.K.5A, was the first twin-engined aircraft to be designed and built in Turkey. Two versions of the basic design have been produced, the M.K.E.K.5 light ambulance providing accommodation for two stretcher cases and a medical attendant, and the M.K.E.K.5A six-seat light transport (*illustrated*). Nine examples of the former and one of the latter have been produced, and the M.K.E.K.5A is now registered in Denmark. Both versions have two 130 h.p. D.H. Gipsy Major engines.

Max. speed, 127 m.p.h.; cruising, 99 m.p.h.; initial climb, 630 ft./min.; service ceiling, 13,120 ft.; range, 405 miles; empty weight, 3,190 lb.; loaded, 4,180 lb.; span, 48 ft.; length, 32 ft. 9½ in.; height, 10 ft. 2 in.

M.K.E.K.7 — TURKEY

Formerly the T.H.K.2 but redesignated M.K.E.K.7 when the aircraft factory of the Turkish Air League was taken over by the Makine-Kimya Endustrusu Kurumu, this single-seat aerobatic training monoplane was produced during World War II, twenty-five machines being completed. The M.K.E.K.7, which is fully aerobatic and of all-wood construction, is powered by a 135 h.p. M.K.E.K.-built de Havilland Gipsy Major 1 engine.

Max. speed, 164.5 m.p.h.; cruising, 136 m.p.h.; initial climb, 1,710 ft./min.; empty weight, 1,080 lb.; loaded, 1,455 lb.; span, 26 ft. 3 in.; length, 22 ft. 10½ in.; height, 6 ft. 10 in.; wing area, 112 sq. ft.

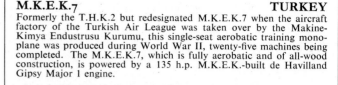

M.L.UTILITY AIRCRAFT — G.B.

Produced by M.L. Aviation Co. Ltd., this utility aircraft is of extremely unorthodox conception, its most unusual feature being an inflatable wing below which is slung a rudimentary cockpit structure. The wing can be rolled up and placed in a container for transportation, and no more than 50 h.p. is required for flight. The wing is cheap to manufacture, and the aircraft carries two persons with a Walter Mikron engine mounted aft of the fuselage nacelle. Take-off and landing speeds into wind are 18–20 m.p.h. The aircraft illustrated is intended as a prototype for both civil and military derivatives.

Approx. cruising speed, 45 m.p.h.; range, 100 miles; empty weight, 550 lb.; normal loaded, 950 lb.; span, 39 ft.; length, 25 ft.

MONOCOUPE 90A — U.S.A.

The Model 90 was introduced by the Monocoupe Corporation in 1930, and this two-seat cabin monoplane was progressively improved until 1942 when production was suspended. A variety of engines have been installed, including the 90 h.p. Lambert R-226, 125 h.p. Warner Scarab and 145 h.p. Warner Super-Scarab radials. The Model 90AF, introduced in 1937, was powered by the 90 h.p. Franklin 4AC-199-E3, and some fifty Model 90 Monocoupes are currently active in the U.S.A., and several in Europe. The specification relates to the Lambert-powered Model 90A.

Max. speed, 130 m.p.h.; cruising, 110 m.p.h.; initial climb, 900 ft./min.; range, 600 miles; empty weight, 973 lb.; loaded, 1,610 lb.; span, 32 ft. 0 in.; length, 20 ft. 6 in.

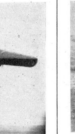

MONOCOUPE 90AL-115 — U.S.A.

Production of the Model 90AF, suspended in 1942, was resumed in 1947 by the Monocoupe Engine and Airplane Corporation, with an improved, higher-powered version known as the Model 90AL-115. This version is powered by a 115 h.p. Lycoming 0-235-C engine, and the generally-similar Model 90AL-125 is powered by a 125 h.p. Lycoming 0-290-A. Only a small number of post-war Monocoupes were built, and no more than five are currently active in the U.S.A. Like earlier Models, it is a side-by-side two-seater.

Max. speed, 156 m.p.h.; cruising, 135 m.p.h.; initial climb, 1,100 ft./min.; range, 600 miles; empty weight, 1,000 lb.; loaded, 1,610 lb.; span, 32 ft.; length, 22 ft. 11½ in.; height, 6 ft. 10 in.

MONOCOUPE METEOR 2 — U.S.A.

The Meteor 2 four-seat cabin monoplane was introduced in 1954 by Monocoupe Aircraft. Of all-metal construction, the Meteor is the result of four-and-a-half years' research and is powered by two 150 h.p. Lycoming 0-320 engines. The manufacturers claim that new constructional methods result in a considerable reduction in weight and manufacturing costs. All fuel is carried in wingtip tanks and full blind-flying equipment is installed.

Max. speed, 193 m.p.h.; max. range, 800 miles; empty weight, 1,750 lb.; loaded, 3,100 lb.; span, 32 ft.; length, 25 ft.; height, 6 ft. 1 in.; wing area, 160 sq. ft.

MOONEY M-18C WEE SCOTSMAN   U.S.A.

The M-18C Wee Scotsman (originally known as the Mite) has been produced in two versions, the M-18C with the 65 h.p. Continental A65-8, and the M-18L with the 65 h.p. Lycoming 0-145-B2. The latter version is now no longer in production owing to the discontinuation of the Lycoming engine. The M-18C incorporates the Mooney "Safe-Trim" control system which comprises a gear linking the tail trim with the wing flaps, automatically establishing proper settings for take-off, climb, approach and landing.
Specification: Single-seat light monoplane. Engine: One 65 h.p. Continental A65-8. Weights: Empty, 540 lb.; loaded, 850 lb. Performance: Max. speed, 142 m.p.h.; cruising, 130 m.p.h.; initial climb rate, 1,090 ft./min.; service ceiling, 21,000 ft.; range, 420 miles. Dimensions: Span, 26 ft. 10½ in.; length, 17 ft. 8 in.; height, 6 ft. 3¼ in.; wing area, 95.05 sq. ft.

MOONEY M-20   U.S.A.

The Mooney M-20 four-seat cabin monoplane was flown for the first time on August 10, 1953, and is basically a scaled-up development of the earlier M-18 Wee Scotsman single-seater. The M-20 embodies the Mooney "Safe-Trim" control system which comprises a gear linking the tail trim with the wing flaps so as to establish automatically proper settings for take-off, climb, approach and landing. The M-20 is powered by a 150 h.p. Lycoming engine and is of mixed construction.
Max. speed, 173 m.p.h. at sea level; economical cruising, 150 m.p.h.; initial climb rate, 950 ft./min.; max. range, 1,000 miles; empty weight, 1,335 lb.; loaded, 2,450 lb.; span, 35 ft.; length, 23 ft. 2⅝ in.; height, 8 ft. 3½ in.

MORAA   GERMANY

The Moraa ultra-light two-seat monoplane is virtually a powered version of the Doppelraab two-seat glider, designed by Fritz Raab of Munich and built by Alfons Puetzer K.G. of Bonn. The prototype illustrated here is powered by a 30 h.p. Volkswagen engine, but a higher-powered Porsche engine is proposed for production machines. The Moraa has a single control column which can be operated by both occupants, and two sets of rudder pedals.

Max. speed, 68 m.p.h.; cruising speed, 62 m.p.h.; minimum speed, 31 m.p.h.; empty weight, 727 lb.; loaded, 1,168 lb.; span, 43 ft. 11½ in.; length, 21 ft. 3¾ in.; height, 5 ft. 6½ in.; wing area, 194 sq. ft.

MORANE-SAULNIER M.S.181   FRANCE

The M.S.180 and the more powerful M.S.181 were produced by the Morane-Saulnier company in 1930 for the flying schools of the Cie Français d'Aviation. Powered by the 40 h.p. Salmson 9Ad and 60 h.p. Salmson 5Ac radial engines respectively, the M.S.180 and 181 were standard equipment with C.F.A. flying schools for several years, and two M.S.181s are still active in France. The M.S.185 is generally similar to the M.S.181 but powered by a 40 h.p. Salmson 9Ad. One example of the M.S.185 is also flying in France.
Max. speed, 88 m.p.h.; cruising, 72 m.p.h.; initial climb, 630 ft./min.; range, 365 miles; empty weight, 630 lb.; loaded, 960 lb.; span, 29 ft. 6 in.; length, 19 ft. 10 in.

MORANE-SAULNIER M.S.230-E   FRANCE

First introduced in 1930, the M.S.230 elementary trainer was one of the most famous Morane-Saulnier designs of the inter-war years, and more than one thousand aircraft of this type were produced during the 'thirties. Powered by a 250 h.p. Salmson 9Ab radial engine, a considerable number of M.S.230-Es are currently active with French aero clubs, and a few remain in service with the *Armée de l'Air*. The M.S.230 was produced under licence in Belgium (as the M.S.233) and Portugal, and a small batch were produced after World War II.
Max. speed, 127 m.p.h.; climb to 9,840 ft., 11 minutes, 18 seconds; empty weight, 1,748 lb.; loaded, 2,533 lb.; span, 35 ft. 2 in.; length, 22 ft. 9 in.; height, 8 ft. 11 in.; wing area, 212 sq. ft.

MORANE-SAULNIER M.S.315-E FRANCE

The M.S.315-E first appeared in 1932, and is very similar to the earlier M.S.230 but smaller and powered by a 135 h.p. Salmson 9Nc engine. The M.S.315 was produced in substantial quantities pre-war, and production was resumed after the war by the S.N.C.A. du Centre, thirty-three post-war machines being built. Sixty-seven M.S.315s are currently flying with French aero clubs, one of these being an M.S.315-II with a 175 h.p. Salmson 9Nd. The M.S.315-E is a tandem two-seat primary training monoplane.

Max. speed, 106 m.p.h.; range, 600 miles; ceiling, 13,000 ft.; loaded weight, 2,112 lb.; span, 39 ft. 4 in.; length, 24 ft. 11 in.; height, 8 ft. 6 in.

MORANE-SAULNIER M.S.340 FRANCE

Introduced in 1933, the M.S.340 parasol-wing two-seat light training aircraft was produced in prototype form only with a 105 h.p. de Havilland Gipsy III engine. Several different engines were installed in the production models: the M.S.341 which appeared in 1934 has a 130 h.p. Renault 4 Pei, the M.S.342 (*illustrated*) has a 130 h.p. de Havilland Gipsy Major, and the M.S.343 has a 175 h.p. Salmson. The M.S.340 prototype is still airworthy in France, and one example of each of the three production versions is currently active.

Max. speed, 124 m.p.h. at sea level; cruising, 111 m.p.h.; climb to 6,560 ft., 12 minutes; service ceiling, 18,040 ft.; empty weight, 1,206 lb.; loaded, 1,802 lb.; span, 33 ft. 7 in.; length, 22 ft. 3 in.; height, 7 ft. 8 in.; wing area, 170 sq. ft.

MORANE-SAULNIER M.S.350 FRANCE

One of the very few biplanes produced by the Morane-Saulnier concern, the M.S.350 was designed in 1935 as a single-seat aerobatic biplane for display flying. Powered by a 220 h.p. Renault 6Q-01 engine, the M.S.350 was employed by the French aerobatic pilot Détroyat at aeronautical displays during 1936–37. Only one prototype was produced and this machine is still flying in France. The M.S.351 was a projected development of the M.S.350 with a 135 h.p. Salmson 9Nc, development of which was abandoned.

Max. speed, 155 m.p.h.; cruising speed, 132.5 m.p.h.; initial climb rate, 920 ft./min.; range, 310 miles; span, 26 ft. 3 in.; length, 19 ft. 8 in.

MORANE-SAULNIER M.S.475 FRANCE

The M.S.475 two-seat advanced trainer is identical to the M.S.474 except that it is fitted with an 850 h.p. Hispano 12Y-45 engine. One hundred and ninety-nine M.S.475 trainers have been delivered to the *Armée de l'Air*. A further development, the M.S.477 powered by a 580 h.p. SNECMA Renault 12S engine, flew on December 28, 1950, but no production contracts for this version were placed. When used as a fighter-trainer, the M.S.475 carries two 7.5-mm. machine guns mounted in the wings and racks for two 110-lb. bombs.

Max. speed, 342 m.p.h. at 16,405 ft.; cruising (70 per cent power), 160 m.p.h.; climb to 16,400 ft., 8 minutes, 30 seconds; range, 746 miles; empty weight, 4,928 lb.; loaded, 6,268 lb.; span, 34 ft. 9 in.; length, 29 ft. 6 in.; height, 11 ft. 10½ in.

MORANE-SAULNIER M.S.502 FRANCE

During the war years, production of the Fieseler Fi 156 Storch monoplane was transferred to the German-controlled Morane-Saulnier plant where production continued after the liberation of France. Production models included the M.S.500 (Argus As 410C engine of 240 h.p.), the M.S.501 (Renault 6Q), and the M.S.502 (230 h.p. Salmson 9AB radial engine). The latter is a commercial version known as the Criquet, fifty-three of which appear on the French Civil Register. The M.S.501 is employed by the *Armée de Terre*.

Max. speed, 106 m.p.h.; cruising speed, 85 m.p.h.; range, 435 miles; empty weight, 2,100 lb.; loaded, 3,140 lb.; span, 46 ft. 9 in.; length, 31 ft. 8 in.; height, 10 ft.; wing area, 279.7 sq. ft.

MORANE-SAULNIER M.S.563 FRANCE

Derived from the M.S.560, which was flown for the first time on September 1, 1945, and the M.S.561, which were powered by the 75 h.p. Train 4D-01 and the 100 h.p. Mathis G-4Z respectively, the M.S.563 is a single-seat fully-aerobatic personal aircraft or intermediate trainer. Powered by a 105 h.p. Walter Minor 4-III engine, the M.S.563 is of all-metal construction and, like its predecessors, was built in prototype form only. The following specification relates to the M.S.561.

Max. speed, 155 m.p.h. at sea level, 145 m.p.h. at 9,840 ft.; initial climb rate, 680 ft./min.; range, 680 miles; service ceiling, 16,400 ft.; empty weight, 1,138 lb.; loaded, 1,490 lb.; span, 28 ft.; length, 23 ft. 8½ in.; height, 7 ft. 2½ in.

MORANE-SAULNIER M.S.472 VANNEAU   FRANCE

The Vanneau advanced trainer stems from the M.S.453 of 1940, and the M.S.470, a derivative of this type developed during the Occupation of France to meet German requirements. The M.S.470 was powered by the 720 h.p. Hispano 12X, and the conversion of this type to use the Gnôme-Rhône radials intended for the Potez 63 resulted in the M.S.472 Vanneau. The Vanneau was first flown on February 12, 1945, and 230 of this type were produced for the French Air Force, while a further 69 of a navalised version, the M.S.474, were delivered to the French Navy. The M.S.479 was a development with a 800 h.p. SNECMA 14X-04 built as a prototype only.
Specification: Two-seat advanced trainer. Engine: One 700 h.p. Gnôme-Rhône 14M-9. Weights: Empty, 3,817 lb.; loaded, 5,290 lb. Performance: Max. speed, 290 m.p.h.; cruising, 258 m.p.h.; range, 950 miles. Armament: Two 7.5-mm. guns. Dimensions: Span, 34 ft. 11 in.; length, 28 ft. 3 in.; height, 11 ft. 10½ in.

MORANE SAULNIER M.S.733 ALCYON   FRANCE

The M.S.733 Alcyon is derived from the M.S.730 (180 h.p. Mathis 8G.20) which first flew in 1950. Like the M.S.730, the M.S.731 (240 h.p. Argus As.10) had a fixed under-carriage, but the M.S.732 (250 h.p. Salmson 8.AS.02) had an undercarriage retracting into large fairings. The Alcyon, which first flew on September 25, 1951, is identical to the M.S.732, apart from undercarriage retraction and engine. Production of 134 Alcyons is nearing completion, one hundred of these having been supplied to the French Air Force, and others to the Cambodian Air Force (*photo*), both as trainers and for police duties.
Specification: Two/three-seat basic trainer. Engine: One 240 h.p. Potez 6D.30. Weights: Empty, 2,780 lb.; loaded, 3,680 lb. Performance: Max. speed, 162 m.p.h.; cruising, 143 m.p.h.; initial climb rate, 825 ft./min.; service ceiling, 15,750 ft.; cruising endurance, 4 hours. Dimensions: Span, 37 ft.; length, 30 ft. 7 in.; height, 7 ft. 11½ in.

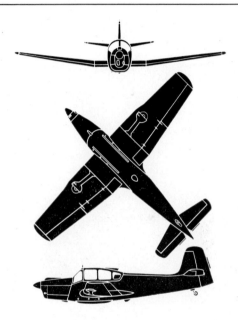

MORANE-SAULNIER M.S.760 PARIS   FRANCE

The M.S.760 Paris four-seat cabin monoplane is a development of the experimental M.S.755 Fleuret fighter-trainer, and flew for the first time on July 29, 1954. Differing from the Fleuret primarily in having a lengthened fuselage and slightly increased wing span, the Paris may be built under licence in the U.S.A. by the Beech Aircraft Corporation. Preparations for quantity production of a military liaison version of the Paris were inaugurated in October 1955, proposed initial orders calling for fifty machines for the *Armée de l' Air* and thirty for the French Navy.
Specification: Four-seat cabin monoplane. Engines: Two 880 lb.s.t. Turboméca Marboré II. Weights: Empty, 4,325 lb.; loaded, 7,480 lb. Performance: Max. speed, 405 m.p.h.; cruising speed, 350 m.p.h. at sea level (530 miles range), 355 m.p.h. at 10,000 ft. (680 miles range); initial climb rate, 2,260 ft./min. Dimensions: Span, 33 ft. 3½ in.; length, 32 ft. 10¾ in.; wing area, 194 sq. ft.

MORANE-SAULNIER M.S.571   FRANCE

Basically a three-seat development of the M.S.560, the prototype of the M.S.571, the M.S.570, flew for the first time on December 19, 1945, powered by a 140 h.p. Renault Pei. The M.S.571 differed from the M.S.570 primarily in providing accommodation for three persons, the earlier machine being a two-seater, and the first of three M.S.571s flew on October 13, 1946. The M.S.572 was a proposed four-seat production variant powered by a 140 h.p. Potez 4D which was not proceeded with.
Max. speed, 152 m.p.h. at 1,640 ft.; cruising (70 per cent power), 137 m.p.h.; initial climb rate, 748 ft./min.; range, 620 miles; empty weight, 1,478 lb.; loaded, 2,312 lb.; span, 34 ft. 2½ in.; length, 27 ft. 11 in.; height, 9 ft. 1 in.

MOSSCRAFT M.A.2   G.B.

Produced in 1937 by Moss Brothers Aircraft Limited, the M.A.2 two-seat light cabin monoplane was originally produced with a 95 h.p. Pobjoy Niagara engine as the M.A.1. The M.A.2 differs in having a 90 h.p. Blackburn Cirrus Minor engine, and one example remains on the British Civil Register. Two models of the M.A.2 with open cockpits were produced in 1938, one being intended for touring and the other for training. The M.A.2 is of wooden construction with plywood covering.

Max. speed, 120 m.p.h.; cruising, 105 m.p.h.; initial climb, 850 ft./min.; range, 400 miles; empty weight, 880 lb.; loaded, 1,400 lb.; span, 34 ft.; length, 23 ft. 3 in.; height, 7 ft.; wing area, 154 sq. ft.

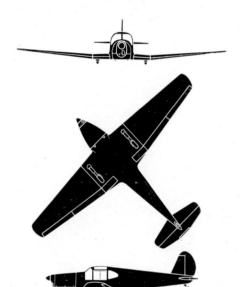

MRAZ M-1D SOKOL   CZECHOSLOVAKIA

The Sokol (Falcon) was secretly designed during the German occupation, and the first prototype, the M-1/1, flew shortly after the German collapse in 1945. The first production model, the M-1A, was a two-seater and was built in small numbers, being replaced by the M-1C three-seater (*photograph*). This was followed by an improved version, the M-1D, with a clear-vision cockpit canopy, and the M-1E twin-float seaplane variant.
Specification: Three-seat cabin monoplane. Engine: One 105 h.p. Walter Minor 4-III. Weights: Empty, 938 lb.; loaded, 1,720 lb. Performance: Max. speed, 150 m.p.h.; cruising speed, 132 m.p.h.; initial climb rate, 590 ft./min.; service ceiling, 15,700 ft.; range, 620 miles. Dimensions: Span, 32 ft. 9¾ in.; length, 24 ft. 1 in.; height, 7 ft. 2¾ in.; wing area, 148.5 sq. ft.

MRAZ M-3 BONZO   CZECHOSLOVAKIA

The M-3 Bonzo was produced by the Chocen plant of the Czech national aircraft industry (the former J. Mraz works) and, like the well-known Sokol, was designed by Ing. J. Mraz. The M-3 Bonzo is a four-seat "family tourer" produced in prototype form only. Of all-wood construction, it is powered by a 160 h.p. Walter Minor 6-III engine. A retractable nosewheel undercarriage is fitted. Ing. J. Mraz was widely known before the war for his light aircraft produced in association with Ing. Benes.
Max. speed, 165 m.p.h.; cruising, 150 m.p.h.; initial climb, 708 ft./min.; ceiling, 16,400 ft.; range, 620 miles; empty weight, 1,278 lb.; loaded, 2,424 lb.; span, 34 ft. 9 in.; length, 25 ft. 4 in.; height, 7 ft. 4½ in.; wing area, 148.5 sq. ft.

NARDI F.N.333-S   ITALY

The F.N.333 amphibian flying-boat, the first post-war product of the Nardi S.A., was first flown on December 4, 1952. This prototype, later destroyed during flight testing, was a three-seater powered by a 145 h.p. Continental engine, but the F.N.333-S is a four-seater powered by a 225 h.p. Lycoming. It employs an unusual form of wing-folding which permits the stabilising floats to remain in constant contact with the surface of the water during the folding process. The F.N.333-S is of all-metal construction.
Max. speed, 168 m.p.h.; cruising, 150 m.p.h.; initial climb, 985 ft./min.; normal range, 450 miles; empty weight, 1,625 lb.; loaded, 2,650 lb.; span, 32 ft. 9½ in.; length, 22 ft. 11¾ in.; height, 8 ft. 8¾ in.; wing area, 145 sq. ft.

NARDI F.N.305   ITALY

The F.N.305 was the first product of the firm founded by the brothers Elio, Luigi, and Euste Nardi, and was designed in 1933. The initial production version was powered by a 180 h.p. Fiat A.70/S radial engine, but later machines had the 185 h.p. Alfa Romeo 115-1 engine, and one example of this variant (*illustrated*) is still flying in Italy. Seating two in tandem, the F.N.305 was intended primarily as a fighter trainer. An experimental version, the F.N.305-D, established a long-distance record by flying from Rome to Addis Ababa.
Max. speed, 211 m.p.h.; cruising, 189 m.p.h.; service ceiling, 22,960 ft.; range, 435 miles; empty weight, 1,320 lb.; loaded, 1,980 lb.; span, 27 ft. 9 in.; length, 22 ft. 11 in.; height, 6 ft. 10½ in.; wing area, 129.12 sq. ft.

NARDI F.N.315   ITALY

Introduced in 1938 as a potential successor to the F.N.305, the F.N.315 tandem two-seat cabin monoplane was designed primarily as a military trainer. The F.N.315 was produced with both the Hirth H.M.508D of 280 h.p., and the Alfa Romeo 115-1 of 185 h.p. It was exported to six countries, and a light attack version was also built experimentally. The sole remaining example is Hirth-powered and carries Swiss registration.
Max. speed, 239 m.p.h. at 8,200 ft.; cruising, 220 m.p.h. at 11,480 ft.; climb to 13,120 ft., 6 minutes, 40 seconds; cruising range, 590 miles; empty weight, 1,562 lb.; loaded, 2,255 lb.; span, 27 ft. 9 in.; length, 22 ft. 11 in.; height, 6 ft. 10½ in.; wing area, 129.12 sq. ft.

NAVAL AIRCRAFT FACTORY N3N-3   U.S.A.

The first product of the Naval Aircraft Factory was the XN3N-1 tandem two-seat primary training floatplane which was produced under the Vinson-Trammell Treaty Navy Bill of 1935 which stipulated that ten per cent of the U.S. Navy's aircraft and aero engines were to be Government manufactured. Delivery of 185 N3N-1 biplanes commenced in June 1936 and was completed in 1938. Subsequently, 650 examples of the improved N3N-3 were built, powered by the 220 h.p. NAF-built Wright R-760-8 engine. A number of N3N-3 biplanes are still operated by the U.S. Navy at Annapolis, and some two hundred surplus machines are used by civil operators, many being modified as crop-dusters with wheel undercarriage.
Max. speed, 105 m.p.h.; cruising, 90 m.p.h.; span, 34 ft.; length, 29 ft.

NIESS MARANHÃO   BRAZIL

Built in quantity by the Fabrica do Galleao at Rio de Janeiro, the Niess Maranhão side-by-side two-seat cabin monoplane is used by several Brazilian flying clubs. Powered by an 85 h.p. Continental C85 engine, the Maranhão has dual controls and is of mixed construction with ply-wood and fabric covering. The Maranhão is very similar externally to the C.A.P.4 Paulistinha, but has a wider fuselage.

Max. speed, 110 m.p.h.; cruising speed, 97 m.p.h.; initial climb rate, 770 ft./min.; range, 280 miles; empty weight, 886 lb.; loaded, 1,270 lb.; span, 34 ft. 6 in.; length, 22 ft.; height, 6 ft. 6 in.

NORD N.3201   FRANCE

The N.3201 has been designed to fulfil the requirements of an official competition for a tandem two-seat primary trainer for the government-sponsored flying training schools. The first prototype, the N.3200, flew on September 10, 1954, with a Salmson-Argus 8AS-04 engine of 260 h.p. being preceded on June 22, 1954, by the N.3201 with a 170 h.p. SNECMA-Régnier engine. Apart from the engine installed, both models are identical. The photograph illustrates the N.3200, and the specification relates to the N.3201.
Max. speed, 150 m.p.h. at sea level; cruising, 124 m.p.h.; initial climb rate, 984 ft./min.; endurance, 2 hours; empty weight, 1,742 lb.; loaded, 2,405 lb.; span, 32 ft. 1½ in.; length, 26 ft. 2½ in.; height, 10 ft. 2¾ in.

NORD N.C.856N   FRANCE

Derived from the N.C.856A Norvigie, the N.C.856N is a four-seat cabin monoplane intended primarily for touring purposes. Powered by a 160 h.p. SNECMA-Régnier 4LO-8 engine, the N.C.856N is generally similar to the three-seat N.C.856H twin-float seaplane variant, an example of which is registered in Monaco. The wing is a single-spar metal structure with fabric covering, and the fuselage is of welded-steel tube with fabric covering over light wooden formers.
Max. speed, 127 m.p.h.; cruising speed, 112 m.p.h.; initial climb, 689 ft./min.; ceiling, 18,040 ft.; range, 360 miles; empty weight, 1,389 lb.; loaded, 2,447 lb.; span, 41 ft.; length, 25 ft. 3¼ in.; height, 7 ft. 6 in.; wing area, 183 sq. ft.

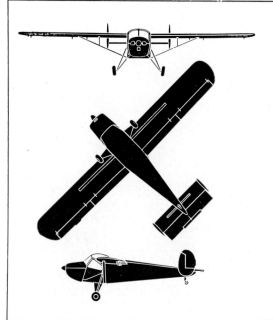

NORD N.C.853S   FRANCE

The N.C.853S was designed by the S.N.C.A. du Centre and production of this light two-seater was taken over in 1949 by the S.N.C.A. du Nord. It is a development of the N.C.850 (75 h.p. Mathis G-4F) of 1947, and N.C.851 (70 h.p. Minié 4DA 28). The N.C.853 first flew on March 15, 1948, and 100 N.C.853s were produced for the *Service de l'Aviation Legère*. The N.C.854 (65 h.p. Continental A-65-8), N.C.858 (90 Continental C-90-8F) and N.C.859 (105 h.p. Walter Minor 4-III) are generally similar apart from the engines.

Specification: Two-seat light cabin monoplane. Engine: One 75 h.p. Minié 4.DC.32A/B. Weights: Empty, 800 lb.; loaded, 1,320 lb. Performance: Max. speed, 102 m.p.h.; cruising speed, 87 m.p.h.; service ceiling, 11,480 ft.; range, 310 miles. Dimensions: Span, 36 ft. 11 in.; length, 22 ft. 5 in.; height, 6 ft. 10 in.; wing area, 166.2 sq. ft.

NORD N.C.856A NORVIGIE   FRANCE

The N.C.856A is a military development of the N.C.856 tourer (105 h.p. Walter Minor 4-III) which flew for the first time on March 12, 1949, but development was discontinued with the liquidation of the S.N.C.A. du Centre. A second prototype, modified for use as an air observation post, was built by the S.N.C.A. du Nord, and flown on March 15, 1951. An order for 112 machines, designated N.C.856A Norvigie, was subsequently placed for the French Army, the first production Norvigie flying on March 12, 1953.

Specification: Two-seat air observation post and liaison monoplane. Engine: One 140 h.p. Régnier 4 LO.4. Weights: Empty, 1,432 lb.; loaded, 1,984 lb. Performance: Max. speed, 118 m.p.h.; cruising speed, 105 m.p.h.; endurance (A.O.P.), 1 hour, (liaison) 3 hours; initial climb rate, 984 ft./min. Dimensions: Span, 41 ft.; length, 25 ft. 3 in.; height, 7 ft. 4½ in.; wing area, 183 sq. ft.

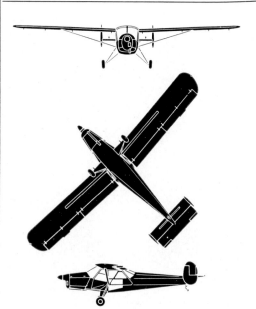

NORD 1101 NORALPHA   FRANCE

The Noralpha is basically the Messerschmitt Me 208 (240 h.p. Argus As 10), two prototypes of which were built in France during the German occupation and later redesignated Nord 1100 Noralpha. No additional Argus-powered machines were built, and the production version, the Nord 1101, had a Renault 6Q-10 engine substituted for the German power plant. Two hundred Noralphas were built, and many of these are in service with the French Air Force for communications and liaison duties. Eight commercial Noralphas are registered in France, being used as air taxis and for touring.

Specification: Four-seat cabin monoplane. Engine: One 240 h.p. Renault 6Q-10. Weights: Empty, 2,090 lb.; loaded, 3,630 lb. Performance: Max. speed, 189 m.p.h.; cruising speed, 172 m.p.h.; service ceiling, 19,350 ft.; range, 745 miles. Dimensions: Span, 37 ft. 8 in.; length, 28 ft.; height, 10 ft. 8 in.; wing area, 187 sq. ft.

NORD 1203/II NORÉCRIN   FRANCE

The Norécrin was first flown on December 15, 1945, as the two-seat Nord 1200. The first production model, the Nord 1201, was a three-seater powered by a 140 h.p. Renault 4 Pei engine. This power plant was replaced by the 135 h.p. Régnier 4LO and the designation changed to Nord 1203. In 1948, a four-seat model, the Nord 1203/II, was placed in production, and an experimental version, the Nord 1204/02, was fitted with a 145 h.p. Continental C145-2. A total of 380 Norécrins had been built when production was suspended, being resumed in 1955 with an order for a further ninety machines.

Specification: Four-seat cabin monoplane. Engine: One 135 h.p. Régnier 4LO. Weights: Empty, 1,437 lb.; loaded, 2,313 lb. Performance: Max. speed, 174 m.p.h.; cruising, 137 m.p.h.; initial climb rate, 985 ft./min.; range, 560 miles. Dimensions: Span, 33 ft. 6¼ in.; length, 23 ft. 8 in.; height, 9 ft. 6 in.; wing area, 410 sq. ft.

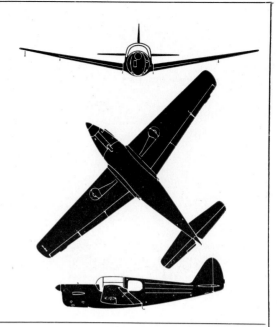

NORD 1402 NOROIT   FRANCE

The Noroit twin-engined Naval amphibian flying-boat is in service with the French Navy. The prototype Noroit, the N.1400-01 (two 1,200 h.p. Gnôme-Rhône 14R), flew on January 6, 1949, and was not fitted with amphibian gear. Four pre-production prototypes followed, the N.1401-02 and -05 with 1,540 h.p. Bristol Hercules 100 engines, and the N.1402-03 and -04 with Arsenal 12H (Junkers Jumo 213A) engines. A batch of twenty N.1402 Noroits was subsequently completed, these being powered by Arsenal 12H engines and employed for air/sea rescue and reconnaissance.

Specification: General-purpose amphibian flying-boat. Engines: Two 2,060 h.p. Arsenal 12H-00. Weights: Empty, 28,660 lb.; loaded, 45,040 lb. Performance: Max. speed, 230 m.p.h. at 8,690 ft.; initial climb rate, 985 ft./min.; max. range, 2,610 miles. Armament: Six 20-mm. cannon (nose, dorsal and tail). Dimensions: Span, 103 ft. 8 in.; length, 72 ft. 3½ in.; height, 22 ft. 5½ in.; wing area, 1,080 sq. ft.

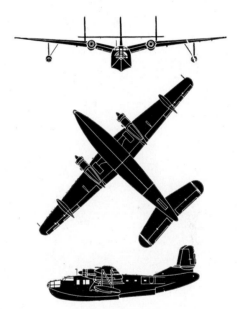

NORD 2501 NORATLAS   FRANCE

The prototype Noratlas, the N.2500, flew on September 10, 1949, powered by two 1,600 h.p. Gnôme-Rhône 14R radials. One hundred and sixty N.2501 Noratlases have been ordered, 140 of these being for the French Air Force. Two civil Noratlases are employed by U.A.T., and three have been ordered by Israel. The N.2502 has two Turboméca Palas turbojets at the wingtips. These enable the Noratlas to maintain a standard take-off and climb performance in high ambient temperatures up to an altitude of 4,500 ft. The first production Noratlas flew on October 24, 1952.

Specification: Military transport. Engines: Two 2,040 h.p. SNECMA-built Bristol Hercules 758. Weights: Empty, 24,445 lb.; loaded, 43,210 lb. Performance: Max. speed, 273 m.p.h. at 4,920 ft.; cruising, 209 m.p.h. at 9,842 ft.; initial climb rate, 1,230 ft./min.; range, 930 miles. Dimensions: Span, 106 ft. 7 in.; length, 71 ft. 6 in.; height, 20 ft. 6 in.; wing area, 1,089.3 sq. ft.

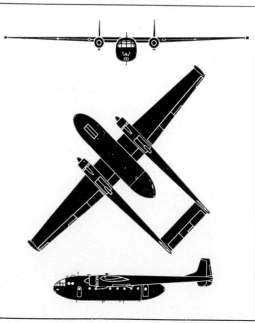

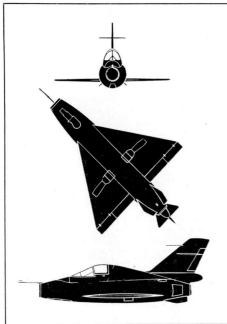

NORD-SFECMAS 1402B GERFAUT II   FRANCE

Designed to furnish data for the higher-powered SFECMAS 1502 Griffon, the Gerfaut flew for the first time on January 15, 1954, and, on August 3, 1954, became the first European aircraft to exceed Mach unity in level flight without recourse to power boosting. After initial flight trials, the Gerfaut was modified by the addition of two ventral strakes, and a larger tail parachute cone. The Nord-SFECMAS 1502 Griffon, first flown on September 20, 1955, is a full combat prototype powered by a 7,717 lb.s.t. Atar 101G turbojet.

Specification: Single-seat research aircraft. Engine: One 6,173 lb.s.t. S.N.E.C.M.A. Atar 101C. Weights: Empty, 6,327 lb.; normal loaded, 7,936 lb.; maximum, 10,150 lb. Performance: Approx. max. speed at sea level, 680 m.p.h.; Mach 1.0 at 32,800 ft.; absolute ceiling, 55,770 ft. Dimensions: Span, 21 ft. 4 in.; length, 32 ft. 5½ in.; height, 13 ft. 8½ in.; wing area, 204.514 sq. ft.

NORTH AMERICAN NA-50A (P-64)   U.S.A.

The NA-50 single-seat fighter appeared in 1939, and six machines of this type were purchased by Siam in 1940. These were taken over by the U.S.A.A.F. as advanced combat trainers in 1941. One example remains and, with Mexican registration, is based at Phoenix, Arizona, where it is used for cloud seeding. The NA-50A is powered by an 875 h.p. Wright R-1820-77 Cyclone 9 engine, and originally carried an armament of two 0.30-in. machine guns in the engine cowling.

Max. speed, 270 m.p.h. at 9,500 ft.; cruising, 255 m.p.h. at 16,500 ft.; range, 645 miles; empty weight, 4,470 lb.; loaded (max.), 6,800 lb.; span, 37 ft. 3 in.; length, 26 ft. 11 in.; wing area, 236 sq. ft.

NORTH AMERICAN NA-25 (0-47B)   U.S.A.

The North American XO-47 three-seat observation monoplane, ordered by the U.S.A.A.F. in 1936, was first flown in 1938, and 164 production machines designated 0-47A were ordered during the same year. The 0-47A was powered by a 975 h.p. Wright R-1820-41 engine, and was succeeded in production by the 0-47B with a 1,060 h.p. Wright R-1820-57 engine and increased fuel capacity. Three of the 0-47Bs produced are used by commercial concerns in the U.S.A., and a few others are believed to be employed in Central and South American countries.

Max. speed, 227 m.p.h.; cruising, 205 m.p.h.; max. range, 881 miles; empty weight, 5,835 lb.; loaded, 8,092 lb.; span, 46 ft. 3⅜ in.; length, 33 ft. 2⅞ in.; height, 12 ft. 0½ in.; wing area, 348.63 sq. ft.

NORTH AMERICAN B-25J (MITCHELL) U.S.A.

A development of the experimental NA-40 of 1938, the NA-62, or B-25 first flew on August 19, 1940, the first major production versions being the B-25B (NA-62B), B-25C (NA-82) and B-25D (NA-87). A total of 9,805 B-25s were delivered to the U.S.A.F., the R.C.A.F., and R.A.F., the latter air forces dubbing the type "Mitchell", and the final production model, the B-25J, still serves with several South American Air Forces. One hundred trainer conversions, designated TB-25J, were delivered to the R.C.A.F. These are powered by two 1,700 h.p. Wright R-2600-29 engines.

Max. speed, 292 m.p.h.; initial climb, 2,090 ft./min.; empty weight, 19,480 lb.; loaded, 27,000 lb.; span, 67 ft. 6 in.; length, 57 ft. 11 in.; height, 15 ft. 9 in.; wing area, 609.8 sq. ft.

NORTH AMERICAN NA-35   U.S.A.

The NA-35 primary trainer was produced by North American Aircraft in 1940, and four machines of this type were produced, one of which remains flying in the U.S.A. After the completion of the fourth machine in July 1941, the designs of the NA-35 were sold to Vega Aircraft, a subsidiary of Lockheed Aircraft Corporation, but no further development was undertaken. The NA-35 is powered by a 165 h.p. Menasco Pirate C4S-2 engine. Slotted flaps are fitted and construction is all-metal.

Max. speed, 137 m.p.h.; cruising, 125 m.p.h.; initial climb, 900 ft./min.; service ceiling, 18,500 ft.; range, 305 miles; loaded weight, 1,760 lb.; span, 29 ft. 8¾ in.; length, 25 ft. 6 in.; height, 9 ft. 4 in.

NORTH AMERICAN F-51D MUSTANG   U.S.A.

Designed and built to a British specification, the prototype Mustang, the XP-51, flew in October 1940, and 15,576 machines of this type were produced when production ceased in 1946. Of these, 7,966 were of the F-51D variant (*illustrated*), powered by the 1,490 h.p. Packard-built Merlin V-1650-7, and the type remains in service with the air forces of Cuba, Dominica, Haiti, Indonesia, Israel, South Korea, the Philippines, and Switzerland. Others are used by reserve units of the R.A.A.F., S.A.A.F., etc.

Max. speed, 437 m.p.h. at 24,000 ft.; climb to 20,000 ft., 6 minutes, 30 seconds; service ceiling, 41,000 ft.; loaded weight, 11,000 lb.; span, 37 ft. 0¼ in.; length, 32 ft. 3¼ in.; height, 13 ft. 8 in.; wing area, 240.06 sq. ft.

NORTH AMERICAN FJ-1 FURY   U.S.A.

The Progenitor of the entire F-86 Sabre series, the first of three Fury prototypes flew on November 27, 1946, and the first of thirty production FJ-1 Furies was delivered to the U.S. Navy in 1947. Several examples still remain. Power is provided by a 4,000 lb.s.t. Allison J35-A-5 turbojet, and the prototype attained a Mach number of 0.87 early in 1947, the highest attained by any U.S. fighter at that time. An armament of six 0.50-in. guns is carried.

Max. speed, 568 m.p.h.; initial climb rate, 5,120 ft./min.; range (internal fuel only), 970 miles; range (with wingtip tanks), 1,550 miles; loaded weight, 12,697 lb.; span, 38 ft. 1½ in.; length, 33 ft. 8 in.

NORTH AMERICAN FJ-2 FURY   U.S.A.

The FJ-2 Fury is virtually a navalised F-86E Sabre and bears little external similarity to the earlier FJ-1 Fury which was withdrawn from carrier service in mid-1953. The XFJ-2 prototype (which did not have folding wing or armament) first flew on February 19, 1952, and the second prototype, the XFJ-2B, differed in having a four 20-mm. MK 12 cannon armament installed. The production FJ-2's wing fold upwards hydraulically, and an A-frame arrester hook is fitted. The FJ-2 is powered by a 6,100 lb.s.t. General Electric J47-GE-27 turbojet.

Approx. max. speed, 680 m.p.h.; initial climb rate, 8,000 ft./min.; tactical radius, 200 miles; empty weight, 10,500 lb.; loaded, 18,000 lb.; span, 37 ft. 1½ in.; length 37 ft. 6½ in.; height, 14 ft. 7½ in.

NORTH AMERICAN FJ-3 FURY   U.S.A.

The FJ-3 Fury differs from its predecessor, the FJ-2, primarily in having a 7,220 lb.s.t. Wright J65-W-3 turbojet, the installation of which called for considerable structural revision and a larger intake duct. The XFJ-3 flew for the first time on July 3, 1953, and, like other carrier-borne fighters of the Fury series, carries an armament of four 20-mm. cannon. Although it corresponds roughly to the land-based F-86H, the FJ-3 is a completely independent development, and very few components are interchangeable.

Approx. max. speed, 720 m.p.h.; initial climb rate, 9,800 ft./min.; service ceiling, 47,000 ft.; tactical radius (with external tanks), 380 miles; span, 37 ft. 1½ in.; length, 37 ft. 7 in.; height, 13 ft. 8 in.; wing area, 287.9 sq. ft.

NORTH AMERICAN FJ-4 FURY   U.S.A.

The FJ-4 is the latest in a line of carrier-based interceptors stemming from the land-based F-86 Sabre. Its predecessors were virtually navalised Sabres, but the FJ-4 has been extensively redesigned, employing a completely new wing which has much increased chord, automatically-drooped leading-edge, large-chord flaps, and inboard flap/ailerons. The first of two prototype XFJ-4s flew on October 28, 1954, and the first production models were delivered to the U.S. Navy in mid-1955. Armament comprises four 20-mm. MK-12 cannon, and underwing loads can comprise two 500-lb. or 1,000-lb. bombs, or four rocket pods of nineteen 2.75-in. missiles.
Specification: Single-seat Naval interceptor. Engine: One 7,800 lb.s.t. Wright J65-W4. Weights: Approx. normal loaded, 17,000 lb.; maximum, 19,300 lb. Performance: Max. speed, 690 (approx.) m.p.h. at sea level; 650 m.p.h. at 36,000 ft. Dimensions: Span, 39 ft. 1 in.; length, 37 ft. 6 in.; height, 13 ft. 3 in.

NORTH AMERICAN F-86F SABRE   U.S.A.

The F-86F Sabre is a progressive development of the F-86E which it supplanted in production in April 1952. The F-86F features a redesigned structure to accommodate a 6,100 lb.s.t. J47-GE-27 turbojet in place of the 5,200 lb.s.t. J47-GE-13 of the E-model. Another change was the provision of racks for underwing ordnance loads in addition to drop-tanks. The F-86F was first flown on March 19, 1952, and continued in production until May 1954. Production was resumed in 1955 with a further order for 500 machines.

Specification: Single-seat fighter-bomber. Engine: One 6,100 lb.s.t. General Electric J47-GE-27. Approx. weights: Empty, 10,950 lb.; loaded, 16,850 lb. Performance: Max. speed, 680 m.p.h. at sea level; 620 m.p.h. at 35,000 ft.; initial climb rate, 8,000 ft./min.; service ceiling, 48,000 ft. Armament: Six 0.50-in. M-3 machine guns. Dimensions: Span, 37 ft. 1 in.; length, 37 ft. 6 in.; height, 14 ft. 7 in.; wing area, 287.9 sq. ft.

NORTH AMERICAN F-86D SABRE   U.S.A.

The F-86D, while developed from and concurrently with the F-86A, is virtually a different aircraft. The prototype, the YF-86D, flew on December 22, 1949, and production machines up to and including the F-86D-40 production batch were powered by the J47-GE-17 of 5,400 lb.s.t. and 7,350 lb. with afterburning. Subsequent machines have the J47-GE-33. It carries twenty-four 2.75-in. missiles in a retractable belly launcher, and the last machine was delivered on September 30, 1955.

Specification: Single-seat all-weather fighter. Engine: One 5,600 lb.s.t. (7,800 lb. with afterburning) General Electric J47-GE-33. Weights: Loaded, 18,800 lb. (increased to 20,000 lb. in the F-86D-50 production batch). Performance: Max. speed, 710–720 m.p.h. at sea level; tactical radius (with two 100 imp. gall. drop tanks), 500 miles; service ceiling, 45,000 ft. Dimensions: Span, 37 ft. 1 in.; length, 41 ft. 8 in.; height, 15 ft.; wing area, 274 sq. ft.

NORTH AMERICAN F-86H SABRE   U.S.A.

The F-86H is a more powerful fighter-bomber derived from the F-86F and intended primarily for low-level attack and differing basically from its predecessors in having a J73-GE-3 turbojet, the 9,300 lb. thrust of which is to be augmented by a Marquardt afterburning tailpipe. The air intake has been deepened by six inches, a clamshell-type cockpit canopy is fitted, the tailplane span has been increased by 2 ft., and improved bomb suspension and release mechanism is fitted. The first production F-86H flew on September 4, 1953, and armament comprises four 20-mm. M-39 cannon and various underwing ordnance loads.

Specification: Single-seat fighter-bomber. Engine: One 9,300 lb.s.t. General Electric J73-GE-3. Weights: Normal loaded, 19,000 lb.; maximum, 21,000 lb. Performance: Max. speed, 690 m.p.h. at sea level; combat radius, 630 miles; service ceiling, 47,000 ft. Dimensions: Span, 37 ft. 1½ in.; length, 38 ft. 10 in.; height, 14 ft. 11¾ in.

NORTH AMERICAN F-100A SUPER SABRE   U.S.A.

The prototype Super Sabre, the YF-100A, flew for the first time on May 23, 1953, and the first production F-100A was completed on October 20, 1953. A further development with strengthened wing to carry increased underwing loads, the F-100C, flew for the first time on January 17, 1955. An all-weather fighter version with rocket armament is designated F-107, and the F-100D is an improved F-100A with boundary layer control. The F-100A has a built-in armament of four M-39 20-mm. cannon.
Specification: Single-seat fighter. Engine: One 9,500 lb.s.t. (14,250 lb. with afterburning) Pratt & Whitney J57-P-7. Weights: Loaded, 28,000 lb. Performance: Approx. max. speed, 850 m.p.h. at 36,000 ft.; initial climb rate, 14,000 ft./min.; service ceiling, 55,000 ft.; combat radius (clean), 575 miles, (with 830 imp. galls. in underwing tanks) 1,100 miles. Dimensions: Span, 38 ft. 9 in.; length, 47 ft.; height, 15 ft.; wing area, 380 sq. ft.

NORTH AMERICAN T-6G TEXAN   U.S.A.

First produced in 1938 as the BC-1 basic combat trainer, the Texan is today the most widely used military trainer in the world. Redesignated AT-6 when the Basic Combat classification was abandoned, and again redesignated T-6 by the U.S.A.F. after the war, more than ten thousand of these trainers have been built in the U.S.A. and Canada. Known as the SNJ-1, 2, 3, 4, and 5 to the U.S. Navy, and as the Harvard 1, 2, 3, and 4 to the R.A.F. and R.C.A.F. the Texan continued in production in Canada at the Canadian Car and Foundry Co. until 1954 as the T-6J for the U.S.A.F. and the Harvard 4 for the R.C.A.F.
Specification: Two-seat basic trainer. Engine: One 550 h.p. Pratt & Whitney Wasp R-1340-AN1. Weights: Empty, 4,271 lb.; loaded, 5,617 lb. Performance: Max. speed, 212 m.p.h.; cruising, 146 m.p.h.; normal range, 870 miles. Dimensions: Span, 42 ft. 0¼ in.; length, 29 ft.; height, 11 ft. 8½ in.; wing area, 253.7 sq. ft.

NORTH AMERICAN T-28B   U.S.A.

The T-28 trainer was designed as a potential replacement for the T-6G Texan, and the prototype flew for the first time on September 26, 1949. As the T-28A, the first trainer was produced in quantity for the U.S.A.F. with a 800 h.p. Wright R-1300-1 engine, and production of this version was completed in 1954. The T-28B is a more powerful version of the basic design for the U.S. Navy, but the two variants differ externally only in minor detail.
Specification: Two-seat basic trainer. Engine: One 1,425 h.p. Wright R-1820-9HD Cyclone. Weights: Empty, 5,780 lb.; loaded, 7,339 lb. Performance: Max. speed, 346 m.p.h.; cruising speed, 250 m.p.h.; initial climb rate, 3,830 ft./min.; service ceiling, 37,000 ft. Dimensions: Span, 40 ft. 7½ in.; length, 32 ft. 11 in.; height, 12 ft. 8 in.; wing area, 268 sq. ft.

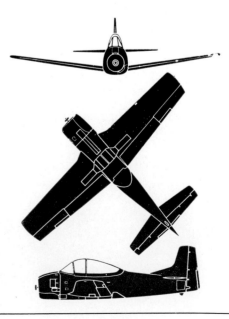

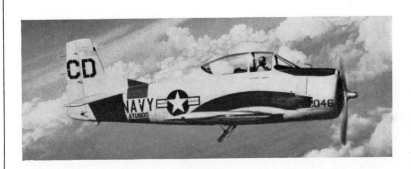

145

K

NORTH AMERICAN F-86K SABRE   U.S.A.

Developed from the F-86D, the F-86K carries an armament of four M39 cannon in place of the all-rocket armament of the "D" sub-type, and is powered by a General Electric J47-GE-33 turbojet delivering 5,600 lb.s.t., and 7,800 lb. with afterburning. One hundred and twenty F-86K Sabres are being assembled by the Italian Fiat company from components imported from the parent concern. The F-86K is eight inches longer than the F-86D due to the need to counterbalance the change in positioning of the armament.

Max. speed, 710–720 m.p.h.; approx. max. range, 1,000 miles; approx. loaded weight, 19,000 lb.; span, 37 ft. 1 in.; length, 42 ft. 4 in.; height, 15 ft.; wing area, 274 sq. ft.

NORTH AMERICAN B-45C TORNADO   U.S.A.

The first U.S. multi-jet aircraft to fly, the prototype Tornado, the XB-45, flying on March 17, 1947. The first production version of the Tornado was the B-45A, ninety-six of which were produced. The version was succeeded in production by the B-45C, ten of which were built, and RB-45C reconnaissance aircraft, thirty-three of which were produced. The B-45C carries a crew of three, and is powered by two General Electric J47-GE-13 turbojets of 5,200 lb.s.t., and two J47-GE-15s, the latter units having water injection which increases thrust to 6,000 lb.

Max. speed, 500 m.p.h. at sea level; combat radius, 1,200 miles; loaded weight, 82,600 lb.; span, 89 ft. 6 in.; length, 74 ft.; height, 25 ft.

NORTH AMERICAN AJ-2 SAVAGE   U.S.A.

The Savage was first flown on July 2, 1948, and forty-three AJ-1s were delivered to the U.S. Navy. This version was succeeded in production by the AJ-2 and AJ-2P which have a taller fin and rudder assembly and no dihedral on the tailplane. The AJ-2P is a photo-reconnaissance version carrying eighteen cameras. A crew of three is carried by the AJ-2 attack bomber, and power is provided by two 2,400 h.p. Pratt & Whitney R-2800-48W Double Wasp piston engines and one 4,600 lb.s.t. Allison J33-A-10 turbojet. The photograph depicts the AJ-1.

Max. speed, 425 m.p.h.; cruising, 290 m.p.h.; initial climb, 2,700 ft./min.; empty weight, 27,558 lb.; loaded, 55,000 lb.; span, 71 ft. 5 in.; length, 65 ft.; height, 21 ft.

NORTHROP DELTA 1-D   U.S.A.

The Delta 1-D is an eight-passenger transport version of the Gamma 2-D high-speed mailplane and was first produced in 1933 by the Northrop Corporation founded in the previous year. Powered by a 575 h.p. Wright Cyclone engine, the Delta normally provided accommodation for one pilot and eight passengers, but a special dual-control version was also produced, and this provided accommodation for two pilots and six passengers. One Delta remains active in the U.S.A.

Max. speed, 219 m.p.h. at 6,300 ft.; cruising, 200 m.p.h.; initial climb rate, 1,390 ft./min.; range, 1,930 miles; empty weight, 4,600 lb.; loaded, 7,350 lb.; span, 47 ft. 7 in.; length, 33 ft. 1 in.; wing area, 363 sq. ft.

NORTHROP F-61B BLACK WIDOW   U.S.A.

The F-61 Black Widow, the first prototype of which flew on May 26, 1942, was the first U.S. combat aircraft designed specifically for the night-fighting role. Seven hundred and six Black Widows, including two prototypes, were produced for the U.S.A.F., and several F-61Bs (*photo*) and F-61Cs are currently employed for weather research, engine and missile testing, and other non-operational roles. The F-61C differs from the F-61B in having 2,100 h.p. Pratt & Whitney R-2800-53 engines in place of the 2,000 h.p. R-2800-65s, and a four-gun dorsal turret.

Max. speed, 375 m.p.h. at 17,000 ft.; climb to 25,000 ft., 13 minutes; service ceiling, 33,000 ft.; loaded weight, 38,000 lb.; span, 66 ft.; length, 49 ft. 7 in.; height, 14 ft. 2 in.; wing area, 664 sq. ft.

NORTHROP C-125 RAIDER   U.S.A.

The Raider was a military development of the experimental N-23 Pioneer, intended to operate from improvised air strips and to replace the glider as an airborne assault vehicle and rescue aircraft. Twenty-three Raiders were built for the U.S.A.F., thirteen as YC-125A assault transports, and ten as C-125B arctic rescue aircraft. The first production YC-125A made its initial flight on August 1, 1949. Both versions are powered by three 1,200 h.p. Wright R-1820-99 radial engines.

Max. cruising speed, 201 m.p.h.; cruising (70 per cent power), 169 m.p.h.; max. climb at sea level, 1,155 ft./min.; max. range, 2,080 miles; empty weight, 26,690 lb.; loaded, 38,000 lb.; span, 86 ft. 6 in.; length, 67 ft. 1 in.; height, 23 ft. 2 in.

NORTHROP F-89D SCORPION
U.S.A.

The first of two XF-89 prototype Scorpions was flown on August 16, 1948, and was followed by forty-eight F-89As powered by two 4,900 lb.s.t. Allison J35-A-21 turbojets. The F-89B was generally similar, but the F-89C, of which 150 were built, changed to 5,000 lb.s.t. Allison J35-A-33 turbojets. The F-89D, illustrated, embodied a further increase in power and changed the six 20-mm. cannon armament for an all-rocket armament. The YF-89E is an experimental version with two Allison YJ71-A-3 turbojets of 9,500 lb.s.t., and the F-89H is a version carrying Hughes GAR-98s.
Specification: Two-seat all-weather fighter. Engines: Two 5,200 lb.s.t. (7,500 lb. with afterburning) Allison J35-A-35. Approx. weights: Loaded, 34,000 lb.; max., 41,000 lb. Performance: Approx. max. speed, 630 m.p.h.; range, 875 miles. Armament: 104 Mighty Mouse missiles in wingtip housings. Dimensions: Span, 56 ft. 2 in.; length, 53 ft. 4½ in.; height, 17 ft. 7 in.

NU-200 SIKUMBANG
INDONESIA

The NU-200 Sikumbang (Bee) was designed in 1953 by Major Nurtanio Pringgoadi-suryo of the Experimental Section of the Indonesian Air Force's Technical Staff. The prototype Sikumbang was first flown on August 1, 1954, and the type is intended as a light ground support monoplane. Of mixed construction, the wing being of all-wood construction with plywood covering and the fuselage being a welded steel-tube structure with metal covering, the Sikumbang will carry a fixed forward-firing armament of two machine guns and various underwing ordnance loads.

Specification: Single-seat ground-attack aircraft. Engine: One 200 h.p. de Havilland Gipsy-Six. Weights: Loaded, 2,400 lb. Performance: Max. speed, 160 m.p.h. at sea level; cruising, 140 m.p.h.; initial climb rate, 1,000 ft./min.; service ceiling, 16,500 ft.; range, 600 miles. Dimensions: Span, 34 ft. 9½ in.; length, 26 ft. 9 in.; height, 11 ft.

NOURY T-65 NORANDA
CANADA

The T-65 Noranda two-seat light cabin monoplane was designed by Mr. J. O. Noury of Noury Aircraft Limited. Soon after the completion of the prototype in 1947, the Noury Aircraft Ltd. was purchased by the Canadian Car and Foundry Company, and further development of the Noranda was abandoned. The sole prototype is still active in Canada, and is powered by a 65 h.p. Continental C65 engine. Mixed construction is employed, with fabric covering, and dual controls are fitted.

Max. speed, 110 m.p.h.; cruising speed, 95 m.p.h.; empty weight, 810 lb.; loaded, 1,380 lb.; span, 33 ft.; length, 23 ft. 6 in.; height, 7 ft.

OKAMURA N-52
JAPAN

The Okamura Seisakujo Kabushiki Kaisha commenced the design and construction of the N-52 side-by-side two-seater light plane in 1952, and the prototype flew for the first time on April 7, 1953. Designed by Professor H. Kimura of the Nihon University, the N-52 is powered by a 65 h.p. Continental A65 engine, but any production machines will be powered by the 85 h.p. Continental C85. The N-52 is of mixed construction with fabric covering. No production plans have been announced at the time of writing.
Max. speed, 108 m.p.h. at sea level; cruising, 101 m.p.h.; initial climb rate, 550 ft./min.; range, 305 miles; empty weight, 660 lb.; loaded, 1,100 lb.; span, 28 ft. 2½ in.; length, 19 ft. 8 in.; height, 8 ft. 6 in.; wing area, 129 sq. ft.

PARTENAVIA P-48-B ASTORE   ITALY

Produced in 1952 by Partenavia S.p.A., and designed by Luigi Pascale, the P-48-B Astore (Goshawk) is a tandem two-seat cabin monoplane powered by a 65 h.p. Continental A65 engine. Built in prototype form only, the P-48-B Astore is primarily of wooden construction with fabric and plywood construction. Dual controls are provided, and the type was designed for use in both the training and touring roles.

Max. speed, 115 m.p.h.; cruising speed, 99 m.p.h.; climb to 3,280 ft., 5 minutes, 50 seconds; service ceiling, 10,827 ft.; range, 342 miles; empty weight, 617 lb.; loaded, 1,036 lb.; span, 26 ft. 9¼ in.; length, 20 ft. 11¾ in.; height, 5 ft. 10½ in.

PARTENAVIA P-52 TIGROTTO   ITALY

Design of the P-52 Tigrotto was initiated by Luigi Pascale in September 1951, and the first prototype was flown in 1953. The Tigrotto is a side-by-side two-seat monoplane entirely of wooden construction. Power is provided by an 85 h.p. Continental C85-12F engine. Full dual controls are fitted, and the comprehensive equipment includes VHF radio. No production plans for the Tigrotto have yet been announced by Partenavia S.p.A.

Max. speed, 147 m.p.h.; cruising, 124 m.p.h.; ceiling, 14,764 ft.; range, 497 miles; empty weight, 948 lb.; loaded, 1,587 lb.; span, 29 ft. 6½ in.; length, 19 ft. 3½ in.; height, 5 ft. 7 in.

PARTENAVIA P-53 AEROSCOOTER   ITALY

Designed by Ing. Luigi Pascale to the specifications of the well-known Italian pilot Mario de Bernardi, the P-53 Aeroscooter ultra-light monoplane is powered by a 22 h.p. Ambrosini P-25 engine. Provision is made in the design for the attachment of a two-blade rotor to the crash pylon above the cabin. This is permitted to autorotate in forward flight, and is claimed to reduce the glide angle considerably. The Aeroscooter is a single-seater of all-metal construction, and it is proposed to install a 35 h.p. C.N.A.C-2 engine in later machines.

Max. speed, 93 m.p.h.; cruising speed, 74.5 m.p.h.; minimum speed, 37 m.p.h.; ceiling, 11,483 ft.; empty weight, 330 lb.; loaded, 551 lb.; span, 27 ft. 2 in.; length, 16 ft. 9½ in.; height, 5 ft. 6¾ in.; wing area, 329.375 sq. ft.

PARTENAVIA P-55 TORNADO   ITALY

The P-55 Tornado side-by-side two-seat cabin monoplane is of exceptionally clean design, and is unusual among aircraft in this category in having a mid-positioned wing and a fully-retractable nosewheel undercarriage. Introduced in 1955 and designed by Luigi Pascale, the P-55 Tornado is powered by a 140 h.p. Lycoming 0-290-D2 engine, and has an exceptionally high performance for the power available. Dual controls are fitted, and the type is intended primarily for competition flying.

Max. speed, 211 m.p.h.; cruising speed, 186 m.p.h.; climb to 3,280 ft., 3 minutes; max. range, 497 miles; empty weight, 868 lb.; loaded, 1,367 lb.; span, 23 ft. 7½ in.; length, 19 ft. 9¾ in.; height, 6 ft. 10¾ in.; wing area, 86.1 sq. ft.

PASOTTI F.6 AIRONE   ITALY

Flown for the first time on July 13, 1954, the F.6 Airone has been designed by Ing. Stelio Frati and built by the Legnami Pasotti. The prototype is powered by two 90 h.p. Continental C90-12F engines, but it is proposed to install two 140 h.p. Lycoming 0-290-D engines, and the specification relates to this higher-powered version. Alternative power plants are the 105 h.p. Walter engine. The Airone is a four-seat low-wing cabin monoplane with dual controls.

Max. speed, 198 m.p.h.; cruising speed, 168 m.p.h.; service ceiling, 21,325 ft.; range, 714 miles; empty weight, 1,984 lb.; loaded, 3,196 lb.; span, 34 ft. 9 in.; length, 23 ft. 9½ in.; wing area, 163.6 sq. ft.

PASPED SKYLARK W-1   U.S.A.

The Skylark W-1 light two-seat sporting monoplane was produced in 1936 by the Pasped Aircraft Company of Glendale, California. Powered by a 125 h.p. Warner Scarab radial engine, the Skylark has an enclosed cockpit seating two side-by-side with dual controls. Mixed construction is employed with wooden wings and welded steel-tube fuselage, and a relatively high performance for the low-power engine is obtained by the use of a low-drag engine cowling, close-fitting undercarriage cowlings and clean contours.

Max. speed, 139 m.p.h.; cruising speed, 125 m.p.h.; initial climb rate, 850 ft./min.; service ceiling, 16,000 ft.; cruising range, 650 miles; empty weight, 1,288 lb.; loaded, 1,885 lb.; span, 35 ft. 10 in.; length, 25 ft.; height, 7 ft. 11 in.; wing area, 187 sq. ft.

PAYEN PA-49 KATY   FRANCE

Designed by N. R. Payen, who produced an aircraft embodying delta wing planform in 1934, the Pa-49 Katy is an exceptionally small single-seat research aircraft flown for the first time on January 22, 1954, and powered by a 330 lb.s.t. Turboméca Palas. The Katy completed the first phase of its flight testing in August 1954, and in October was fitted with split flaps. Projected developments include the Pa-57 Aton with an 880 lb. thrust Marboré II turbojet, the Pa-59 Aldebaran lightweight fighter with a 2,645 lb.s.t. SNECMA R-105, and the Pa-60 Arbalete tourer.

Max. speed, 310 m.p.h.; cruising, 217 m.p.h.; initial climb, 1,150 ft./min.; empty weight, 1,005 lb.; loaded, 1,430 lb.; span, 16 ft. 11 in.; length, 16 ft. 8 in.; height, 7 ft. 2 in.

PELLARINI PL-5C AERAUTO   ITALY

The PL-5C Aerauto two-seat roadable monoplane was designed and built by Luigi Pellarini in 1950. Powered by an 85 h.p. Continental C85, the PL-5C made a tour of Italy in 1950, covering 4,160 miles in fifteen days of which only 1,240 miles were flown. The outer wings fold backwards, and with their leading-edges upward and anchored to the tailplane extremities form a guard to the pusher airscrew which provides the means of ground propulsion. Only one prototype has been completed.

Max. speed, 112 m.p.h.; cruising, 100 m.p.h.; initial climb, 535 ft./min.; service ceiling, 13,120 ft.; range, 500 miles; empty weight, 1,012 lb.; loaded, 1,540 lb.; span, 33 ft. 5½ in.; length, 20 ft. 4 in.; height, 5 ft. 9 in.

PERCIVAL P.1B GULL FOUR   G.B.

The Gull was first introduced in 1932 as a three-seat wooden cantilever monoplane with a 130 h.p. Cirrus Hermes IV engine, and twenty-two P-1A (170 h.p. Javelin III) and P.1B (130 h.p. Gipsy Major 1) Gulls were produced by Parnell Aircraft Ltd. One P.1B Gull is flying in Australia (*illustrated*). In 1934, an improved version, the P.3 Gull Six, appeared with a 200 h.p. Gipsy Six I engine, a new cantilever under-carriage and redesigned cabin. This is externally similar to the Proctor.

Max. speed, 155 m.p.h.; cruising, 133 m.p.h.; range, 760 miles; ceiling, 17,000 ft.; loaded weight, 2,300 lb.; span, 36 ft.; length, 25 ft.; height, 7 ft. 4½ in.

PERCIVAL P.6 MEW GULL II   G.B.

The Mew Gull was produced in 1936 as a racing monoplane with a 160 h.p. Javelin 1A engine. Known by the company designation P.2, this aircraft was later rebuilt as the P.6 with a 200 h.p. D.H. Gipsy Six I. Four Mew Gull IIs were followed by a Mew Gull IIA with a 205 h.p. Gipsy Six R racing engine, but the sole example flying (*illustrated*) is a Mew Gull II with a 205 h.p. de Havilland Gipsy Six Series II engine and a redesigned and deeper cockpit canopy.

Max. speed, 230 m.p.h.; cruising, 190 m.p.h.; initial climb, 1,400 ft./min.; ceiling, 21,000 ft.; range, 750 miles; empty weight, 1,080 lb.; loaded, 2,125 lb.; span, 24 ft. 9 in.; length, 20 ft. 9½ in.; height, 6 ft. 10 in.; wing area, 88.5 sq. ft.

PERCIVAL P.16 Q-SIX I   G.B.

The first twin-engined aircraft to be produced by Percival Aircraft Ltd., the Q-Six six-seater appeared in 1937, and the prototype, G-AEYE, is believed to be the sole example of the type remaining airworthy. Series production commenced in 1938, and twenty-six Q-Sixes were built, in addition to the prototype, including fourteen P.16As, three P.16Ds with retractable undercarriages, and nine P.16E communications aircraft. The Gull-Six has two 205 h.p. D.H. Gipsy Six II engines.

Max. speed, 195 m.p.h.; cruising, 175 m.p.h.; service ceiling, 21,000 ft.; range, 750 miles; empty weight, 3,500 lb.; loaded, 5,500 lb.; span, 46 ft. 8 in.; length, 32 ft. 3 in.; height, 9 ft. 9 in.

PERCIVAL P.40 PRENTICE   G.B.

The Prentice was first flown on March 31, 1946, and was ordered in quantity by the R.A.F. as a standard basic trainer. The Prentice was also adopted by the Indian Air Force and built under licence by Hindustan Aircraft Ltd., and is used by the air forces of Lebanon and Argentina. An experimental version was fitted with a 296 h.p. D.H. Gipsy Queen 51 engine in place of the standard 251 h.p. Gipsy Queen 32, and was known as the Prentice T.2. The Indian Air Force version is designated Prentice T.3.

Max. speed, 143 m.p.h.; cruising, 139 m.p.h.; initial climb, 653 ft./min.; range, 396 miles; empty weight, 3,232 lb.; loaded, 4,200 lb.; span, 46 ft.; length, 31 ft. 3 in.; height, 12 ft. 10½ in.; wing area, 305 sq. ft.

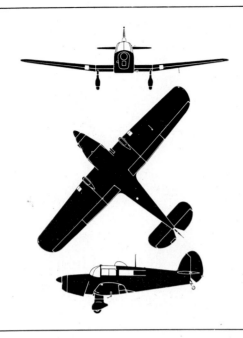

PERCIVAL P.44 PROCTOR 5   G.B.

Derived from the P.10 Vega Gull of 1935 to which it is externally similar, the Proctor was chosen by the R.A.F. and Royal Navy for use as a liaison, training and communications aircraft, and 1,143 Proctors were built during the war. Examples of all R.A.F. versions have been "civilianised"; the three-seat P.28 Proctor I and P.28A Proctor 1A have become the civil P.28B Proctor 1B; the P.30 and P.30A Proctor 2 and 2A have become the Civil P.30B Proctor 2B, and the four-seat P.30A Proctor 4A and the P.30B Proctor 4B have become the P.31C Proctor 4C. A post-war civil production version, the P.44 Proctor 5, is flying in substantial numbers.
Specification: Four-seat cabin monoplane. Engine: One 208 h.p. de Havilland Gipsy Queen II. Weights: Empty, 2,450 lb.; loaded, 3,500 lb. Performance: Max. speed, 157 m.p.h.; cruising, 140 m.p.h.; initial climb rate, 680 ft./min. Dimensions: Span, 39 ft. 6 in.; length, 28 ft. 2 in.; height, 7 ft. 3 in.; wing area, 202 sq. ft.

PETLYAKOV PE-2   U.S.S.R.

The PE-2 (code-named *Buck*), was designed by the late Vladmir M. Petlyakov as a three-seat ground-attack bomber, and entered service in 1940–41. It is now relegated to the role of crew trainer and target tug, and is used in some numbers by the air forces of the U.S.S.R., Poland, Czechoslovakia, and other Russian "satellite" countries for these roles. An air-to-air gunnery trainer with a power-operated dorsal turret and a pilot trainer version with a second, raised cockpit, exist. The PE-2 is powered by two 1,100 h.p. VK-105R engines.

Max. speed, 340 m.p.h. at 16,500 ft.; cruising, 230 m.p.h.; service ceiling, 29,000 ft.; range, 1,200 miles; empty weight, 12,900 lb.; loaded, 18,730 lb.; span, 56 ft. 4 in.; length, 41 ft. 4 in.

PETLYAKOV PE-8   U.S.S.R.

The PE-8 (formerly the TB-7 under the old functional designation system) was the only Russian four-engined strategic bomber to see service during World War 2. The PE-8 has now been relegated to transport duties, several being employed during 1954–55 to supply Soviet research bases in the Arctic Circle. The PE-8 has been powered with 1,100 h.p. M-105, 1,300 h.p. AM-35, 1,500 h.p. M-40F, and 1,700 h.p. M-82 III engines. The following specification relates to the version with AM-35 engines.

Max. speed, 240 m.p.h.; cruising, 200 m.p.h.; range, 1,300 miles; service ceiling, 23,000 ft.; max. loaded weight, 70,500 lb.; span, 131 ft. 3 in.; length, 80 ft. 6 in.

PETROLINI EL BOYERO   ARGENTINA

Designed and built in 1939 by the Instituto Aerotecnico (then known as the Fabrica Militar de Aviones), the Boyero did not enter production until 1947. A licence for its manufacture was originally granted to S. A. Sfreddo y Paolini, but owing to the difficulty in acquiring the necessary equipment during the war, production was shelved and eventually taken over by Petrolini. This concern received a government order for 160 El Boyeros. A 65 h.p. Continental A65 is installed.

Max. speed, 104 m.p.h.; cruising, 87 m.p.h.; ceiling, 13,000 ft.; range, 400 miles; empty weight, 715 lb.; loaded, 1,210 lb.; span, 37 ft. 10 in.; length, 23 ft. 5 in.; height, 5 ft. 11 in.

PIAGGIO P.149   ITALY

Derived directly from the P.148 military trainer, the P.149 four-seat cabin monoplane employs the same basic fuselage and wing as the trainer, but has a re-styled cockpit hood, a retractable nosewheel undercarriage and a 260 h.p. Lycoming GO-435-C2 engine. The P.149 is of all-metal construction, and the prototype flew for the first time in the summer of 1953. It is intended primarily for touring but is adaptable for military liaison duties.
Max. speed, 184 m.p.h.; cruising, 163 m.p.h.; service ceiling, 19,192 ft.; normal range, 503 miles; max. 870 miles; empty weight, 2,189 lb.; loaded, 3,104 lb.; span, 36 ft. 5½ in.; length, 28 ft. 1¼ in.; height, 9 ft. 6 in.; wing area, 202.46 sq. ft.

PIAGGIO P.136-L   ITALY

The Piaggio P.136 amphibian flying-boat was flown for the first time on August 29, 1948, and the first production aircraft (*silhouette*) were powered by 215 h.p. Franklin 6A8-215-B9F engines. A second production series, the P.136-L, differs primarily in having Lycoming engines of higher power and redesigned and enlarged vertical tail surfaces. Fourteen P.136 amphibians have been supplied to the Italian Air Force for air/sea rescue duties and communications. The P.136-L is being assembled in the U.S.A. by Royal Aircraft Corp., under the name Royal Gull.
Specification: Five-seat amphibian flying-boat. Engines: Two 260 h.p. Lycoming GO-435-C2. Weights: Empty, 4,211 lb.; loaded, 5,842 lb. Performance: Max. speed, 181 m.p.h.; cruising speed, 160 m.p.h. at 6,890 ft.; climb to 3,280 ft., 3 minutes 40 seconds; service ceiling, 17,716 ft.; normal range, 373 miles; max., 621 miles. Dimensions: Span, 44 ft. 4¾ in.; length, 35 ft. 5 in.; height, 11 ft. 6 in.; wing area, 268 sq. ft.

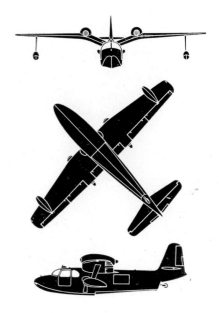

PIAGGIO P.148   ITALY

The Piaggio P.148 all-metal primary trainer was designed by Ing. G. P. Casiraghi and first flew on February 12, 1951. One hundred machines were ordered by the Italian Air Force, and the P.148 is now one of two standard primary trainers, the other being the Macchi M.416 (licence-built Fokker S.11 Instructor). The P.148 has two side-by-side seats for pupil and instructor, with complete dual controls, and a third seat can be installed to the rear. The rear part of the canopy slides back for access, and this may be jettisoned in an emergency.
Specification: Two/three-seat primary trainer. Engine: One 190 h.p. Lycoming 0-435-A. Weights: Empty, 1,947 lb.; loaded, 2,646 lb. Performance: Max. speed, 147 m.p.h.; cruising speed, 125 m.p.h.; climb to 3,280 ft., 3 minutes 50 seconds; duration, 3.9 hours; normal range, 435 miles. Dimensions: Span, 36 ft. 5 in.; length, 27 ft. 7½ in.; height, 7 ft. 10½ in.; wing area, 200.2 sq. ft.

PIAGGIO P.150   ITALY

Intended to compete with the Fiat G.49 and the Macchi M.B.323 as a replacement for the North American T-6 Texan basic trainer, the P.150 is basically a scaled-up version of the P.148 primary trainer with a 600 h.p. Pratt & Whitney Wasp R-1340-S3H1 radial engine. The P.150 was first flown in November 1952, but no production orders for the type have so far been announced. A second prototype was to have been powered by a geared Alvis Leonides engine.

Max. speed, 237 m.p.h. at 5,000 ft.; cruising, 195 m.p.h.; initial climb, 1,663 ft./min.; service ceiling, 25,200 ft.; range, 880 miles; empty weight, 4,277 lb.; loaded, 5,600 lb.; span, 42 ft. 4½ in.; length, 30 ft. 4 in.; height, 9 ft. 2½ in.

PILATUS P.4   SWITZERLAND

The P.4 was produced in 1952 by the Pilatus Flugzeugwerke A.G., as a five-seat cabin monoplane for passengers, cargo or ambulance duties. The sole prototype P.4 is powered by a 190 h.p. Lycoming 0-435 engine, but it was proposed that production machines would have the 260 h.p. Lycoming and a cantilever undercarriage. Development was abandoned owing to inadequate orders. The P.4 is of all-metal construction with fabric covering.

Max. speed, 150 m.p.h.; cruising, 130 m.p.h.; initial climb, 900 ft./min.; range, 550 miles; empty weight, 1,970 lb.; loaded, 3,300 lb.; span, 39 ft.; length, 28 ft. 3 in.; height, 8 ft. 3 in.; wing area, 226 sq. ft.

PILATUS P.2   SWITZERLAND

Built by the Pilatus Flugzeugwerke A.G., the P.2 advanced trainer has been built in two series for the Swiss Air Force. Powered by the Czech-built Argus As 410A-2 engine, the P.2 is of extremely rugged construction, and was designed for operation from high-altitude, alpine airfields. One series of aircraft was equipped as armament trainers, having racks under the wings for rocket projectiles and light bombs. The P.2 is fully aerobatic and has a high placard diving speed in relation to its low wing loading and landing speed.

Specification: Two-seat advanced trainer. Engine: One 465 h.p. Argus As 410A-2. Weights: Empty, 3,040 lb.; loaded, 3,970 lb. Performance: Max. speed, 211 m.p.h. at 8,200 ft.; economical cruising, 190 m.p.h. at 14,700 ft.; initial climb rate, 1,280 ft./min.; service ceiling, 22,000 ft.; range, 480 miles. Dimensions: Span, 36 ft.; length, 29 ft. 9 in.; height, 8 ft. 10 in.; wing area, 183 sq. ft.

PILATUS P.3   SWITZERLAND

The Pilatus P.3 is a robust, all-metal basic trainer designed to meet the requirements of the Swiss Air Force for a low-powered trainer capable of operating from alpine training bases. The first of two prototypes of the P.3 was flown on September 3, 1953, the two prototypes differing in that the first machine has a two-blade airscrew whereas the second machine employs an airscrew of three-blade type. Provision is made for the attachment of a pair of rocket launchers for 5-cm. Oerlikon training missiles, and a bomb rack and camera gun may be fitted.

Specification: Two-seat basic trainer. Engine: One 260 h.p. Lycoming GO-435-C2. Weights: Empty, 2,280 lb.; loaded, 3,310 lb. Performance: Max. speed, 190 m.p.h. at sea level; cruising speed, 156 m.p.h.; initial climb rate, 1,440 ft./min.: (at 6,560 ft.), 726 ft./min.; service ceiling, 18,050 ft. Dimensions: Span, 34 ft. 1½ in.; length, 28 ft. 8½ in.; height, 10 ft.; wing area, 177.6 sq. ft.

PIPER J-3 CUB   U.S.A.

Derived from the externally similar J-2 Cub of 1936, the J-3 (*photo*) was introduced in the following year, and was fitted with various Franklin, Lycoming and Continental engines of 50–130 h.p. By the end of 1941 more than 10,000 Cubs had been delivered, and wartime models included the L-4 series of air observation posts and liaison machines with extended cockpit canopy (*silhouette*). Production of the J-3 was resumed after the war, the post-war model being known as the PA-11 Cub Special (see specification). Several thousand pre-war and post-war Cubs are currently active in the U.S.A.

Specification: Tandem two-seat cabin monoplane. Engine: One 65 h.p. Continental A65. Weights: Empty, 730 lb.; loaded, 1,220 lb. Performance: Max. speed, 100 m.p.h.; cruising, 87 m.p.h.; initial climb rate, 514 ft./min.; range, 300 miles. Dimensions: Span, 35 ft. 2½ in.; length, 22 ft. 4½ in.; height, 6 ft. 8 in.; wing area, 178.5 sq. ft.

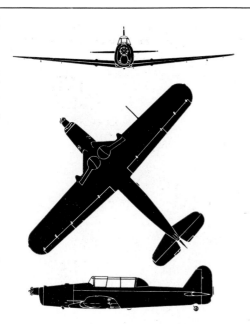

PIPER PA-12 SUPER CRUISER U.S.A.

The PA-12 Super Cruiser and the externally similar PA-14 Family Cruiser are post-war developments of the J-5B Cruiser of 1940, the first three-seat Piper light plane. Whereas the Cruiser is powered by a 75 h.p. Continental A75-8 (J-5B), the Super Cruiser, like the later J-5C Cruiser, has a 104 h.p. Lycoming 0-235-C and several refinements. The Family Cruiser (115 h.p. Lycoming 0-235-C1) appeared in 1948 as a four-seat development of the Super Cruiser, and was followed on the production line in 1950 by the PA-20 Pacer. More than 2,000 PA-12s and PA-14s are currently active in the U.S.A.

Specification: Three-seat cabin monoplane. Engine: One 104 h.p. Lycoming 0-235-C. Weights: Empty, 960 lb.; loaded, 1,750 lb. Performance: Max. speed, 115 m.p.h.; cruising, 105 m.p.h.; service ceiling, 12,600 ft.; range, 600 miles. Dimensions: Span, 35 ft. 5½ in.; length, 22 ft. 10 in.; height, 6 ft. 10 in.; wing area, 179.3 sq. ft.

PIPER PA-18 SUPER CUB U.S.A.

Introduced in 1950 as a development of the Cub, the Super Cub was produced in three versions: the Super Cub 95 (90 h.p. Continental C90), the Super Cub 125 (125 h.p. Lycoming 0-290-D), and the Super Cub 135 (135 h.p. Lycoming 0-290-D2). The L-18B is a military liaison version of the Super Cub 95, and the L-21B (*photo*) is a military version of the Super Cub 135 fitted with tandem wheels for operation from rough ground. The following specification refers to the Super Cub 135.

Specification: Tandem two-seat cabin monoplane. Engine: One 135 h.p. Lycoming 0-290-D2. Weights: Empty, 895 lb.; loaded, 1,500 lb. Performance: Max. speed, 127 m.p.h.; cruising speed, 112 m.p.h.; max. range, 500 miles. Dimensions: Span, 35 ft. 3 in.; length, 22 ft. 5 in.; height, 6 ft. 7½ in.; wing area, 178.5 sq. ft.

PIPER PA-20 & PA-22 U.S.A.

The PA-20 Pacer and PA-22 Tri-Pacer four-seat cabin monoplanes were introduced in 1950 as a development of the 1949 Clipper. Versions produced include the Pacer 115 (108 h.p. Lycoming 0-235-C1), the Pacer 125 (125 h.p. Lycoming 0-290-D) illus-trated by the photo, and the Pacer 135 described here. A nosewheel version of the Pacer 135, known as the Tri-Pacer 135 (*silhouette*), has been in production since February 1951. The Pacer and Tri-Pacer models introduced in 1953 had 10 h.p. more power than did previous models. The Pacer and Tri-Pacer are identical apart from their landing gear. Figures quoted in parentheses refer to the Tri-Pacer 135.

Specification: Four-seat cabin monoplane. Engine: One 135 h.p. Lycoming 0-290-D2. Weights: Empty, 975 (1,005) lb.; loaded, 1,950 lb. Performance: Max. speed, 139 (137) m.p.h.; cruising, 134 (132) m.p.h.; range, 580 miles. Dimensions: Span, 29 ft. 4 in.; length, 20 ft. 4¾ in.; height, 6 ft. 2½ in.; wing area, 147.5 sq. ft.

PIPER PA-15 VAGABOND U.S.A.

The PA-15 Vagabond was introduced in 1948 as a low-priced two-seat side-by-side cabin monoplane powered by a 65 h.p. Lycoming engine. The PA-17 is externally similar to the PA-15, and also known as the Vagabond, but is a dual-control trainer model with a 65 h.p. Continental engine. Both versions of the Vagabond are similar structurally to other Piper single-engined cabin monoplanes; the wing having spruce spars and aluminium ribs and the fuselage a welded steel-tube structure, the whole fabric-covered.

Max. speed, 102 m.p.h.; cruising speed (75 per cent power), 90 m.p.h. initial climb rate, 510 ft./min.; empty weight, 650 lb.; loaded, 1,150 lb.; span, 29 ft. 3⅜ in.; length, 18 ft. 8 in.; height, 5 ft. 11½ in.

PIPER PA-16 CLIPPER U.S.A.

The PA-16 Clipper is a four-seat version of the PA-15 Vagabond, a lengthening of the fuselage permitting an increase in the length of the cabin and the accommodation of two additional persons. The Clipper is powered by a 115 h.p. Lycoming 0-235-C1 engine. The rear seat area can easily be converted as cargo space, and a rear door of the port side can be used as a cargo loading hatch. More than five hundred Clippers are currently active in the U.S.A.

Max. speed, 125 m.p.h.; cruising, 112 m.p.h.; initial climb, 600 ft./min.; service ceiling, 11,000 ft.; range, 480 miles; empty weight, 850 lb.; loaded, 1,650 lb.; span, 29 ft. 4 in.; length, 20 ft. 1½ in.; height, 16 ft. 2½ in.

PIPER PA-23 APACHE U.S.A.

The Apache, which first flew on March 2, 1952, at which time it was known as the Twin-Stinson, is the first Piper aircraft of Stinson lineage to be built since the production of the Piper Stinson Station Wagon was completed in 1949, and the first Piper to have the name of a famous American Indian tribe. The Piper Aircraft Corporation took over the Stinson Division of the Consolidated Vultee Aircraft Corp. on December 1, 1948, and the first production batch of ten Apaches was commenced by Piper early in 1953, quantity production following on the successful trials with these.

Specification: Four-seat light cabin monoplane. Engines: Two 150 h.p. Lycoming 0-320. Weights: Empty, 2,160 lb.; loaded, 3,500 lb. Performance: Cruising speed (65 per cent power), 150 m.p.h. at sea level; range, 720 miles. Dimensions: Span, 37 ft.; length, 27 ft. 1¼ in.; height, 9 ft. 6 in.; wing area, 204 sq. ft.

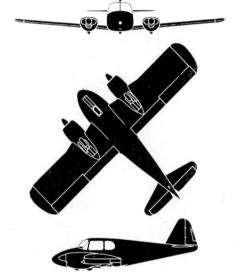

PITCAIRN PA-7S U.S.A.

The Pitcairn PA-7S sporting biplane was generally similar to the PA-7M Mailwing single-seat mail-carrying biplane produced in some numbers during the early 'thirties and designed in 1927. The PA-7S illustrated above is an extensively modified crop-dusting version with a modified metal fuselage. The PA-7S is of mixed construction and is powered by a 220 h.p. Wright Whirlwind J-6 radial engine.

Max. speed, 150 m.p.h.; cruising, 128 m.p.h.; service ceiling, 16,000 ft.; empty weight, 1,820 lb.; loaded, 3,050 lb.; span, 33 ft.; length, 23 ft. 9 in.; height, 9 ft. 6½ in.; wing area, 243.5 sq. ft.

POLIKARPOV PO-2 U.S.S.R.

The PO-2 (formerly U-2), code-named *Mule*, was first flown in 1927 and was subsequently produced in extremely large numbers. It has even been produced since World War II in Poland as the C.S.S.13. The PO-2 is currently flying in the U.S.S.R., Czechoslovakia, Poland, Rumania, China and Yugoslavia, and the most widely used version is a tandem two-seater powered by a 110 h.p. M-11 radial engine. Other versions in existence include one with three open tandem seats, one with two passenger seats in an enclosed cabin, and an ambulance version with a built-up rear fuselage. The PO-2 is used for agricultural purposes, training, and as a light freighter.

Max. speed, 96 m.p.h.; approx. cruising speed, 75 m.p.h.; initial climb rate, 640 ft./min.; empty weight, 1,342 lb.; loaded, 1,910 lb.; span, 37 ft. 5 in.; length, 26 ft. 8 in.; height, 9 ft. 6 in.

POLIKARPOV I-15   U.S.S.R.

Nikolai N. Polikarpov was responsible for the design of the majority of Russian single-seat fighters of the 'thirties. His I-15 single-seat fighter biplane (sometimes referred to as the TsKB I-15 Chato or Chikka) appeared in 1935, and was a modification of the I-13 powered by a 750 h.p. M-25 radial. I-15s were sent to the aid of China in December 1937, and 226 I-15s and thirty-four I-15Bs (1,000 h.p. M-63 radial) were sent to aid the Communist forces in Spain. After the termination of the Spanish Civil War, a number of I-15s were captured and later used as attack aircraft under the designation A.4. Several remain in Spain.
Max. speed, 223 m.p.h.; climb to 16,400 ft., 6.5 minutes; ceiling, 31,500 ft.; range, 465 miles; loaded weight, 3,558 lb.; span, 29 ft. 11 in.; length, 22 ft. 2 in.

POLIKARPOV I-16   U.S.S.R.

The first Russian single-seat fighter monoplane to enter production, Polikarpov's I-16 (sometimes referred to as the TsKB I-16 Rata or Mosca) first appeared during the 1935 Autumn Manœuvres near Kiev. The initial production model was powered by a 750 h.p. M-25 radial (the later I-16B and I-16C has the 1,000 h.p. M-62 and 1,100 h.p. M-88B respectively), and a number of these were sent to Spain. Many crated I-16s were captured at the end of the Civil War, and these were assembled at Jerez in 1939 under the direction of Luis Arias. Several I-16s are still in use as fighter trainers in Spain under the designation C.8.
Max. speed, 279 m.p.h. at sea level, 254 m.p.h. at 16,400 ft.; cruising, 223 m.p.h.; service ceiling, 29,527 ft.; range, 404 miles; empty weight, 2,791 lb.; loaded, 3,703 lb.; span, 30 ft. 5 in.; length, 21 ft. 3 in.

PORTERFIELD 35-70   U.S.A.

The Model 35 was placed in production by the Porterfield Aircraft Corporation in April 1935, and was subsequently produced with several different engines. The initial models were the 35-70 with the 70 h.p. Le Blond engine, and the 35-90 with the 90 h.p. Warner Scarab. The 35-65 and 35-75 were versions with 65 h.p. and 75 h.p. Warner engines respectively. A few Model 35-70 with the 70 h.p. Le Blond engines are flying in the U.S.A., together with several Warner-powered Model 35-90s. One Model 35-70 fitted with a 75 h.p. Continental A75 engine is flying in Australia.
Max. speed, 115 m.p.h.; cruising, 105 m.p.h.; initial climb rate, 600 ft./min.; service ceiling, 15,000 ft.; range, 360 miles; empty weight, 813 lb.; loaded, 1,310 lb.; span, 32 ft.; length, 20 ft.; height, 6 ft. 7 in.

PORTERFIELD CP-65   U.S.A.

In 1939, the Porterfield Aircraft Corporation introduced a new range of light two-seat cabin monoplanes developed from the earlier Model 35. These were the Models CP-50, CP-55, CP-65, FP-65 and LP-65, the initial letter indicating the type of engine installed (i.e., Continental, Franklin, or Lycoming) and the horse power being indicated by the model number. All models were externally similar, and the photograph depicts the CP-55. Some eighty Porterfield monoplanes are currently registered in the U.S.A., the majority being of the CP-65 and LP-65 versions. The specification relates to the Model CP-65.
Max. speed, 110 m.p.h.; cruising, 100 m.p.h.; initial climb rate, 685 ft./min.; range, 290 miles; empty weight, 671 lb.; loaded, 1,160 lb.; span, 34 ft. 9 in.; length, 22 ft. 8 in.; height, 6 ft. 11¼ in.

POTEZ 36/14   FRANCE

The Potez 36 two-seat monoplane was introduced in 1929 as the first of a series of touring aircraft produced by the Société des Avions Henry Potez. Two versions of the Potez 36 remain active in France: the Potez 36/14 powered by a 95 h.p. Renault 4Pb engine (of which four examples are flying), and the Potez 36/21 with a 100 h.p. Potez 6Ac engine (of which two examples are flying). The specification relates to the Potez 36/14.

Max. speed, 93 m.p.h.; climb to 3,280 ft., 9 minutes 30 seconds; absolute ceiling, 13,120 ft.; range, 431 miles; empty weight, 994 lb.; loaded, 1,676 lb.; span, 33 ft. 3 in.; length, 25 ft. 2 in.; height, 8 ft. 1 in.; wing area, 215 sq. ft.

POTEZ 431   FRANCE

The Potez 43 series of two-seat cabin monoplanes achieved some popularity during the early 'thirties, and were fitted with a variety of different engines. Some ten examples of the Potez 43 are currently flying in France, including the Potez 431 (100 h.p. Potez 6Ac) to which the specification refers, the Potez 434 (120 h.p. de Havilland Gipsy Major), the Potez 435 (Renault 4 Pdi of 120 h.p.), and the similarly powered Potez 437 and 438, the Potez 436 (140 h.p. Renault 4, POI), and the Potez 439A (130 h.p. Potez 6Ba).

Max. speed, 106 m.p.h.; cruising, 92 m.p.h.; empty weight, 1,030 lb.; loaded, 1,850 lb.; span, 37 ft.; length, 24 ft. 5 in.; height, 7 ft. 9 in.; wing area, 204 sq. ft.

POTEZ 58   FRANCE

The Potez 58 three-seat light cabin monoplane was produced in some numbers and with several engines during the mid 'thirties, first appearing in 1933. Three examples of this type are currently flying in France; two Potez 584 with 120 h.p. de Havilland Gipsy Major engines, and one Potez 585 with a 130 h.p. Potez 6 Ba engine. The specification relates to this latter version. The Potez 58 series touring monoplanes are of wooden construction with plywood covering.

Max. speed, 118 m.p.h.; cruising speed, 99 m.p.h.; normal range, 466 miles; max. 747 miles; empty weight, 1,120 lb.; loaded, 1,980 lb.; span, 37 ft.; length, 24 ft. 5 in.; height, 7 ft. 8 in.

POTEZ 60   FRANCE

The Potez 60 was introduced by the Henry Potez concern in 1934. This tandem two-seat light parasol monoplane became extremely popular, and large numbers were produced for the flying clubs participating in the officially-sponsored *Aviation Populaire* movement. The Potez 60 is powered by a 60 h.p. Potez 3B engine, and seven machines of this type are currently active in France. One additional machine was modified in 1948 to take a 75 h.p. Minié 4DC-30 engine and is referred to as the Potez 60/48.

Max. speed, 90 m.p.h.; climb to 1,640 ft., 3 minutes, 45 seconds; ceiling, 9,840 ft.; range, 404 miles; empty weight, 629 lb.; loaded, 1,232 lb.; span, 32 ft. 9½ in.; length, 22 ft. 10 in.; height, 7 ft. 8 in.

POTEZ 75   FRANCE

The first product of the resuscitated Potez Company, the Potez 75 two-seat police and ground-attack monoplane was flown for the first time on June 1, 1953. Powered by a 450 h.p. Potez 8D.32 engine driving a pusher airscrew, the Potez 75 was designed as a simple and inexpensive aircraft for use by reserve units and small air forces with limited maintenance facilities. It can be used as a control aircraft for guided missiles and carries various combinations of bombs and rockets.

Max. speed, 170 m.p.h.; cruising, 150 m.p.h.; initial climb, 1,575 ft./min.; max. range, 465 miles; empty weight, 3,690 lb.; loaded, 5,290 lb.; span, 42 ft. 8 in.; length, 29 ft. 10 in.

PRAGA E.114 AIR BABY   CZECHOSLOVAKIA

A pre-war design resurrected after World War II, the E.114 Air Baby was built in two versions after the war: the E.114D with a 75 h.p. Praga D engine, and the E.114M with a 65 h.p. Walter Mikron III. One hundred and ten post-war E.114s had been built when production ceased in 1948. The E.114 was built under licence in Britain before the war by F. Hills and Sons, and was known as the Hillson-Praga. The pre-war E.114 and the Hillson-Praga, several examples of both of which are flying, have the 40 h.p. Praga B.

Max. speed, 116 m.p.h.; cruising, 103 m.p.h.; range, 435 miles; empty weight, 772 lb.; loaded, 1,290 lb.; span, 36 ft. 1 in.; length, 21 ft. 8 in.; height, 8 ft. 6 in.

PRAGA E.117   CZECHOSLOVAKIA

The Praga E.117, a refined version of the E.114 Air Baby of 1934, is another pre-war Czechoslovak design that was resurrected after World War II. Of mixed wood and metal construction, the E.117 has an entirely new wing and is a side-by-side two-seat cabin monoplane powered by a 75 h.p. Praga D engine. The E.117 was built in smaller numbers than the more popular E.114, but a few aircraft of this type are still flying.

Max. speed, 128 m.p.h. at sea level; cruising speed, 112 m.p.h.; initial climb rate, 558 ft./min.; ceiling, 11,500 ft.; range, 370 miles; empty weight, 838 lb.; loaded, 1,367 lb.; span, 35 ft. 5¼ in.; length, 22 ft. 3½ in.; height, 7 ft. 10½ in.

PRETI PM-280 TARTUCA   ITALY

The PM-280 Tartuca (Tortoise) was produced in 1948 by the Instituto di Aeronautica of the Politecnico di Milano to the designs of Ing. Ermenegildo Preti, who was also responsible for the Agusta P.110 and P.111. A single-seat low-wing monoplane of all-wood construction, the Tartuca is fitted with flaps and a retractable undercarriage, and is powered by a 60 h.p. C.N.A. D4 engine. From the time that the design of the Tartuca was commenced to the first flight tests only ten weeks elapsed.

Max. speed, 161 m.p.h.; climb to 3,280 ft., 5 minutes 50 seconds; range 342 miles; ceiling, 10,827 ft.; empty weight, 550 lb.; loaded, 770 lb.; span, 16 ft. 5 in.; length, 16 ft. 6 in.; wing area, 53.8 sq. ft.

RAWDON T-1   U.S.A.

The Rawdon T-1 two-seat monoplane was designed and built by Rawdon Brothers Aircraft, Inc., as a general purpose aircraft, suitable for training, touring and crop-spraying. The T-1 was first produced in 1938, and some five pre-war built machines are still active. The design was resurrected in 1953, and the post-war model is powered by a 135 h.p. Lycoming 0-290 engine. The T-1S is a special agricultural version, equipped with spray tank and spray bars.

Max. speed, 138 m.p.h.; cruising, 120 m.p.h.; initial climb, 900 ft./min.; service ceiling, 18,000 ft.; range, 500 miles; empty weight, 1,300 lb.; loaded, 1,900 lb.; span, 33 ft. 4 in.; length, 24 ft. 2 in.; height, 7 ft. 3 in.

REARWIN 9000L SPORTSTER   U.S.A.

The Model 9000 first appeared in 1935, and several versions with different engines had been produced when production ceased in 1939. The 9000L is the most common version today, and examples are flying with both the 90 h.p. Le Blond and the 90 h.p. Warner Scarab engines. The Model 7000 and Model 8500 are similar except for engines, the former having a 70 h.p. Le Blond and the latter having an 85 h.p. Le Blond. Examples of all three models are flying in the U.S.A., and Model 9000s are flying in Australia and New Zealand.

Max. speed, 123 m.p.h.; cruising speed, 110 m.p.h.; initial climb, 1,000 ft./min.; service ceiling, 15,000 ft.; range, 450 miles; empty weight, 861 lb.; loaded, 1,460 lb.; span, 35 ft.; length, 22 ft. 3½ in.; height, 6 ft. 9 in.; wing area, 166 sq. ft.

REARWIN 6000M SPEEDSTER   U.S.A.

Introduced in 1935 by the newly-formed Rearwin Airplanes, Inc., the Speedster was produced in two versions: the Model 6000 with the 95 h.p. American Cirrus engine, and the Model 6000M with the 125 h.p. Menasco C-4. One or two examples of both versions currently remain in the U.S.A. The Speedster is a tandem two-seat cabin monoplane of mixed construction with metal and fabric covering. Complete dual controls are fitted. The specification relates to the Model 6000M.

Max. speed, 166 m.p.h.; cruising, 140 m.p.h.; initial climb rate, 750 ft./min.; range, 600 miles; empty weight, 1,052 lb.; loaded, 1,668 lb.; span, 32 ft.; length, 21 ft. 6 in.; height, 6 ft. 6 in.; wing area, 145 sq. ft.

REID AND SIGRIST R.S.4 BOBSLEIGH   G.B.

The R.S.4 commenced life as the R.S.3 two-seat primary and intermediate trainer which first flew on July 9, 1945. In 1951 this prototype was modified for a series of prone-pilot experiments at the R.A.E., Farnborough. For these trials the pilot's seat was moved aft to the position originally occupied by the second seat, and a modified nose enclosing a prone-pilot position was fitted. In this form the machine became known as the R.S.4 Bobsleigh and flew on June 13, 1951. It is powered by two 130 h.p. de Havilland Gipsy Major Series I engines.

Max. speed, 158 m.p.h.; cruising, 146 m.p.h.; initial climb, 1,100 ft./min.; service ceiling, 17,740 ft.; empty weight, 2,450 lb.; loaded, 3,300 lb.; span, 34 ft.; length, 26 ft. 9 in.

REPUBLIC 2PA-204A (AT-12)   U.S.A.

The Republic (formerly Seversky) 2PA-204A Guardsman was first flown in January, 1940, and was a modification of the 2PAL. A two-seat fighter-bomber powered by a 1,050 h.p. Pratt & Whitney R-1830-45 engine, the 2PA-204A was ordered for the Swedish Air Force but only two of the fifty-two machines ordered reached Sweden, the remaining fifty being taken over by the U.S.A.A.F. as advanced trainers under the designation AT-12. Powered by a 1,200 h.p. Pratt & Whitney Twin Wasp, one AT-12 is currently included on the U.S. civil register.

Max. speed, 315 m.p.h.; cruising, 285 m.p.h.; initial climb, 2,600 ft./min.; range, 675 miles; loaded weight, 6,022 lb.; span, 36 ft.; length, 26 ft. 10 in.; height, 9 ft. 9½ in.

REPUBLIC F-47D THUNDERBOLT   U.S.A.

The prototype Thunderbolt, the XP-47B, first flew on May 8, 1941, and a total of 15,329 Thunderbolt fighters were produced during the war years. The version produced in the greatest numbers was the F-47D powered by a 2,300 h.p. Pratt & Whitney R-2800-59 or -63 engine, and the F-47D-25 production batch marked the transition from the "turtle-back" type canopy to the "bubble" canopy which appeared on all later models. The F-47D serves with the air forces of Yugoslavia, Brazil, Chile, Colombia, Dominica, Ecuador, Mexico, Peru and Turkey.

Max. speed, 426 m.p.h. at 30,000 ft.; climb to 15,000 ft., 5.1 minutes; loaded weight, 14,500 lb.; span, 40 ft. 9¼ in.; length, 36 ft. 1¼ in.; height, 14 ft. 2 in.; wing area, 300 sq. ft.

REPUBLIC F-84G THUNDERJET   U.S.A.

Design of the Thunderjet was initiated in November 1944, and the first prototype, designated XP-84, was first flown on February 28, 1946. Two prototypes were followed by thirteen pre-production YP-84s (4,000 lb.s.t. Allison J35-A-15), five hundred similarly-powered F-84Bs, one hundred and ninety-one F-84Cs (J35-A-13), three hundred and eighteen F-84Ds, and one hundred and twenty F-84Es (5,000 lb.s.t. J35-A-17). The final production model, the F-84G, continued in production until July 1953, when a total of 4,457 Thunderjets had been completed.

Specification: Single-seat fighter-bomber. Engine: One 5,600 lb.s.t. Allison J35-A-29. Weights: Empty, 11,460 lb.; loaded, 18,000 lb. Performance: Max. speed, 605 m.p.h. at sea level; combat radius, 850 miles (with two 191.5 imp. gall. drop-tanks), 1,000 miles. Armament: Six 0.50-in. M-3 guns and 32 5-in. HVAR, or two 11.5-in. and sixteen 5-in. rockets. Dimensions: Span, 36 ft. 4 in.; length, 38 ft. 5 in.; height, 12 ft. 10¼ in.

REPUBLIC F-84F THUNDERSTREAK   U.S.A.

Originally intended as a simple adaptation of the F-84E to take swept wing and tail surfaces, the prototype Thunderstreak, the XF-84F, flew on June 3, 1950. The design was later extensively modified, and few components are now interchangeable with those of the Thunderjet. The first production F-84F flew on November 22, 1952, powered by a YJ65-W-1 turbojet, and a single-piece, "all-flying" tail surface was fitted between the 250th and 300th production Thunderstreak. The installation of a liquid-fuel rocket motor in the tail to assist take-off with heavy loads has been considered.

Specification: Single-seat fighter-bomber. Engine: One 7,220 lb.s.t. Wright J65-W-3. Weights: Loaded (clean), 19,340 lb.; normal (with external load of two 191 imp. gall. and two 375 imp. gall. external tanks), 26,030 lb.; max., 28,000 lb. Performance: Max. speed, 720 m.p.h. at sea level; initial climb rate, 7,500 ft./min.; service ceiling, 48,000 ft.; normal combat radius, 850 miles. Dimensions: Span, 33 ft. 7¼ in.; length, 43 ft. 4¾ in.

REPUBLIC RF-84F THUNDERFLASH   U.S.A.

The second XF-84F Thunderstreak was modified late in 1951 by the replacement of the nose air intake with twin wing root intakes. This arrangement was not adopted for the fighter-bomber but was incorporated in the RF-84F Thunderflash photo-reconnaissance fighter. The root intakes permit the installation of a camera bay in the nose which can accommodate several combinations of remotely-controlled and automatic vertical and oblique cameras. A version of the RF-84F is employed by the FICON system, a reconnaissance fighter being carried in the bomb-bay of a Convair GRB-36J.

Specification: Single-seat reconnaissance-fighter. Engine: One 7,220 lb.s.t. Wright J65-W-3. Weights: Approx. normal loaded, 20,000 lb.; max. 26,000 lb. Performance: Max. speed, 720 m.p.h.; normal range, 1,500 miles; max. 2,500 miles; service ceiling, 48,000 ft. Armament: Four 0.5-in. M-3 guns. Dimensions: Span, 33 ft. 7¼ in.; length, 47 ft. 7¾ in.; height, 15 ft.

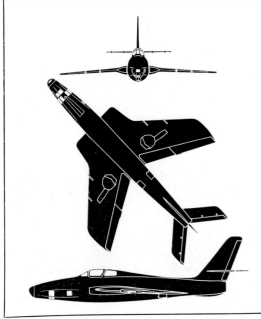

REPUBLIC XF-84H U.S.A.

Flown for the first time on July 22, 1955, the XF-84H is a supersonic airscrew testbed derived from the basic F-84F Thunderstreak design, but it is not a conversion, having been built from the outset for its specialised role. Powered by a 5,850 e.s.h.p. Allison XT40-A-1 turbo-prop designed for afterburner thrust augmentation, the XF-84H is intended to provide data for a turboprop-driven attack bomber, and two further prototypes are under construction, one of which will be fitted with two sets of three-blade airscrews, both sets rotating in the same direction, with special controls counteracting torque, and one XF-84H is expected to undergo U.S. Navy carrier trials. A one-piece "slab" type tailplane is mounted at the tip of the vertical tail surfaces.

REPUBLIC YF-84J U.S.A.

The YF-84J is an experimental version of the F-84F Thunderstreak powered by a 9,300 lb.s.t. General Electric J73-GE turbojet, and the first of two examples ordered for evaluation by the U.S.A.F. flew on May 7, 1954. The YF-84J features a redesigned and deepened air intake, a deeper fuselage and redesigned dive brakes. An armament of six 0.50-in. machine guns is carried and underwing loads of bombs and rocket missiles exceeding 6,000 lb. may be carried.

Max. speed, 720 (plus) m.p.h. at sea level; range (with external load), 1,000 (plus) miles; service ceiling, 45,000 ft.; span, 33 ft. 7 in.; length, 43 ft.; height, 14 ft. 4 in.

REPUBLIC RC-3 SEABEE U.S.A.

Flown for the first time in November 1944, the Seabee was designed as a simple, low-cost amphibian flying boat, and 1,060 Seabees had been produced when production ceased in October 1947. Some four hundred of these are still active in the U.S.A., and others are flying in Canada, Central and South America, Sweden, and Switzerland. The construction of the Seabee is extremely simple, and manufacturing man hours had been reduced to two hundred per aircraft when production terminated.
Specification: Four-seat amphibian flying boat. Engine: One 215 h.p. Franklin 6A8-215-B7F. Weights: Empty, 1,950 lb.; loaded, 3,000 lb. Performance: Max. speed, 120 m.p.h.; cruising speed, 103 m.p.h.; initial climb rate, 700 ft./min.; service ceiling, 12,000 ft.; range, 560 miles. Dimensions: Span, 37 ft. 8 in.; length, 27 ft. 11 in.; height, 10 ft. 1 in.; wing area, 196 sq. ft.

REPUBLIC XF-91 U.S.A.

Designed initially as a high-altitude interceptor, the XF-91 embodies several unusual design features. First flown on May 9, 1949, and powered by a 5,200 lb.s.t. General Electric J47-GE-3 augmented by a 6,000 lb. thrust Reaction Motors XLR-11-RM-9 rocket motor. The wing is of variable-incidence type and features inverse taper, having greater chord and depth at the tip than at the root. The XF-91 was initially fitted with orthodox swept vertical tail surfaces, but these were supplanted by a V-type or "butterfly" unit as illustrated.

Max. speed, Mach 1.0 (plus); approx. max. loaded weight, 30,000 lb.; span, 31 ft. 3 in.; length, 46 ft. 8 in.; height, 18 ft. 1 in.

REY R.1 FRANCE

The Rey R.1 was designed to test a new variable wing incidence system, and the first of two prototypes flew on December 16, 1949 powered by two 216 h.p. Renault 6QR engines. The outer wing panels are articulated on an oblique hinge-line and these orientate automatically in turbulent air, the varying incidence absorbing the loads imposed and resulting in smoother flight in gusty weather. The Rey R.1 carries a test crew of two and is of wooden construction.

Max. speed, 202 m.p.h.; climb to 3,280 ft., 4 minutes, 10 seconds; ceiling, 19,025 ft.; empty weight, 4,950 lb.; loaded, 6,490 lb.; span, 43 ft. 2½ in.; length, 30 ft. 2 in.; height, 11 ft. 11 in.

RILEY TWIN NAVION U.S.A.

The Riley Twin Navion is a conversion of the North American- or Ryan-built single-engined Navion to take two Lycoming engines. So extensive is the conversion of the basic Navion airframe to Twin Navion standards that more than 2,000 engineering drawings and 1,837 specially-manufactured parts are utilised. Most conversions have been made by Riley Aircraft, but late in 1953 rights in the Twin Navion were acquired by the Temco Aircraft Corporation, and the 1955 Temco-built model (described by the specification), first flown in October 1954, has more powerful engines, and fuel capacity has been increased from 60 U.S. galls. to 106 U.S. galls. with wingtip tanks.
Specification: Four-seat cabin monoplanes. Engines: Two 170 h.p. Lycoming 0-340-A1A. Weights: Empty, 2,350 lb.; loaded, 3,600 lb. Performance: Normal cruising speed, 170 m.p.h.; initial climb rate, 1,400 ft./min.; range, 850 miles. Dimensions: Span, 34 ft.; length, 27 ft. 2 in.; height, 10 ft. 4 in.

ROSE PARRAKEET U.S.A.

Originally produced in 1936 by the Rose Airplane Corporation with a 40 h.p. Continental A40 engine, the Parrakeet single seat sports biplane was returned to production in 1948 when the manufacturing rights were acquired by the Hannaford Aircraft Company. As the Hannaford Parrakeet, it is available in three versions with 40 h.p., 65 h.p., and 85 h.p. engines respectively. The standard post-war production model is powered by a 65 h.p. Continental, but a number of pre-war Parrakeets are flying and the specification refers to this version.

Max. speed, 100 m.p.h.; cruising, 85 m.p.h.; initial climb, 750 ft./min.; range, 340 miles; empty weight, 470 lb.; loaded, 728 lb.; span, 20 ft.; length, 16 ft.; height, 5 ft. 8 in.

RUBIK R-18 KANYA HUNGARY

The R-18 Kanya general-purpose two-seat cabin monoplane and glider tug was produced by the Sportarutermelö factory at Esztergom, and was designed by Erno Rubik. Powered by a 130 h.p. Walter Major 4-I engine, the Kanya has a minimum speed of 38 m.p.h. resulting from the use of full-span Handley Page slots and large flaps. Dual controls are provided and construction is mixed with fabric covering. The manufacturer of the Kanya, the Sportarutermelö N.V., is a national concern for the production of sporting equipment.

Max. speed, 110 m.p.h.; cruising speed, 75 m.p.h.; absolute ceiling, 19,700 ft.; range, 380 miles; empty weight, 900 lb.; loaded, 1,520 lb.; span, 38 ft.; length, 25 ft.; height, 7 ft.; wing area, 150 sq. ft.

RYAN STM-2 U.S.A.

The STM-2 tandem two-seat primary trainer was a development of the STA-1 of 1934, fifteen of which were delivered to the U.S.A.A.F. as YPT-16s with Menasco C-4-S engines of 150 h.p. These were later replaced by 132 h.p. Kinner R-440-1 engines and the type became the PT-16A. Thirty were delivered as PT-20s with the Menasco engine, subsequently replaced by the Kinner, and a number were supplied to the Netherlands East Indies Air Force. Eight Menasco-powered STM-2s are flying in Australia, and a number of externally similar STA-2s are flying in the U.S.A.
Max. speed, 160 m.p.h.; cruising, 135 m.p.h.; initial climb, 1,400 ft./min.; service ceiling, 21,000 ft.; range, 350 miles; empty weight, 1,027 lb.; loaded, 1,600 lb.; span, 30 ft.; length, 21 ft. 5 in.

RYAN ST-3KR U.S.A.

The Ryan ST-3KR was introduced in 1940 as a development of the STA-1 with a 125 h.p. Kinner B-54 radial engine. One hundred were delivered to the U.S.A.A.F. as the PT-21 with a 132 h.p. Kinner R-440-3, and 1,023 were delivered as the PT-22 with the 160 h.p. Kinner R-540-1. Nearly two hundred ST-3KR monoplanes are currently active in the U.S.A. The ST-3KR is a tandem two-seater with dual controls, and is of all-metal construction. Specification relates to the 160 h.p. Kinner-powered version.

Max. speed, 131 m.p.h.; cruising, 123 m.p.h.; initial climb, 1,000 ft./min.; range, 352 miles; empty weight, 1,313 lb.; loaded, 1,860 lb.; span, 30 ft. 1 in.; length, 22 ft. 5 in.; height, 6 ft. 10 in.

RYAN (L-17) NAVION 205   U.S.A.

Originally designed by North American Aviation, Inc., which concern produced more than 1,000 aircraft of this type, the Navion has been produced by the Ryan Aeronautical Company, which acquired the design and manufacturing rights in 1947. The U.S.A.F. purchased a number of North American-built Navions for liaison duties under the designation L-17A and, in 1948, ordered a further 158 machines from Ryan under the designation L-17B. The L-17C is the L-17A modified by Ryan. A more powerful version, the Navion Super 260, appeared in 1951 powered by a 260 h.p. Lycoming GO-435-C2 engine, and the Model 72 was a two-seat primary training version.

Specification: Four-seat cabin monoplane. Engine: One 205 h.p. Continental E-185-3. Weights: Empty, 1,782 lb.; loaded, 2,750 lb. Performance: Max. speed, 163 m.p.h.; cruising, 155 m.p.h.; initial climb rate, 900 ft./min. Dimensions: Span, 33 ft. 4½ in.; length, 27 ft. 3 in.; height, 8 ft. 7⅞ in.; wing area, 185 sq. ft.

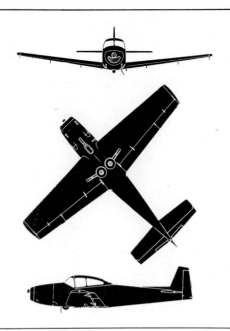

SAAB-17A   SWEDEN

The SAAB-17 attack bomber was first flown in 1940, and a large number of aircraft of this type were supplied to the Swedish Air Force. Three different engines were installed in production series, but remaining machines are of the SAAB-17A type powered by the 1,065 h.p. SFAB-built Pratt & Whitney R-1830 (STWC-3). Sixty-six SAAB-17As have been sold to the Ethiopian Air Force, and fifteen are employed by Svensk Flygtjanst A.B. as target tugs.

Max. speed, 270 m.p.h.; cruising speed, 242 m.p.h.; loaded weight, 8,350 lb.; span, 45 ft. 1 in.; length, 32 ft. 10 in.; height, 14 ft. 6 in.; wing area, 307 sq. ft.

SAAB-18A   SWEDEN

The SAAB-18A was produced in several versions for the Swedish Air Force, the first prototype appearing in 1942. The initial production model, the SAAB-18A (*illustrated*), was used by Swedish bomber units as the B 18A and, as the S 18 reconnaissance aircraft, still serves in small numbers. An improved version, the SAAB-18B, differs primarily in having the 1,065 h.p. SFA-built Pratt & Whitney R-1830 engines replaced by 1,475 h.p. SFA-built DB 605Bs. Bomber and attack variants were designated B 18B and T 18B respectively.

Max. speed, 289 m.p.h.; cruising, 258 m.p.h.; empty weight, 13,448 lb.; loaded, 17,960 lb.; span, 55 ft. 9 in.; length, 43 ft. 5 in.; height, 14 ft. 3 in.; wing area, 471 sq. ft.

SAAB-35 DRAKEN   SWEDEN

The SAAB-35 Draken, or J 35, single-seat interceptor fighter first appeared in October 1955, and is intended as a replacement for the J 34 (Hawker Hunter F.4) during 1958–59. The SAAB-35 Draken features the radical double-delta wing planform that was first flight-tested on the SAAB-210 research aircraft. The SAAB-210, which flew for the first time in December 1951, is virtually a half-scale flying model of the SAAB-35, and is powered by a 1,050 lb.s.t. Armstrong Siddeley Adder A.S.A.1 turbojet. The production version of the J 35 will utilise a more powerful afterburning Avon turbojet than that installed in the prototypes, and is expected to attain Mach 1.5 in level flight.

Specification: Single-seat interceptor. Engine: One 7,500 lb.s.t. (9,500 lb. with afterburning) SFA-built (RM5) Rolls-Royce Avon R.A.7R. Weights: No details available. Performance (production model): Approx. max. speed, 990 m.p.h. at 40,000 ft. Approx. dimensions: Span, 32 ft.; length, 40 ft.

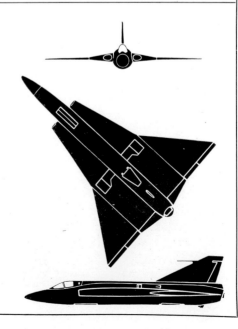

L

SAAB-29F SWEDEN

The SAAB-29 (designated J 29 by the *Flygvapnet*) flew for the first time on September 1, 1948, and was subsequently produced in considerable numbers for Swedish fighter, attack, and photo-reconnaissance elements. The second production version, the J 29B, differed from its predecessor in having increased internal tankage; the S 29C, which first flew on June 3, 1953, was a photo-reconnaissance version with a camera nose; the J 29D was an experimental model fitted with a Swedish-designed afterburner, and the J 29E had "saw tooth" wing leading-edge extensions to raise the local critical Mach number. The current J 29F has both afterburner and wing extension.

Specification: Single-seat fighter. Engine: One 5,000 lb.s.t. (6,500 lb. with afterburning) SFA-built Ghost 50. Weights (J 29A): Empty, 9,479 lb.; loaded, 13,360 lb. Performance: Max. speed, 658 m.p.h. at 5,000 ft.; initial climb (with afterburning), 15,000 ft./min.; max. range, 1,677 miles. Dimensions: Span, 36 ft. 1 in.; length, 33 ft. 2½ in.; height, 12 ft. 3½ in.; wing area, 258 sq. ft.

SAAB-91B SAFIR SWEDEN

The Safir three-seat cabin monoplane was first flown in 1945, and in the initial production series, the SAAB-91A, was powered by the 145 h.p. D.H. Gipsy Major X engine, and seventeen aircraft of this type are used as primary trainers by the Imperial Ethiopian Air Force. Re-engined with a Lycoming as the SAAB-91B, the Safir is employed as a standard primary trainer of the *Flygvapnet* as the Sk 50, and nine machines of this type have been delivered to Ethiopia. Others are used by the West German *Deutsch Lufthansa* and by *SABENA* as crew trainers, and 120 SAAB-91Bs were built under sub-contract by the De Schelde company. The SAAB-91C is a four-seat version developed by the Dutch company.

Specification: Three-seat cabin monoplane. Engine: One 190 h.p. Lycoming 0-435-A. Weights: Empty, 1,580 lb.; loaded, 2,560 lb. Performance: Max. speed, 171 m.p.h.; cruising speed, 137 m.p.h.; initial climb rate, 1,140 ft./min.; range, 650 miles. Dimensions: Span, 34 ft. 9 in.; length, 25 ft. 6 in.; height, 7 ft. 2 in.; wing area, 146.3 sq. ft.

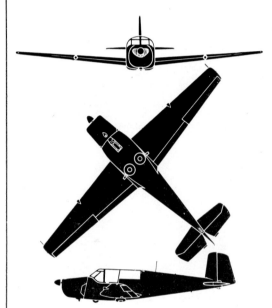

SAAB-90A-2 SCANDIA SWEDEN

The prototype Scandia was flown for the first time on November 16, 1946, and twelve SAAB-90A-2 Scandia thirty-two/forty-seat airliners were built by the parent company for Scandinavian Airlines and the Brazilian VASP airline. Owing to the company's military commitments orders for additional Scandias were sub-contracted to three Dutch aircraft manufacturers, Fokker, De Schelde and Aviolanda, these concerns co-operating in the construction of six further Scandias for VASP.

Specification: Thirty-two/forty-seat commercial transport. Engines: Two 1,800 h.p. Pratt & Whitney R-2180-E1 Twin Wasp. Weights: Empty, 21,960 lb.; loaded, 35,280 lb. Performance: Max. speed, 280 m.p.h. at 8,500 ft.; max. cruising speed, 242 m.p.h. at 10,000 ft.; initial climb rate, 1,350 ft./min.; normal range, 900 miles. Dimensions: Span, 91 ft. 10 in.; length, 69 ft. 11 in.; height, 23 ft. 3 in.; wing area, 922 sq. ft.

SAAB-32 LANSEN — SWEDEN

Flown for the first time on November 3, 1952, the Lansen (Lance) will enter service with the Swedish Air Force in 1956 as the A 32. Two variants currently under development are the S 32 photo-reconnaissance aircraft powered by a 9,500 lb.s.t. Rolls-Royce Avon R.A.14, and the J 32 night and all-weather fighter version with a 10,000 lb.s.t. Avon R.A.28. The three prototypes of the Lansen are powered by imported Avon R.A.7R engines, but the production A 32 has the licence-built Avon R.A.7R. Built-in armament comprises four 20-mm. Swedish Hispano cannon, and a variety of under-wing ordnance loads may be carried.

Specification: Two-seat attack aircraft. Engine: One 7,500 lb.s.t. (9,500 lb. with after-burning) RM 5 (Rolls-Royce Avon R.A.7R). Weights: Approx. loaded, 22,000 lb. Performance: Approx. max. speed, 720 m.p.h. at sea level; approx. max. range, 1,500 miles. Dimensions: Span, 42 ft. 8 in.; length, 49 ft. 2 in.; height, 16 ft. 5 in.

S.A.I. KZ-III — DENMARK

Two prototypes of the KZ-III were built during the German occupation of Denmark, ostensibly for use by the Danish Air Ambulance Service. One was test flown in Denmark, but the other was smuggled to Sweden in a railway truck and test flown in that country. Production of the KZ-III commenced after the liberation of Denmark, and sixty cabin monoplanes of this type were built during 1946–47, after which it was replaced on the production lines by the KZ-VII Laerke. For air ambulance duties, the KZ-III has a hinged panel in the fuselage portside through which a stretcher may be loaded.

Specification: Two-seat light cabin monoplane. Engine: One 100 h.p. Blackburn Cirrus Minor II. Weights: Empty, 850 lb.; loaded, 1,435 lb. Performance: Max. speed, 115 m.p.h.; cruising speed, 106 m.p.h.; initial climb rate, 700 ft./min.; range, 310 miles. Dimensions: Span, 31 ft. 6 in.; length, 21 ft. 6 in.; height, 6 ft. 9 in.; wing area, 140 sq. ft.

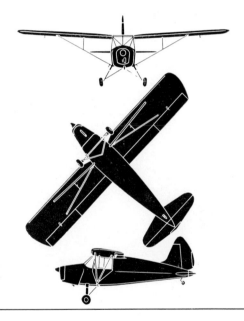

S.A.I. KZ-VII LAERKE — DENMARK

The KZ-VII Laerke is a higher-powered, four-seat development of the KZ-III. Flown for the first time on October 11, 1946, the Laerke is used in small numbers by the Danish Air Force for communications duties. Fifty-five machines were built, and seven of these were supplied to Switzerland with 145 h.p. Continental C-145-2 engines and Aeromatic constant-speed airscrews. Twelve examples of an air observation post version, the KZ-X, were supplied to the Danish Army. This was first flown on September 29, 1951, but after several accidents due to tailplane failure, the KZ-X was withdrawn from service.

Specification: Four-seat cabin monoplane. Engine: One 125 h.p. Continental C-125. Weights: Empty, 1,022 lb.; loaded, 1,911 lb. Performance: Max. speed, 125 m.p.h.; cruising, 115 m.p.h.; initial climb, 590 ft./min.; range, 450 miles. Dimensions: Span, 31 ft. 6 in.; length, 21 ft. 6 in.; height, 6 ft. 11 in.; wing area, 140 sq. ft.

S.A.I. KZ-II-T
DENMARK

The KZ-II has been produced in three versions: the pre-war KZ-II *Sport* (105 h.p. Hirth H.M.504A-II) with open cockpits, the KZ-II *Kupe* (90 h.p. D.H. Gipsy Minor) cabin monoplane, and the post-war KZ-II-T primary trainer with a 145 h.p. de Havilland Gipsy Major 10. Fifteen of the latter version were built for the Royal Danish Air Force, and the remaining nine KZ-II-Ts have been sold to private owners and flying clubs. A Hirth-powered KZ-II *Sport* and a Minor-powered KZ-II *Kupe* are flying in Sweden, and two KZ-II *Sports* in Switzerland.
Max. speed, 146 m.p.h.; cruising speed, 124 m.p.h.; initial climb, 885 ft./min.; service ceiling, 16,405 ft.; empty weight, 1,212 lb.; loaded, 1,874 lb.; span, 33 ft. 6 in.; length, 25 ft.; height, 6 ft. 10¾ in.; wing area, 161.5 sq. ft.

S.A.I. KZ-IV
DENMARK

The KZ-IV six-seat ambulance aircraft was produced during the German occupation of Denmark for the *Zoneredningskorpset* which operates an air ambulance service. The KZ-IV, two examples of which were produced, the first being flown on May 4, 1944, has accommodation for two stretcher cases and a medical attendant. The first KZ-IV is powered by two 130 h.p. D.H. Gipsy Major I engines, and the second machine (KZ-IVA) built in 1948 has two 145 h.p. Gipsy Major 10 engines. The specification relates to the first KZ-IV.
Max. speed, 138 m.p.h.; cruising, 125 m.p.h.; service ceiling, 14,700 ft.; range, 560 miles; empty weight, 2,650 lb.; loaded, 4,400 lb.; span, 52 ft. 6 in.; length, 32 ft. 2 in.; height, 8 ft. 8½ in.

S.A.I. KZ-VIII
DENMARK

The KZ-VIII single-seat aerobatic trainer was first flown on November 12, 1949. Two prototypes were commenced but only one of these was completed and this is now registered in Switzerland (HB-EPB). Powered by a 145 h.p. de Havilland Gipsy Major 10 engine, the KZ-VIII is of all-wood construction and fully aerobatic, stressed for 12G. The sliding "bubble" canopy is jettisonable, and three-position split-flaps are fitted between the ailerons and the fuselage.
Max. speed, 171 m.p.h.; initial climb rate, 480 ft./min.; empty weight, 895 lb.; loaded (aerobatic), 1,265 lb. (normal), 1,430 lb.; span, 23 ft. 7 in.; length, 19 ft. 2 in.; height, 5 ft. 11 in.; wing area, 93 sq. ft.

SAIMAN 202-M
ITALY

The Saiman 202-M was first introduced in 1936, and participated in a number of international competitions in pre-war years. During the war the type was employed as a liaison and communications two-seat cabin monoplane by the *Regia Aeronautica*, and at least one example remains airworthy in Italy. The Saiman 204 is externally similar but is arranged as a four-seater and has a 180 h.p. Alfa Romeo 115 engine. The Saiman 202-M is powered by a 130 h.p. Alfa Romeo 110 engine. Construction is all-wood with fabric and plywood covering.
Max. speed, 143 m.p.h.; cruising, 124 m.p.h.; absolute ceiling, 16,400 ft.; range, 683 miles; empty weight, 1,364 lb.; loaded, 2,068 lb.; span, 35 ft. 7 in.; length, 25 ft. 3 in.; height, 6 ft. 7 in.; wing area, 190 sq. ft.

SAN-101
FRANCE

The SAN-101 is the first product of the Société Aéronautique Normande, and flew for the first time at the end of 1949. A tandem two-seat cabin monoplane, the SAN-101 is powered by a 65 h.p. Continental C65 engine, but a 100 h.p. Renault 4PG1 engine may also be installed, and it is estimated that this will increase cruising speed from 74 m.p.h. to 96 m.p.h. The SAN-101 is externally very similar to the American Piper Cub, and only one prototype has been built to date.
Max. speed, 98 m.p.h.; cruising speed, 74 m.p.h.; range, 373 miles; weight: no details available; span, 38 ft. 2½ in.; length, 24 ft.

SAVOIA-MARCHETTI S.M.79
ITALY

The S.M.79 originally appeared in 1935 as an eight-passenger commercial monoplane powered by three 650 h.p. Alfa Romeo 125 R.C. radials, but the bomber version ordered by the *Regia Aeronautica* had three 850 h.p. Alfa Romeo 126 RC 34 radials. The final wartime production version was powered by 1,000 h.p. Piaggio P.XI RC 40 radials, and several of these are flying in Italy now, re-engined with 1,215 h.p. Pratt & Whitney R-1830-S1C3G engines. Three are flying in Lebanon and others are employed by the Spanish Air Force.
Max. speed, 260 m.p.h.; cruising, 225 m.p.h.; service ceiling, 22,960 ft.; range, 1,000 miles; empty weight, 14,960 lb.; loaded, 23,100 lb.; span, 66 ft. 3 in.; length, 53 ft. 2 in.; height, 13 ft. 6 in.; wing area, 656.3 sq. ft.

SAVOIA-MARCHETTI S.M.82   ITALY

The S.M.82 Marsupiale was introduced in 1938 and entered service as a bomber-transport with the *Regia Aeronautica* in 1941. In 1942, a Marsupiale flew from Rome to Tokio with a Campini power plant, and the type was used for bombing raids on the Barheim Islands and Palestine. A number of S.M.82s survived the war and are employed by the Italian Air Force. Some retain the original 950 h.p. Alfa 128 RC 21 radial engines, but others have been re-engined with 1,215 h.p. Pratt & Whitney R-1830-S1C3G radials.

Max. speed, 224 m.p.h.; cruising speed, 186 m.p.h.; range, 2,361 miles; empty weight, 26,400 lb.; loaded, 38,360 lb.; span, 97 ft. 5 in.; length, 73 ft. 10 in.; height, 18 ft.; wing area, 1,276 sq. ft.

SCAN-20   FRANCE

Designed and built in secret during the German occupation of France, the SCAN-20 four-seat trainer flying-boat was flown for the first time on October 6, 1945, and twenty-three machines were subsequently built for the French government. Powered by a 325 h.p. Béarn 6D, the SCAN-20 is fitted with dual controls, the instructor and pupil being seated side-by-side, with two additional seats aft. The SCAN-20 was built by the Société de Constructions Aéro Navale.

Max. speed, 143 m.p.h. at 6,560 ft.; cruising, 124 m.p.h.; ceiling, 16,405 ft.; range, 621 miles; max. loaded weight, 5,511 lb.; span, 49 ft. 2½ in.; length, 38 ft. 6 in.; height, 11 ft. 10½ in.; wing area, 344 sq. ft.

SCOTTISH AVIATION PIONEER C.C.1   G.B.

The Pioneer C.C.1 is being delivered to the R.A.F. for use in the casualty evacuation, air observation post and light transport roles, and sixteen machines of this type are on order for the R.A.F. Originally designed to fulfil specification A.4/45, the first prototype Pioneer flew in 1947 with a 240 h.p. Gipsy Queen 34 engine. This engine was replaced by an Alvis Leonides in the second prototype, known as the Prestwick Pioneer II, and has been standardised for production machines. Pioneer C.C.1s have a removable rectangular panel in the fuselage to facilitate the loading of stretchers.
Specification: Five-seat general-purpose monoplane. Engine: One 560 h.p. Alvis Leonides 501/4. Weights: Empty, 3,835 lb.; loaded, 5,800 lb. Performance: Max. speed, 162 m.p.h.; cruising (50 per cent power), 121 m.p.h.; service ceiling, 23,000 ft.; range, 420 miles. Dimensions: Span, 49 ft. 9 in.; length, 34 ft. 4¾ in.; height, 11 ft. 4½ in.; wing area, 390 sq. ft.

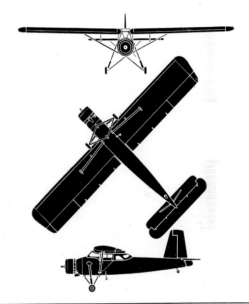

SCOTTISH AVIATION TWIN PIONEER   G.B.

The Twin Pioneer, first flown on June 25, 1955, employs the high-lift devices successfully introduced on the single-engined Pioneer, and was, in fact, known as the Pioneer 4 during its initial design stages. The outer wing panels and engines are almost identical to those of the Pioneer; the wing centre section has built-in slots on each side of the engine nacelles, and very large powered slats similar to those of the Pioneer are fitted. The Twin Pioneer has been designed expressly to provide inexpensive air transport over under-developed areas.
Specification: Sixteen-passenger light transport. Engines: Two 570 h.p. Alvis Leonides 503/8. Weights: Empty, 9,075 lb.; loaded, 13,500 lb. Performance: Cruising speed, 159 m.p.h. at 11,000 ft. (40 per cent power), 124 m.p.h. at 5,000 ft.; initial climb rate, 880 ft./min.; normal still-air range, 620 miles. Dimensions: Span, 76 ft. 6 in.; length, 45 ft. 3 in.; height, 13 ft. 8 in.; wing area, 657 sq. ft.

SECAN TYPE S.U.C.₁₀ COURLIS   FRANCE

First flown on May 9, 1946, the S.U.C.10 Courlis (Curlew) was manufactured by the Société d'Etudes et de Constructions Aéro-Navales, one hundred and thirty-five aircraft of this type being built. Only seventeen Courlis four-seat cabin monoplanes now appear on the French civil register, and these are powered by the 180 h.p. Mathis 8GR or 175 h.p. Mathis 8G-40 engines. The Courlis is of all-metal construction, and the hinged entrance door allows the fitting of a stretcher and simplifies the loading of bulky freight.

Max. speed, 143 m.p.h.; cruising speed, 124 m.p.h.; service ceiling, 13,120 ft.; range, 621 miles; empty weight, 2,180 lb.; loaded, 3,386 lb.; span, 37 ft. 8 in.; length, 26 ft. 10 in.; height, 8 ft. 9½ in.

SETCA MILAN   FRANCE

Designed and built by Messrs. Laboureix and Lagrevol, the SETCA Milan was first flown in 1947, obtained its CNRA in August 1949, and in 1952 was awarded a normal *certificat de navigabilité*. Powered by a 90 h.p. Régnier 4-EO engine, the Milan is of all-wood construction, and its cabin provides accommodation for two persons seated side-by-side. Dual controls are provided. Only one prototype of the Milan has so far been completed, and no production plans have been announced.

Max. speed, 122 m.p.h.; cruising speed, 112 m.p.h.; range, 434 miles; empty weight, 1,210 lb.; loaded, 1,742 lb.; span, 32 ft. 9½ in.; length, 24 ft. 1¼ in.

SF-23 SPERLING   GERMANY

The SF-23 Sperling two-seat cabin monoplane was designed and built by Dipl. Ing. Egon Scheibe who has been responsible for several glider and sailplane designs, including the Mue 13-E Bergfalke I and II, the Spatz, and the Zugvogel, and the prototype flew for the first time in August 1955, powered by an 85 h.p. Continental C85. Production machines will have either the 65 h.p. or 85 h.p. Continental, and a price of approximately £1,400 is currently quoted.

Max. speed, 112 m.p.h.; cruising speed, 98–104 m.p.h.; empty weight, 661 lb.; loaded, 1,146 lb.; span, 32 ft. 4½ in.; length, 19 ft. 8¼ in.; wing area, 99.35 sq. ft.

SHCHERBAKOV SHCHE-2   U.S.S.R.

The SHCHE-2 light transport, designed by Alexei Shcherbakov, was first reported in service with the Soviet Air Force in 1944, being employed for casualty evacuation and for dropping supplies to partisans. Powered by two 145 h.p. M-11D engines, the SHCHE-2 was used for a short time as a ten-seat feeder-liner by *Aeroflot*, but has now been largely replaced by the Antonov AN-2, and the type has been used by the Polish Air Force to train paratroops. Others have been used by Yugoslavia.

Max. speed, 110 m.p.h.; cruising speed, 82.5 m.p.h.; range, 400 miles; span, 72 ft.; length, 50 ft.

SHORT SUNDERLAND M.R.₅   G.B.

First flown in 1937, the Sunderland reconnaissance flying boat continued in production until October 1945. The initial production version, the Sunderland 1, was powered by Bristol Pegasus 18s in the Sunderland 2. The Mk.3 featured a modified hull and adopted as standard the dorsal turret fitted to late production Mk.2s, and the Mk.5 switched to Pratt & Whitney engines. With a crew of ten, the Sunderland M.R.5 is employed for maritime reconnaissance, transport and air/sea rescue duties by R.A.F. Coastal Command.

Specification: Reconnaissance flying boat. Engines: Four 1,200 h.p. Pratt & Whitney R-1830-90B Twin-Wasp. Weights: Empty, 45,000 lb.; loaded, 66,400 lb. Performance: Max. speed, 242 m.p.h.; cruising speed, 155 m.p.h.; initial climb rate, 880 ft./min.; service ceiling, 14,000 ft. Dimensions: Span, 112 ft. 9½ in.; length, 88 ft. 6¾ in.; height, 37 ft. 3 in.; wing area, 1,487 sq. ft.

SHORT S.16/1 SCION   G.B.

The S.16 Scion light five-passenger transport appeared in 1932, and was subsequently built under licence as the S.16/1 by Pobjoy Airmotors and Aircraft Ltd. One example remains airworthy in the United Kingdom, and another is flying in Australia. The Scion, sometimes referred to as the Scion Junior, is powered by two 90 h.p. Pobjoy Niagara engines, and has an all-metal structure fabric-covered. The Scion was used with both wheel and float undercarriages. The two existing machines both have wheel undercarriages, but VH-UUP was originally a floatplane.

Max. speed, 128 m.p.h.; cruising, 112 m.p.h.; initial climb, 625 ft./min.; ceiling, 13,000 ft.; range, 390 miles; empty weight, 1,875 lb.; loaded, 3,200 lb.; span, 42 ft.; length, 31 ft. 6 in.; height, 8 ft.

SHORT S.25 HYTHE   G.B.

During 1943, several Sunderland 3 maritime reconnaissance flying-boats were fitted out for transport duties and supplied to B.O.A.C. Twenty-four were eventually delivered to B.O.A.C. and, in 1946, these were brought up to a higher standard of comfort and re-named Hythe. Powered by four 1,000 h.p. Bristol Pegasus 48 engines, the Hythe H.1 accommodated sixteen passengers and 3.5 tons of freight, and the H.3 accommodated twenty-two passengers and two tons of freight. One Hythe is owned by Aquila Airways.

Max. cruising speed, 178 m.p.h. at 5,000 ft.; max. range, 2,350 miles; service ceiling, 16,000 ft.; empty weight, 35,862 lb.; loaded, 50,000 lb.; span, 112 ft. 9 in.; length, 85 ft. 6 in.; height, 32 ft. 10½ in.; wing area, 1,687 sq. ft.

SHORT S.25/V SANDRINGHAM 4   G.B.

The Sandringham is a civil conversion of the Sunderland, modifications being confined to secondary structural changes. The bow and tail of the hull have been redesigned, and several variations were built. Versions currently flying include the Sandringham 2 and 3 supplied to the Cia. Argentina de Aeronavigacion Dodero, and the Sandringham VI supplied to Norwegian Air Lines. These are powered by four 1,200 h.p. Pratt & Whitney R-1830-90C-3 Twin Wasp engines, and accommodate 21–62 passengers.

Max. speed, 238 m.p.h.; max. cruising, 221 m.p.h.; initial climb, 1,000 ft./min.; range, 1,410 miles; empty weight, 41,370 lb.; loaded, 56,000 lb.; span, 112 ft. 9½ in.; length, 86 ft. 3 in.; height, 32 ft. 10½ in.

SHORT S.45A SOLENT 3   G.B.

The Solent is a civil version of the Seaford flying-boat which differed from the Sunderland in having Hercules engines, a larger hull and strengthened wings. Twelve Solents were ordered by B.O.A.C. for use on the England-Australia route. Three former B.O.A.C. Solent 2s were recently purchased by Aquila Airways from T.E.A.L., one Solent 3 is operated by South Pacific Airlines, and a Solent 4 is owned by Tasman Empire Airways. The Solent 2 and 3 are powered by four Bristol Hercules 637 engines.

Max. speed, 273 m.p.h.; max. economical cruising, 244 m.p.h.; initial climb, 830 ft./min.; max. range, 2,190 miles; empty weight, 48,210 lb.; loaded, 78,000 lb.; span, 112 ft. 9½ in.; length, 88 ft. 6¾ in.; height, 34 ft. 3¼ in.

SHORT S.B.5   G.B.

The S.B.5 is essentially a flying scale model of the English Electric P.1A fighter, built to provide data on the low-speed flight characteristics of the full-scale design. The S.B.5 was designed so that flight trials could be conducted with the wing at sweep angles of 50°, 60° and 69°, and the tailplane in high- and low-set positions. Flown for the first time on December 2, 1952, and powered by a 3,500 lb.s.t. Rolls-Royce Derwent turbojet. The ailerons are arranged across the wingtips in a similar fashion to those of a delta.

Span (69° sweep), 25 ft. 11¾ in. (50° sweep), 35 ft. 2¼ in.; length, 47 ft. 4 in.; height (high tailplane), 16 ft. 7 in.

SHORT S.B.4 SHERPA   G.B.

The S.B.4 Sherpa was built to test in flight the characteristics of the aero-isoclinic wing—a swept wing in which the angle of incidence remains constant under flexion—and flew for the first time on October 4, 1953. The Sherpa is powered by two 353 lb.s.t. Blackburn-Turboméca Palas turbojets, and its rotatable wingtips are used as ailerons, elevators and tailplane. This wing is designed for use by long-range, high-altitude aircraft.

Normal operating speed, 117–170 m.p.h.; endurance, 50 minutes at 117 m.p.h. at 10,000 ft.; loaded weight, 3,125–3,268 lb.; span, 38 ft.; length, 31 ft. 10½ in.; height, 9 ft. 1½ in.; wing area, 261.5 sq. ft.

SHORT S.A.6 SEALAND 1 G.B.

The Sealand amphibian flying boat, which first flew on January 22, 1948, is employed in Borneo, Egypt, Yugoslavia, Norway and Pakistan, and ten Sealands powered by Gipsy Queen 70/4 engines are in service with the Indian Navy. The Sealand 1 accommodates five to eight passengers and, with the landing gear removed, ten passengers. The latter version is known as the Sealand 3. A projected Leonides-powered variant, the Sealand 2, was abandoned after construction of a prototype had commenced.
Specification: Five/eight-passenger amphibian flying boat. Engines: Two 340 h.p. de Havilland Gipsy Queen 70/3. Weights: Empty, 7,065 lb.; loaded, 9,100 lb. Performance: Max. speed, 185 m.p.h. at 5,000 ft.; normal cruising speed, 127 m.p.h. at 5,000 ft.; initial climb rate, 780 ft./min.; max. range, 522 miles. Dimensions: Span, 61 ft. 6 in.; length, 42 ft. 2 in.; height, 15 ft.; wing area, 358.6 sq. ft.

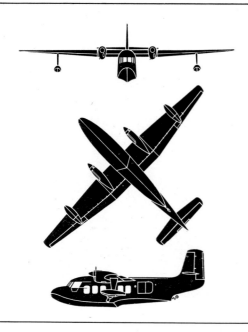

SHORT STURGEON T.T.3 G.B.

The S.B.9 Sturgeon T.T.3 naval target tug is a modification of the earlier Sturgeon T.T.2 to meet simplified requirements. The extended nose with its synchronised photographic equipment of the earlier version has been removed and, as the aircraft is no longer required to operate from carrier decks all deck-landing equipment has been eliminated. The hydraulic wing-folding gear formerly fitted has been replaced by manually operated mechanism, and all existing Sturgeon T.T.2 aircraft are receiving these modifications. The Sturgeon was originally conceived as a reconnaissance-bomber.
Specification: Two-seat Naval target-tug. Engines: Two 2,080 h.p. Rolls-Royce Merlin 140. Weights: Empty, 16,967 lb.; loaded, 22,000 lb. Performance: Max. cruising speed, 366 m.p.h. at 24,200 ft.; continuous cruising, 312 m.p.h. at 15,000 ft.; initial climb rate, 2,280 ft./min.; service ceiling, 35,200 ft. Dimensions: Span, 59 ft. 9 in.; length, 42 ft. 2 in.; height, 13 ft. 2½ in.; wing area, 560.4 sq. ft.

SHORT SEAMEW A.S.1 G.B.

The Short S.B.6 Seamew light anti-submarine aircraft flew for the first time on August 23, 1953, and is now in production for the Fleet Air Arm and the R.A.F. Coastal Command. Primarily designed for operation from escort carriers of N.A.T.O. forces, the Seamew is also suitable for inshore maritime patrol, operating from small, semi-prepared coastal strips. The wing is power-folded for carrier stowage, and relatively heavy military loads may be carried. Typical combinations are: (1) one homing torpedo, four sonobuoys and four rocket projectiles; (2) twenty sonobuoys and six rocket missiles; (3) four depth charges, eight markers and six rocket missiles.
Specification: Two-seat light anti-submarine aircraft. Engine: One 1,590 s.h.p. Armstrong Siddeley Mamba A.S.Ma.6. Weights: Loaded, 14,000 lb. Performance: No details available for publication. Dimensions: Span, 55 ft.; span folded, 23 ft.; length, 41 ft.; height, 13 ft. 6 in.; height, folded, 15 ft. 9 in.

SHORT S.A.4 SPERRIN　　　　　　G.B.

Built to meet specification B.14/46 calling for a five-seat four-jet, long-range medium-bomber, the Sperrin is employed for research by the Ministry of Supply, and the first prototype (*illustrated*) is shown with a de Havilland H-4 Gyron turbojet under test in the lower half of its port engine nacelle. The first of two Sperrin prototypes flew on August 10, 1951, and the second on August 12, 1952. The Sperrin is normally powered by four 6,500 lb.s.t. Rolls-Royce Avon R.A.3 turbojets, one superimposed upon another in two paired nacelles.

Max. speed, 564 m.p.h. at 15,000 ft.; range (with 10,000 lb. load), 3,860 miles; max. loaded weight, 115,000 lb.; span, 109 ft.; length, 102 ft. 2½ in.; height, 28 ft. 6 in.; wing area, 1,896.7 sq. ft.

SIAI-MARCHETTI S.M.101　　　　ITALY

Flown for the first time on December 20, 1947, the S.M.101 was designed as a six-seat light transport, and is powered by a 235 h.p. Walter Bora radial engine. It was proposed that a 300 h.p. engine would replace the Bora in production aircraft, but only one prototype S.M.101 was completed. Welded steel-tube construction is employed with fabric covering. Fowler-type trailing-edge flaps are fitted to the wing and dual controls are provided.

Max. speed, 149 m.p.h. at sea level; cruising, 140 m.p.h. at 9,020 ft.; range, 777 miles; service ceiling, 15,750 ft.; empty weight, 2,910 lb.; loaded, 4,828 lb.; span, 54 ft. 1 in.; length, 33 ft. 6 in.; height, 9 ft. 9½ in.; wing area, 322 sq. ft.

SIEBEL SI 204D　　　　　　GERMANY

Used in large numbers by the *Luftwaffe* during World War II as a crew trainer and light transport, the Si 204D was built during the war by the former Hanriot (later S.N.C.A. du Centre) factory, production continuing after the war, 350 being completed as the N.C.701 and N.C.702 Martinet (the latter having a stepped cockpit canopy). It was also produced during and after the war by the Aero factory in Czechoslovakia as the C.3 and C.3B (for the Czech Air Force) and C.103 civil feeder-liner. The Si 204D has two 575 h.p. Argus As 411 engines.

Max. speed, 219 m.p.h. at 9,840 ft.; cruising, 185 m.p.h.; range, 500 miles; empty weight, 8,639 lb.; loaded, 11,902 lb.; span, 69 ft. 9 in.; length, 39 ft. 5 in.; height, 13 ft. 9½ in.; wing area, 495.14 sq. ft.

SIAI-MARCHETTI S.M.95　　　　ITALY

Designed during the war years as a military transport, the prototype S.M.95 did not fly until 1945. This was powered by four Alfa Romeo 131 RC 14/50 engines for initial flights, but these were later replaced by Alfa 128 RC 18 engines, and production aircraft were powered by both the Bristol Pegasus 48 and the Pratt & Whitney R-1830-S1C3G. The specification relates to the version of the S.M.95 powered by the latter engines.

Max. speed, 242 m.p.h. at 9,840 ft.; cruising, 215 m.p.h. at 11,500 ft.; service ceiling, 22,300 ft.; empty weight, 31,950 lb.; loaded, 48,480 lb.; span, 112 ft. 5 in.; length, 81 ft. 3 in.; height, 17 ft. 3 in.

SIAI-MARCHETTI S.M.102　　　　ITALY

Originally flown in 1948 powered by two 500 h.p. Ranger SVG-770-C1B engines, the S.M.102 was intended as an eight-passenger feeder-liner. The type was subsequently modified to take two 450 h.p. Pratt & Whitney R-985 Wasp Junior radials, and a small production batch was built for the Italian Air Force for communications and light transport duties. The S.M.102 is of mixed construction.

Max. speed, 208 m.p.h. at 3,280 ft.; cruising, 180 m.p.h. at 11,480 ft.; climb to 5,000 ft., 6 minutes; service ceiling, 19,700 ft.; max. range, 932 miles; empty weight, 7,600 lb.; loaded, 11,125 lb.; span, 59 ft.; length, 43 ft.; height, 11 ft. 5 in.

SIKORSKY S.43　　　　　　U.S.A.

The S.43 commercial amphibian was first produced in 1935 by the Sikorsky Aviation Corporation as a fifteen passenger transport. A small number of S-43 amphibians were procured by the U.S.A.A.F. as the Y10A-8 and by the U.S. Navy as the JRS-1 in 1937. A commercial S.43 impressed by the U.S.A.A.F. in 1942 was designated OA-11. Three S-43s are currently active, two powered by two 875 h.p. Pratt & Whitney Hornet engines, and one (S-43-W) with two 1,200 h.p. Pratt & Whitney Twin Wasps. The example illustrated has had the wingtip floats removed.
Max. speed, 194 m.p.h.; cruising, 169 m.p.h.; initial climb, 1,100 ft./min.; cruising range, 803 miles; empty weight, 12,570 lb.; loaded, 19,000 lb.; span, 86 ft.; length, 51 ft. 2 in.; height, 17 ft. 8 in.

SIPA S.12   FRANCE

The S.12 series of advanced trainers built by the Société Industrielle pour l'Aéronautique (SIPA) is derived from the Arado Ar 396 developed in France during the German occupation. The Ar 396V-1 first flew on December 29, 1944, and twenty-eight of the first production version, the S.10, were produced. Progressive developments included the S.11 (fifty built), the S.111 (fifty-three built), and S.12 (fifty built). The latter was the first all-metal version. The final production version was the S.121, fifty of which were delivered to the *Armée de l'Air*. All five versions are externally similar, and the photograph depicts the S.12.

Specification: Two-seat advanced trainer. Engine: One 580 h.p. SNECMA 12S-02. Weights: Empty, 4,107 lb.; loaded, 5,126 lb. Performance: Max. speed, 224 m.p.h.; cruising speed, 199 m.p.h.; initial climb rate, 1,476 ft./min. Dimensions: Span, 36 ft. 1 in.; length, 30 ft. 7½ in.; height, 8 ft.; wing area, 197.1 sq. ft.

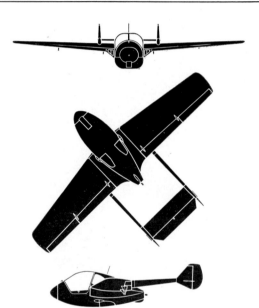

SIPA S.200 MINIJET   FRANCE

Design of the S.200 Minijet was commenced in February 1951, and the first of two prototypes was flown on January 14, 1952. A pre-production batch of five Minijets is currently nearing completion. The Minijet was designed for the dual role of high-speed, short-range liaison aircraft and transitional trainer. The cabin in the central fuselage nacelle seats two persons side-by-side, the entire canopy hinging forward for access. The second prototype has attachment points for wingtip auxiliary fuel tanks and is stressed for aerobatics.

Specification: Two-seat liaison and training aircraft. Engine: One 330 lb.s.t. Turboméca Palas. Weights: Empty, 990 lb.; loaded, 1,675 lb. Performance: Max. speed, 248 m.p.h. at sea level; cruising speed, 223 m.p.h. at 3,280 ft.; initial climb rate, 1,132 ft./min.; ceiling, 26,240 ft.; range (without auxiliary tanks), 350 miles. Dimensions: Span, 26 ft. 2 in.; length, 17 ft.; height, 5 ft. 10 in.; wing area, 104 sq. ft.

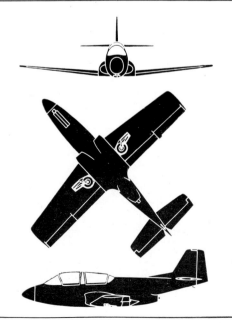

SIPA S.300   FRANCE

The S.300 tandem two-seat elementary trainer was flown for the first time on September 4, 1954, and was designed as a potential replacement for current piston-engined elementary trainers. Design emphasis has been placed on structural simplicity and ease of maintenance, and the outer wing panels are generally similar to those of the earlier S.200 Minijet. Provision is made for the installation of a more powerful turbojet, such as the Turboméca Marboré II. The S.300 is claimed to be the World's first jet trainer designed from the outset for *ab initio* instruction.

Specification: Tandem two-seat elementary trainer. Engine: One 350 lb.s.t. Turboméca Palas. Weights: Empty, 1,153 lb.; loaded, 1,940 lb. Performance: Max. speed, 224 m.p.h. at sea level; cruising speed, 193 m.p.h.; initial climb rate, 894 ft./min.; ceiling, 16,500 ft.; range, 435 miles. Dimensions: Span, 26 ft. 3 in.; length, 22 ft.; height, 5 ft. 10½ in.; wing area, 104.4 sq. ft.

SIPA S.901 — FRANCE

The S.901 is the production version of the S.90 of 1947 which gained first place in an officially-sponsored contest for two-seat light touring aircraft. The S.901 first flew on June 25, 1948, and one hundred machines have since been produced for government-sponsored schools. Experimental variants of the basic design include the S.90 (75 h.p. Mathis 4G-60), S.91 (85 h.p. Continental C85-12F), S.92 (85 h.p. Mathis 4GB-62), S.93 (75 h.p. Salmson 5AQ-01), S.94 (90 h.p. Continental C90-8F), S.902 (85 h.p. Continental C85-12-F), and the S.903 (990 h.p. Continental C90-12-F).
Specification: Two-seat light touring and training cabin monoplane. Engine: One 75 h.p. Minié 4 DC-30 or DC-32. Weights: Empty, 805 lb.; loaded, 1,320 lb. Performance: Max. speed, 124 m.p.h.; cruising speed, 109 m.p.h.; initial climb rate, 492 ft./min.; range, 310 miles. Dimensions: Span, 28 ft. 8 in.; length, 18 ft. 10½ in.; height, 5 ft. 9 in.; wing area, 120.5 sq. ft.

SIPA S.1000 COCCINELLE — FRANCE

The Coccinelle, first flown on June 11, 1955, was designed and built in two months. It features absolute structural simplicity and can be operated from almost any field. The three undercarriage wheels are interchangeable and are of the same type as those fitted to current motor-scooters. A number of automobile parts are embodied in the design, such as oil pressure and temperature indicators, and the hydraulic brakes are those of a Renault 4 cv car. Either 65 h.p. or 90 h.p. Continental engines may be installed, and the specification relates to the Coccinelle with the latter power. First production deliveries are scheduled for April 1956 when production will attain one aircraft per day.
Specification: Two-seat ultra-light cabin monoplane. Engine: One 90 h.p. Continental C90. Weights: Empty, 740 lb.; loaded, 1,260 lb. Performance: Max. speed, 125 m.p.h.; cruising speed, 112 m.p.h.; range, 375 miles. Dimensions: Span, 25 ft. 11 in.; length, 17 ft. 10 in.; height, 7 ft. 3 in.

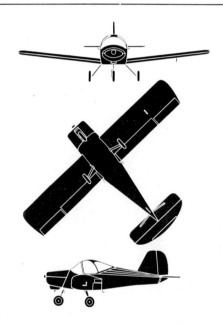

SLINGSBY S.29A MOTOR-TUTOR — G.B.

The S.29A Motor-Tutor is a powered adaptation of the Tutor primary sailplane, the only modifications necessary being those relating to the installation of the 37 h.p. Aeronca J.A.P. engine, and the fitting of a robust and simple undercarriage. The Motor-Tutor is of wooden construction with fabric covering, and the cockpit provides the pilot with excellent view in all directions. It retains most of the quick assembly and dis-assembly features of the Tutor glider, greatly facilitating maintenance and stowage.

Cruising speed, 65 m.p.h.; initial climb rate, 490 ft./min.; service ceiling, 16,500 ft.; range, 240 miles; empty weight, 555 lb.; loaded, 798 lb.; span, 43 ft. 3¾ in.; length, 20 ft.; height, 6 ft. 2 in.; wing area, 170 sq. ft.

SPARTAN ARROW — G.B.

The Arrow, first produced in 1930, was a variation of the Spartan two/three-seat light biplane but differed little externally from the earlier machine. Any one of three engines could be installed: the de Havilland Gipsy II, the Cirrus III, or the Cirrus Hermes. The specification relates to the Arrow with the latter engine. One example remains active in the U.K., and another is registered in Sweden.

Max. speed, 103 m.p.h.; cruising, 82 m.p.h.; initial climb, 630 ft./min.; climb to 5,000 ft., 11 minutes; empty weight, 992 lb.; loaded, 1,750 lb.; span, 30 ft. 7 in.; length, 25 ft.; height, 9 ft. 6 in.; wing area, 251 sq. ft.

SPARTAN 7-W EXECUTIVE U.S.A.

Flown for the first time on January 1, 1936, the Executive was built in some numbers between 1937 and 1940, fourteen machines of this type remaining active in the U.S.A. The design was revived after the war, and in 1946 the Model 12 Executive appeared. Like the Model 7-W, the Model 12 is powered by a 450 h.p. Pratt & Whitney R-985 engine, but differs in having the tailwheel undercarriage of the earlier model replaced by a retractable nosewheel gear. Only one prototype Model 12 has been built. The Executive is a five-seat cabin monoplane.

Max. speed, 212 m.p.h.; cruising, 208 m.p.h.; initial climb, 1,430 ft./min.; max. range, 1,000 miles; empty weight, 2,987 lb.; loaded, 4,400 lb.; span, 38 ft. 11½ in.; length, 26 ft. 9⅝ in.; height, 8 ft. 5 in.

STAMPE S.V.4B BELGIUM

The S.V.4 two-seat primary training biplane was first introduced in the early 'thirties by the Stampe-et-Vertongen concern. The design was revived after the war, and a number of S.V.4B trainers (125 h.p. de Havilland Gipsy Major II) were built by Société Stampe et Rénard for the Belgian Air Force. The type was also placed in production by the S.N.C.A. du Nord as the S.V.4C (140 h.p. Renault 4POI or 4P-03), this concern building 700 for the government-sponsored flying clubs. Some five hundred S.V.4 biplanes are currently active in France.

Max. speed, 112 m.p.h.; cruising speed, 90 m.p.h.; climb to 3,280 ft., 4 minutes, 55 seconds; empty weight, 1,034 lb.; loaded, 1,672 lb.; span, 31 ft. 10 in.; length, 23 ft. 3 in.; height, 8 ft. 6 in.

STAMPE-RENARD MONITOR III BELGIUM

The S.R.7 Monitor III, also known as the Farman F-521 Monitor III, was built in France by the Société des Usines Farman with the collaboration of the Stampe-Rénard concern. In its original form (Monitor I) it incorporated the fuselage, tail assembly and engine of the S.V.4C biplane married to a wooden wing, but the Monitor II differed in having a metal wing and a 240 h.p. Salmson-Argus replacing the 140 h.p. Renault 4 Pei. The latest version, the Monitor III, which flew on June 15, 1954, has a 170 h.p. SNECMA-Régnier 4L-22 engine.

Max. speed, 143 m.p.h.; cruising speed, 118 m.p.h.; initial climb, 787 ft./min.; empty weight, 1,232 lb.; loaded, 2,083 lb.; span, 30 ft. 11 in.; length, 22 ft. 2½ in.; height, 7 ft. 11 in.

STARCK A.S.57/3 FRANCE

Designed by Avions André Starck, the A.S.57 was built in small numbers with various power plants. The prototype was flown for the first time on April 4, 1946, and seven examples are currently flying in France. These comprise two examples of the A.S.57/3 powered by the 95 h.p. Régnier 4-EO, four examples of the A.S.57/4 with the 105 h.p. Walter Minor 4-III, and one A.S.57/5 with a Hirth 504A-2 of 105 h.p. The specification refers to the Régnier-powered A.S.57/3.

Max. speed, 124 m.p.h.; cruising speed, 115 m.p.h.; ceiling, 19,000 ft.; range, 497 miles; empty weight, 683 lb.; loaded, 1,322 lb.; span, 28 ft.; length, 21 ft. 2 in.; wing area, 118 sq. ft.

STARCK A.S.71 JAC FRANCE

The A.S.70 and A.S.71 are single-seat cantilever low-wing monoplanes intended for sporting flying or aerobatic purposes. They differ solely in the type of power plant installed, both being of welded steel-tube and wooden construction with fabric covering. The A.S.70 is powered by a 45 h.p. Salmson 9 ADL radial (*specification*), and the A.S.71 (*photograph*) has a 65 h.p. Walter Mikron III. Only one prototype of each version has been built.

Max. speed, 115 m.p.h.; cruising, 104 m.p.h.; range, 260 miles; empty weight, 467 lb.; loaded, 705 lb.; span, 24 ft. 3 in.; length, 17 ft. 7 in.; wing area, 86 sq. ft.

STARCK A.S.80 LAVADOUX FRANCE

The A.S.80 was designed primarily for construction from kits of parts by amateurs, and several engines may be installed. Examples of the A.S.80 are flying with the 65 h.p. Continental A65, the 75 h.p. Régnier 4D2, and the 75 h.p. Minié 4 DC-30, but the 75 h.p. Praga or the 65 h.p. Walter Minor may also be installed. A tandem two-seat cabin monoplane, the A.S.80 is of wooden construction with fabric covering. The specification relates to the Régnier-powered version.

Max. speed, 98 m.p.h.; cruising, 88 m.p.h.; initial climb, 590 ft./min.; range, 200 miles; empty weight, 720 lb.; loaded, 1,210 lb.; span, 32 ft. 10 in.; length, 21 ft. 7½ in.; height, 6 ft. 3 in.

STEARMAN B-2   U.S.A.

The Model B two-seat cabin monoplane powered by a 75 h.p. Continental A75 engine, first appeared in 1941 as the Ariel Model B. In February 1942, Ariel Aircraft Inc. changed its name to Stearman Aviation Inc. (not related to the Stearman Aircraft Company), but production of the Model B was not resumed until 1944 when three machines were produced. The Models A and C differed in having a 65 h.p. Lycoming 0-145-B2 and a 80 h.p. Franklin 4AC-176 respectively.

Max. speed, 125 m.p.h.; cruising, 110 m.p.h.; initial climb, 930 ft./min.; range, 430 miles; empty weight, 680 lb.; loaded, 1,200 lb.; span, 30 ft.; length, 20 ft. 2½ in.

STEARMAN 4E   U.S.A.

The Model 4 series was introduced by the Stearman Aircraft Company in 1930, and the version currently flying in the largest numbers is the Model 4E with a 450 h.p. Pratt & Whitney Wasp. The similarly-powered Model 4D, and the Model 4CM1 with a 550 h.p. Pratt and Whitney Wasp are also flying. The Model 4 series were originally three-seat biplanes, but most remaining machines have been converted for agricultural purposes.

Max. speed, 158 m.p.h.; initial climb, 1,400 ft./min.; service ceiling, 18,000 ft.; range, 645 miles; empty weight, 2,426 lb.; loaded, 3,936 lb.; span, 38 ft.; length, 26 ft. 4 in.; height, 10 ft. 2 in.

STEARMAN-HAMMOND Y-1S   U.S.A.

The Model Y was designed in 1934 by the Hammond Aircraft Corporation, the first prototype being completed in 1935. Redesigned for production, the Model Y-1S was produced in small numbers by the later Stearman-Hammond Aircraft Corporation, but further development was abandoned in 1938. Powered by a 125 h.p. Menasco C-4 engine, the Model Y-1S seats two persons side-by-side and is of all-metal construction. At least one Model Y-1S remains active in the U.S.A.

Max. speed, 119 m.p.h.; cruising (75 per cent power), 110 m.p.h.; cruising range, 500 miles; loaded weight, 2,150 lb.; span, 40 ft.; length, 26 ft. 10¾ in.; height, 7 ft. 7 in.; wing area, 210 sq. ft.

STINSON S.M.8A DETROITER   U.S.A.

The S.M.8A Detroiter four-seat cabin monoplane of mixed construction is a progressive development of the S.M.2, and is very similar externally. Produced during 1930–31, the S.M.8A Detroiter is powered by a 215 h.p. Lycoming radial, and seven examples are currently active in the U.S.A. Two S.M.2s are also flying, one powered by a 160 h.p. Kinner and the other by a 235 h.p. Wright Whirlwind.

Max. speed, 125 m.p.h.; cruising, 105 m.p.h.; initial climb, 650 ft./min.; ceiling, 15,000 ft.; range, 350 miles; empty weight, 2,152 lb.; loaded, 3,265 lb.; span, 42 ft. 1 in.; length, 28 ft. 11 in.; height, 8 ft. 9 in.; wing area, 234 sq. ft.

STINSON SR-5A RELIANT   U.S.A.

The Reliant was developed from the earlier SM series (e.g., SM-8A Detroiter) and was introduced in 1935. Subsequently, the Reliant was progressively improved, being followed by the SR-6, -7, -8, -9, and -10. The Reliant was initially a four-seat cabin monoplane, but the SR-8 and subsequent models were five-seaters. Production of the civil Reliants was terminated in 1940, but an extensively modified version (the V-77) continued in production for the Fleet Air Arm. The SR-5A Reliant has a 225 h.p. Lycoming R-680 engine.

Max. speed, 138 m.p.h.; cruising, 120 m.p.h.; initial climb, 725 ft./min.; service ceiling, 14,500 ft.; empty weight, 2,250 lb.; loaded, 3,325 lb.; span, 43 ft. 3 in.; length, 27 ft.; height, 8 ft. 5 in.

STINSON S.M.6000B (MODEL U)   U.S.A.

The Model 6000B ten-passenger commercial transport, powered by three 240 h.p. Lycoming R-680-BA engines, appeared in 1931, and acted as a prototype for the production Model U which appeared in small numbers during 1932–33. One example of the Model 6000B and one example of the Model U are active in the U.S.A., and the latter differs in having a revised cockpit with provision for two pilots, the earlier model carrying only one pilot. The Model U is of all-metal construction with fabric covering.

Max. speed, 142 m.p.h.; cruising, 121 m.p.h.; initial climb, 900 ft./min.; service ceiling, 14,000 ft.; empty weight, 6,230 lb.; loaded, 9,300 lb.; span, 66 ft.; length, 43 ft. 6 in.; height, 8 ft. 9 in.; wing area, 574 sq. ft.

STINSON (VULTEE) V-74 VIGILANT   U.S.A.

Originally designated 0-49 by the U.S.A.A.F., and later redesignated L-1, the Vigilant two-seat army co-operation monoplane appeared in 1940, and 324 machines of this type were produced during 1940–41 for the U.S.A.A.F. The Vigilant is powered by a 300 h.p. Lycoming R-680-E3A engine and has full-length automatic slots on the wing leading-edge and hand-operated slotted flaps. Two privately-owned Vigilants are registered in the U.S.A., and one in Holland.

Max. speed, 123 m.p.h.; cruising, 90 m.p.h.; initial climb, 1,160 ft./min.; service ceiling, 20,000 ft.; range, 350 miles; empty weight, 2,591 lb.; loaded, 3,322 lb.; span, 51 ft.; length, 34 ft.

STINSON (VULTEE) V-76 SENTINEL   U.S.A.

The V-76 was first flown in 1941 as a two/three-seat liaison and observation post aircraft, and 3,283 aircraft of this type were delivered to the U.S.A.A.F. as the L-5. Others were used by the U.S. Navy as the OY-1 and by the R.A.F. as the Sentinel. The Sentinel is powered by a 190 h.p. Lycoming 0-435-1 engine, and is still used in small numbers by the U.S.A.A.F. and the U.S. Marine Corps. It is also used by the air forces of the Philippine Republic, Mexico, Thailand, Italy and Japan, and more than a hundred civil Sentinels are registered in the U.S.A.

Max. speed, 129 m.p.h.; cruising speed, 112 m.p.h.; service ceiling, 15,800 ft.; empty weight, 1,472 lb.; loaded, 2,158 lb.; span, 34 ft.; length, 24 ft. 1¼ in.; height, 7 ft. 1 in.

STINSON (VULTEE) V-77 RELIANT   U.S.A.

The V-77 Reliant was an extensively modified version of the civil SR-10 Reliant, and five hundred were produced for the Fleet Air Arm during 1940–43 by Stinson Aircraft after this concern had been taken over by Vultee Aircraft, Inc. Employed by the Royal Navy as a navigational trainer during World War 2, the V-77 Reliant is powered by a 290 h.p. Lycoming R-680-13 engine, and nearly one hundred and fifty machines of this type are operated by private owners in the U.S.A. Examples of the V-77 are flying in several parts of the world.

Max. speed, 141 m.p.h.; cruising, 130 m.p.h.; initial climb, 850 ft./min.; service ceiling, 14,000 ft.; empty weight, 2,810 lb.; loaded, 4,000 lb.; span, 41 ft. 10½ in.; length, 29 ft. 4¼ in.; height, 8 ft. 7 in.

STINSON 108 VOYAGER   U.S.A.

The Model 108 Voyager was a post-war production version of the Model 105 Voyager (90 h.p. Franklin) of 1939. Two versions powered by the 165 h.p. Franklin 6A4-150-B3 engine were produced in quantity, the standard Voyager and the externally-similar Station Wagon utility model. Production was continued by the Piper Aircraft Corp. after that concern had taken over the Stinson Division of the Consolidated-Vultee Aircraft Corporation on December 1, 1948. The Voyager is a four-seat cabin monoplane, and some 2,000 aircraft of this type are flying in the U.S.A.

Cruising speed, 130 m.p.h.; service ceiling, 14,000 ft.; range, 554 miles; empty weight, 1,295 lb.; loaded, 2,400 lb.; span, 33 ft. 11 in.; length, 25 ft. 2 in.; height, 7 ft. 6 in.

STITS SA3A PLAYBOY   U.S.A.

Designed by Ray Stits, the Playboy was designed primarily for construction by amateurs, and the Stits Aircraft Company furnish complete plans and building instructions or a kit of parts. A considerable number of Playboys are under construction in the U.S.A. The Model SA3A (*illustrated*) is a single-seater normally powered by an 85 h.p. Continental C85, and the Model SA3B is a two-seater powered by a 135 h.p. Lycoming engine. A projected development is the three-seat Executive with a 150 h.p. Lycoming 0-320 engine.

Max. speed, 135 m.p.h.; landing speed, 45 m.p.h.; max. range, 400 miles; empty weight, 600 lb.; normal loaded, 902 lb.; span, 22 ft. 2 in.; length, 17 ft. 4 in.; height, 5 ft.; wing area, 96 sq. ft.

SUD-EST S.E.2410 GROGNARD   FRANCE

The Grognard was designed as a single-seat ground attack aircraft and embodied several novel features at the time of its appearance. Two 4,850 lb.s.t. Hispano-Suiza Nene 101 are staggered one above the other in the rear fuselage. The Grognard flew for the first time on April 30, 1950, and has been used as an armament test-bed. A second prototype, the S.E.2415 two-seater with reduced wing-sweep and lengthened fuselage was destroyed during tests.

Max. speed, 645 m.p.h. at 4,920 ft.; initial climb rate, 5,315 ft./min.; empty weight, 24,508 lb.; loaded, 31,967 lb.; span, 44 ft. 6½ in.; length, 50 ft. 6 in.; height, 17 ft.; wing area, 495 sq. ft.

SUD-EST S.E.161 LANGUEDOC   FRANCE

The Languedoc is a progressive development of the Bloch 160 and, as the Bloch 161, first flew in 1939. Production at the Toulouse plant of the S.N.C.A. du Sud-Est began in 1941, the Languedoc having been ordered by both the Vichy government and the *Deutsch Lufthansa*. However, none was completed until after World War 2 when one hundred were built. Sixty of these have been supplied to the *Armée de l'Air* and *Aeronavale*. Some of these are used for testing engines, missiles, etc., and the Languedoc serves with *Aviacion y Comercio S.A.*
Specification: Commercial and military transport. *Engines*: Four 1,200 *h.p. Pratt & Whitney R-1830-92 Twin Wasp. Weights*: Empty, 27,890 *lb*.; loaded, 45,364 *lb. Performance*: Max. speed, 273 *m.p.h.* at sea level; cruising, 233 *m.p.h.* at 7,548 *ft.*; normal range, 1,678 *miles*, max. 1,988 *miles. Dimensions*: Span, 96 *ft.* 5 *in.*; length, 79 *ft.* 7 *in.*; height, 16 *ft.* 10 *in.*; wing area, 1,197.8 *sq. ft.*

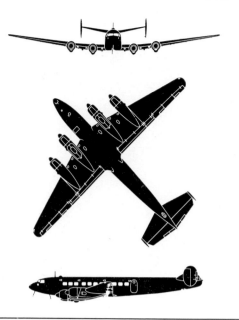

SUD-EST S.E.2010 ARMAGNAC   FRANCE

Flown for the first time on January 12, 1949, the Armagnac was designed as an eighty-four/one-hundred-and-seven passenger commercial transport, and eight production machines were completed, the first production aircraft flying on December 30, 1950. The Armagnac is powered by four 3,500 h.p. Pratt & Whitney R-4360-B13 Wasp Major engines. One Armagnac, the S.O.2060, is currently employed as a test-bed for the SNECMA Vulcain turbojet which is mounted in a nacelle under the fuselage.
Max. speed, 307 *m.p.h.* at 14,760 *ft.*; cruising speed, 281 *m.p.h.*; range, 3,730 *miles*; empty weight, 83,190 *lb.*; loaded, 165,000 *lb.*; span, 160 *ft.* 7 *in.*; length, 129 *ft.* 11 *in.*; height, 44 *ft.* 3 *in.*; wing area, 2,542 *sq. ft.*

SUD-EST S.E.2310   FRANCE

The S.E.2310 is a variation of the S.E.2300 which flew for the first time on October 26, 1945. The S.E.2310 differs from the 2300 in having a fixed nosewheel undercarriage and a third seat fitted as standard. One prototype S.E.2300 was built (140 h p. Renault 4 Pei) and two S.E.2310s (the S.E.2310/11 with a 135 h.p. Régnier 4 1-00 and the S.E.2310/ III with a 170 h.p. Régnier 4 LO-2). All three prototypes are currently flying in France. The S.E.2300/2310 aircraft are of all-metal construction.
Max. speed, 140 *m.p.h.*; cruising speed, 127 *m.p.h.*; range, 559 *miles*; empty weight, 1,543 *lb.*; loaded, 2,385 *lb.*; span, 33 *ft.* 3 *in.*; length, 24 *ft.* 3½ *in.*; wing area, 161.4 *sq. ft.*

SUD-EST S.E.535 MISTRAL   FRANCE

The Mistral is a version of the de Havilland Vampire single-seat fighter-bomber built under licence by the S.N.C.A. du Sud-Est. The Mistral is powered by a 5,000 lb.s.t. Hispano-Suiza Nene 102 (replacing the Goblin of the British-built Vampire), fed by enlarged wing-root intakes, and 247 machines had been delivered to the *Armée de l'Air* when production was completed in 1954. The Mistral has an ejector seat and embodies considerable structural redesign.

Max. speed, 574 *m.p.h.*; climb to 39,360 *ft.*, 9 *minutes*, 41 *seconds*; empty weight, 7,656 *lb.*; loaded, 10,912 *lb.*; span, 38 *ft.*; length, 30 *ft.* 9 *in.*; height, 6 *ft.* 2 *in.*

SUD-EST S.E.5000 BAROUDEUR   FRANCE

Designed to operate from small, semi-prepared advanced bases, the Baroudeur is intended to operate from a take-off trolley and land on skids. The first prototype was powered by a 5,280 lb.s.t. SNECMA Atar 101B turbojet and flew on August 1, 1953, being followed by a second prototype powered by a 6,170 lb.s.t. Atar 101C. Three pre-production Baroudeurs powered by 7,280 lb.s.t. Atar 101E turbojets have been ordered, and these will carry an armament of two 30-mm. DEFA cannon. The following specification relates to the pre-production version.
Max. speed, 709 *m.p.h.* at sea level; initial climb, 10,500 *ft./min.*; empty weight, 9,854 *lb.*; loaded, 15,256 *lb.*; span, 32 *ft.* 10 *in.*; length, 44 *ft.* 3 *in.*; height, 11 *ft.* 9 *in.*; wing area, 272 *sq. ft.*

SUD-EST S.E.210 CARAVELLE — FRANCE

Designed for stage lengths up to 1,500 miles, the S.E.210 Caravelle will carry a maximum of seventy passengers. The first of two prototypes flew in May 1955, powered by two 10,000 lb. thrust Avon R.A.26 turbojets, but production machines will employ the 11,000 lb. thrust Avon R.A.29s. The Caravelle embodies several radical features, not least of which is the positioning of the two turbojets in rear-fuselage-mounted pods. This feature results in an aerodynamically clean wing and reduces cabin noise level. No production orders for the Caravelle have been announced at the time of writing.
Specification: Medium-range commercial transport. Engines: Two 10,000 lb.s.t. Rolls-Royce Avon R.A.26. Weights: Empty, 41,800 lb.; max. loaded, 88,000 lb. Performance: Cruising speed, 478 m.p.h. at 31,496 ft.; range (with 7,260 lb. payload), 2,435 miles; (with 20,944 lb.), 1,472 miles. Dimensions: Span, 112 ft. 6 in.; length, 103 ft. 4 in.; height, 29 ft. 4 in.; wing area, 1,579.06 sq. ft.

SUD-OUEST S.O.94R — FRANCE

The S.O.94R is a development of the S.O.90 which was built during the war by the Groupe Technique de Cannes. The first S.O.94 flew on March 3, 1947, and fifteen machines of this type were delivered to the French Navy, most of them being radar trainers (*illustrated*), designated S.O.94R. This is powered by two 580 h.p. Renault 12S-00 engines and, as a personnel transport, can accommodate ten passengers. A retractable nosewheel type undercarriage is fitted.

Max. speed, 276 m.p.h.; cruising, 233 m.p.h.; range, 800 miles; empty weight, 7,700 lb.; loaded, 13,640 lb.; span, 53 ft.; length, 41 ft. 9 in.; height, 14 ft. 5 in.; wing area, 350.7 sq. ft.

SUD-OUEST S.O.95 CORSE II — FRANCE

The S.O.95 Corse II, first flown on July 17, 1947, is generally similar to the previously-described S.O.94, differing primarily in having a retractable tailwheel-type undercarriage in place of the earlier machine's nosewheel gear. Forty-five S.O.95 light transports were produced by the S.N.C.A.S.O., and the majority of these have been delivered to the French Navy as personnel transports and trainers under the designation S.O.95M. The S.O.95 Corse II is powered by two 590 h.p. Renault 12S-02-201 engines.
Max. speed, 221 m.p.h. at sea level; max. cruising, 208 m.p.n.; empty weight, 8,863 lb.; loaded, 12,346 lb.; span, 59 ft.; length, 40 ft. 5 in.; height, 14 ft. 1 in.; wing area, 405 sq. ft.

SUD-OUEST S.O.30P BRETAGNE — FRANCE

The prototype Bretagne, the S.O.30N, was completed in November 1942, but did not fly until February 26, 1945. Two production models were built, the S.O.30P-1 with 2,000 h.p. Pratt & Whitney R-2800-B42 engines, and the S.O.30P-2 with two 2,400 h.p. Pratt & Whitney R-2800-CA18 engines. Forty production machines were built as thirty-seat commercial transports, but the majority of these are now employed by the *Armee de l'Air* and the French Navy. Specification relates to the S.O.30P-2.
Cruising speed, 267 m.p.h.; range, 746 miles; empty weight, 29,357 lb.; loaded weight, 44,370 lb.; span, 88 ft. 2 in.; length, 62 ft. 2 in.; height, 19 ft. 4 in.; wing area, 925 sq. ft.

SUD-OUEST S.O.7060 DEAUVILLE — FRANCE

The S.O.7060 Deauville two/three-seat light cabin monoplane was developed from the S.O.7050 and S.O.7055 two-seat cabin monoplanes, and differs from the latter primarily in having the 75 h.p. Mathis 4GO engine replaced by a 105 h.p. Walter Minor 4-III. The first of two Deauville prototypes flew on March 22, 1948, but no production has been undertaken. It is of all-metal construction, and dual controls are provided. A third seat may be fitted aft of the side-by-side front seats.

Max. speed, 127 m.p.h.; cruising, 105 m.p.h. at 3,280 ft.; range, 500 miles; empty weight, 1,140 lb.; loaded, 1,760 lb.; span, 34 ft.; length, 21 ft. 10 in.; height, 7 ft. 11 in.; wing area, 161.4 sq. ft.

SUD-OUEST (BLOCH) M.B.175   FRANCE

The M.B.175 is a development of the M.B.174 reconnaissance bomber of 1938 which was built in small numbers by the S.N.C.A. du Sud-Ouest for the *Armée de l'Air*. The M.B.175 appeared early in the war and, after the fall of France, one machine was fitted with two Daimler-Benz DB 601 engines for *Luftwaffe* tests. In 1945, the S.N.C.A. du Sud-Ouest received an order for the French Navy for eighty M.B.175s modified for use as attack and torpedo bombers. These differ from the wartime version in having revised nose and cockpit contours, and redesigned tail assembly.
Specification: Three-seat naval attack bomber. Engines: Two 1,000 h.p. Gnôme-Rhône 14N-48/49. Weights: Empty, 10,361 lb.; loaded, 18,959 lb. Performance: Max. speed, 335 m.p.h.; cruising, 317 m.p.h.; range, 2050 miles. Armament: Three 20-mm. cannon, eight rocket projectiles and one 450-mm. torpedo. Dimensions: Span, 58 ft. 11 in.; length, 40 ft. 9¼ in.; height, 10 ft.; wing area, 456.6 sq. ft.

SUD-OUEST S.O.4050 VAUTOUR   FRANCE

Design of the Vautour was initiated in June 1951, and the first of three prototypes was flown on October 16, 1952. Six pre-production and 140 production Vautours have been ordered in three versions: the S.O.4050A single-seat close support aircraft (*photo*), the S.O.4050B two-seat level bomber, and the S.O.4050N two-seat night and all-weather fighter. A reconnaissance variant is also under development. The third prototype has been experimentally fitted with two 8,000 lb. thrust A.S. Sapphire A.S. Sa.6, and the second pre-production Vautour has two 9,260 lb. thrust Avon R.A.14s.
Specification: Single- or two-seat bomber and all-weather fighter. Engines: Two 7,275 lb.s.t. SNECMA Atar 101E-3. Weights: Normal loaded, 30,865 lb.; max. 39,684 lb. Performance: Max. speed, 686 m.p.h. at sea level; initial climb rate, 10,500 ft./min.; service ceiling, 44,290 ft.; normal range, 1,240 miles. Dimensions: Span, 49 ft. 6½ in.; length, 51 ft. 1 in.; height, 14 ft. 1¼ in.; wing area, 484.376 sq. ft.

SUD-OUEST S.O.9000 TRIDENT I   FRANCE

The S.O.9000 Trident I was initially designed as a supersonic short-range interceptor fighter but, when the first of two prototypes was flown on March 2, 1953, the decision to relegate the machine to the development role had been reached. Initially, 880 lb. thrust Turboméca Marboré II turbojets were attached to the wingtips, but these were replaced by Vipers in 1955. The three combustion chambers of the liquid-fuel rocket motor may be used separately or in concert. The Trident I has provided flight data for the externally similar but fully operational S.O.9050 Trident II which first flew on July 17, 1955. The latter will eventually have 2,425 lb.s.t. Turboméca Gabizo units.
Specification: Single-seat interceptor. Engines: One 9,930 lb.s.t. S.E.P.R. 48 rocket motor and two 1,640 lb.s.t. A.S.V.5 turbojets. Weights: Loaded, 12,100 lb. Performance: Max. speed, 1,056 m.p.h. at 36,000 ft.; ceiling, 72,000 ft. Dimensions: Span, 26 ft. 9 in.; length, 45 ft. 11 in.; height, 12 ft. 1½ in.; wing area, 99 sq. ft.

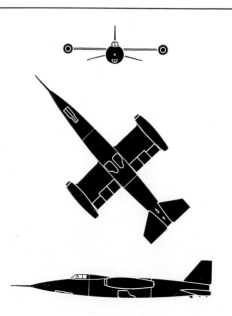

SUD-OUEST S.O.6025 ESPADON   FRANCE

The Espadon (Swordfish) was designed as a single-seat fighter, the first prototype (the S.O.6020) flying on November 12, 1948. Several versions of the Espadon were built in prototype form and have been extensively employed as test-beds. The second prototype was used to flight test the 2,755 lb. thrust SEPR 251 rocket motor (being redesignated S.O.6026), and the third prototype, or S.O. 6025 (*illustrated*), has a SEPR 251 rocket and fuel tanks in a ventral fairing. The basic power plant of all Espadons is the 5,000 lb.s.t. Rolls-Royce Nene. Specification relates to the lighter S.O.6021, fourth prototype.

Max. speed, 621 m.p.h. at sea level; climb to 33,000 ft., 9 minutes, 5 seconds; endurance, 1 hour, 5 minutes; empty weight, 10,474 lb.; loaded, 13,422 lb.; span, 34 ft. 9 in.; length, 49 ft. 2 in.

SUPERMARINE TYPE 378 SPITFIRE L.F.16 G.B.

The first prototype Spitfire flew on March 5, 1936, and a considerable number of variants of the basic design were produced during the ten years in which this famous fighter remained in production. The Spitfire L.F.16 (*illustrated*) is one of the most common of remaining variants, a few flying in the U.K., and others serving with the Israeli and Burmese Air Forces. The L.F.16 is similar to the L.F.9 apart from having the British-built Merlin 61 supplanted by a 1,705 h.p. Packard-built Merlin 266. L.F.9s are flying in Egypt and Israel, and a few remain in Italy. Some Spitfire F.22s (Griffon 85) serve in Syria and Thailand.

Max. speed, 408 m.p.h.; range, 660 miles; initial climb, 4,800 ft./min.; loaded weight, 7,300 lb.; span, 32 ft. 8 in.; length, 31 ft. 4 in.

SUPERMARINE TYPE 384 SEAFIRE F.17   G.B.

A naval version of the Spitfire, the Seafire was introduced in 1941, the first versions being "hooked" Spitfire F.5s. Wing folding was introduced with the Seafire F.3 which was powered by a 1,415 h.p. Rolls-Royce Merlin 46, 50A or 56, or a 1,475 h.p. Merlin 45, 50 or 55. A few Seafire F.3s remain in service with the Irish Air Corps. The last Fleet Air Arm squadron equipped with Seafires (F.17s) was disbanded in November 1954, but a few remain in the U.K. The Seafire F.17 has a 1,825 h.p. Rolls-Royce Griffon 6 engine. Photo depicts a Seafire F.47, a few examples of which remain.

Max. speed, 395 m.p.h.; initial climb rate, 4,680 ft./min.; loaded weight, 8,020 lb.; span, 36 ft. 11 in.; length, 32 ft. 3 in.; height, 13 ft. 6 in.; wing area, 242 sq. ft.

SUPERMARINE TYPE 347 SEA OTTER   G.B.

Designed as a successor to the Walrus as an air-sea rescue amphibian, the Sea Otter first appeared in 1940, and was employed as the A.S.R. Mk.2. Powered by an 870 h.p. Bristol Mercury 30 radial engine, the Sea Otter is employed in Australia for air-sea rescue duties, and several civil machines are used for bush-fire spotting. The Sea Otter has single-bay folding wings, a hydraulically retractable landing gear, and normally carries a crew of three. It is of mixed construction.

Max. speed, 150 m.p.h.; cruising, 100 m.p.h.; initial climb, 795 ft./min.; max. range, 690 miles; empty weight, 6,876 lb.; loaded, 10,000 lb.; span, 46 ft.; length, 39 ft. 9 in.; height, 16 ft. 2 in.

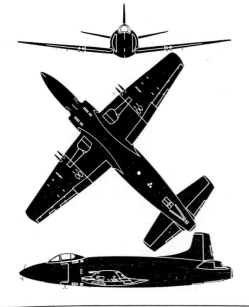

SUPERMARINE ATTACKER F.B.2   G.B.

The first prototype Attacker, the Type 392, flew on July 27, 1946, and was intended as a land-based interceptor to specification E.10/44. The first carrier-borne prototype, to specification E.1/45, the Type 398, followed on June 17, 1947. Subsequently, 145 Attacker F.1 and F.B.2 fighters were delivered to the Royal Navy, and these are now mostly relegated to the training role. In addition, as the Type 538, thirty-six land-based Attackers were delivered to the Pakistani Air Force.

Specification: Single-seat naval fighter-bomber. Engine: One 5,100 lb.s.t. Rolls-Royce Nene 102. Weights: Empty, 8,434 lb.; normal loaded, 12,300 lb.; max. 17,350 lb. Performance: Max. speed, 590 m.p.h. at sea level; cruising, 380 m.p.h.; initial climb rate, 6,350 ft./min.; max. range, 1,190 miles. Armament: Four 20-mm. cannon. Dimensions: Span, 36 ft. 11 in.; length, 37 ft. 6 in.; height, 9 ft. 6½ in.; wing area, 226.4 sq. ft.

SUPERMARINE SWIFT F.R.5   G.B.

The Supermarine Type 541, prototype Swift, was first flown on August 1, 1951, and several production variants intended for the high-altitude single-seat interceptor role were subsequently developed. High-altitude flight difficulties resulted in the discontinuation of the Swift interceptor and its withdrawal from service, but limited production of the Swift F.R.5 photo-reconnaissance fighter intended for low- and medium-altitudes has been undertaken for the R.A.F. The wing leading-edge features a "saw-tooth", a clear-view canopy is fitted, and the nose houses three cameras.
Specification: Single-seat reconnaissance fighter. Engine: One 7,500 lb.s.t. (9,500 lb. with afterburning) Rolls-Royce Avon R.A.7R. Weights: No details available. Performance: Max. speed, 725 (plus) m.p.h. at sea level; initial climb rate, 15,000 (plus) ft./min. Armament: Two 30-mm. Aden cannon. Dimensions: Span, 32 ft. 4 in.; length, 42 ft. 3 in.; height, 12 ft. 6 in.

SUPERMARINE TYPE 508   G.B.

Developed as an experimental single-seat carrier-borne fighter, the Type 508 is powered by two 6,500 lb.s.t. Rolls-Royce Avon R.A.3 turbojets, and first flew on August 31, 1951. A second prototype, designated Type 529, is externally similar and flew on August 29, 1952. These prototypes have served to provide data for the Type 544 carrier-based strike fighter currently in production for the Fleet Air Arm, the production machine differing externally in having swept wings and more orthodox swept tail surfaces. An interim prototype, the Type 525, was destroyed during flight tests.

Span, 41 ft.; length, 50 ft.; height, 11 ft. 7½ in.; wing area, 340 sq. ft.

TACHIKAWA R-52   JAPAN

The R-52 was completed in September 1952, and was the first aircraft built entirely from Japanese materials and powered by a Japanese engine (a 130 h.p. Shinphu 2 radial) to be completed after World War 2. Derived from the pre-war R-38, the R-52 tandem two-seat parasol-wing trainer was the first product of the Shin Tachikawa Kasushiki Kaisha, and the prototype has been presented by the Yomiuri Press for student instruction. The R-52 is of mixed construction with fabric covering.
Max. speed, 124 m.p.h.; cruising, 93 m.p.h.; initial climb, 722 ft./min.; range, 310 miles; empty weight, 1,500 lb.; loaded, 2,105 lb.; span, 35 ft.; length, 24 ft. 3 in.; height, 9 ft. 2 in.

TACHIKAWA R-53   JAPAN

The Tachikawa R-53 is a revised version of the previously-described R-52, and differs primarily in having a 155 h.p. Blackburn Cirrus Major engine. Essentially a parasol-wing tandem two-seat primary trainer, the R-53 is of mixed construction with a welded steel-tube fuselage structure and a wood and duralumin wing structure, the whole covered by fabric. No production plans for the R-53 have been announced at the time of writing.

Max. speed, 129 m.p.h.; cruising, 93 m.p.h.; range, 465 miles; service ceiling, 14,270 ft.; empty weight, 1,470 lb.; loaded, 2,090 lb.; span, 35 ft.; length, 24 ft. 9 in.; height, 8 ft. 2 in.

TACHIKAWA R-HM   JAPAN

The R-HM is a refined two-seat cabin version of Monsieur Henri Mignet's controversial pre-war *Pou de Ciel*, or "Flying Flea", powered by a 90 h.p. Continental C90-12F engine. It is generally similar to the H.M.310 Estafette produced by Aviões Mignet do Brasil. The R-HM is a tandem monoplane or heavily-staggered biplane, lift being divided between the two surfaces which give a slot effect. Another variant, the H.M.210 powered by a Minié Horus 4 Do engine, is flying in France.

Max. speed, 99 m.p.h.; cruising speed, 74.5 m.p.h.; range, 298 miles; empty weight, 910 lb.; loaded, 1,422 lb.; span, 26 ft. 3 in.; length, 16 ft. 8 in.; height, 6 ft. 6 in.; wing area, 201.5 sq. ft.

TAYLORCRAFT MODEL A (CUB)   U.S.A.

C. G. Taylor introduced the popular Taylor Cub in 1931. One of the first major production models, the Model A, was produced in substantial numbers by the Taylor-Young Airplane Co., and later by the Taylor Aircraft Co. The Model A, production of which was discontinued in 1939, was normally powered by a 37 h.p. Continental A40-4 engine, but other Continental engines up to 65 h.p. could be installed. The Model A is a tandem two-seat cabin monoplane of mixed construction.

Max. speed, 87 m.p.h.; cruising speed, 74 m.p.h.; initial climb, 450 ft./min.; range, 210 miles; empty weight, 563 lb.; loaded, 970 lb.; span, 35 ft. 2½ in.; length, 22 ft. 5 in.; height, 6 ft. 8 in.; wing area, 178 sq. ft.

TAYLORCRAFT MODEL BC-12   U.S.A.

The Taylorcraft Model B was introduced in 1939 when the corporate name of the company was changed from Taylor Aircraft Co. to Taylorcraft Aviation Corporation. Whereas the Model A featured tandem-seating, the Model B introduced side-by-side seating for the two occupants. The initial production model (BC) had a 50 h.p. Continental engine. This was followed by the BC-65 with a 65 h.p. Continental, and in 1940 by the BC-12, which embodied minor improvements. After World War 2, the type was returned to production as the BC-12D, and some 2,000 aircraft of this type are active in the U.S.A. The Models BF and BL are fitted with 65 h.p. Franklin and 65 h.p. Lycoming.

Max. speed, 105 m.p.h.; cruising, 95 m.p.h.; initial climb, 450 ft./min.; empty weight, 670 lb.; loaded, 1,150 lb.; span, 36 ft.; length, 22 ft.

TAYLORCRAFT MODEL D   U.S.A.

The Model D Tandem Trainer appeared in 1941, and was produced in large numbers for the Civilian Pilot Training Programme and the Civil Air Patrol. Generally similar in arrangement and construction to the previously-described Model B, the Model D differed mainly in having a narrower fuselage with tandem seating and dual controls. The Model D was powered by either the 65 h.p. Lycoming 0-145-B2 (DL), the 65 h.p. Continental A65 (DC), or the 65 h.p. Franklin 4AC-176 (DF). Several hundred examples of the Model DC are flying in the U.S.A., together with a few DLs and DFs.

Max. speed, 102 m.p.h.; cruising, 92 m.p.h.; initial climb, 600 ft./min.; range, 300 miles; empty weight, 720 lb.; loaded, 1,200 lb.; span, 35 ft. 5 in.; length, 22 ft. 9 in.

TAYLORCRAFT L-2M   U.S.A.

The Taylorcraft L-2 was a two-seat air observation post and military liaison model of the civil Model D. Seventy were originally procured by the U.S.A.A.F. in 1941 as the 0-57, and 336 examples of an improved model, the 0-57A, were procured in the following year. The 0-57A was redesignated L2A, and a further 490 for field artillery observation were delivered as L-2Bs. The final production model was the L-2M which was similar to the L-2A but fitted with spoilers, 900 being procured. The L-2M has a 65 h.p. Continental 0-170-3 engine. Many civil conversions are flying in the U.S.A.

Max. speed, 90 m.p.h.; cruising, 85 m.p.h.; empty weight, 815 lb.; loaded, 1,325 lb.; span, 36 ft.; length, 22 ft. 5 in.; height, 6 ft. 8 in.; wing area, 183.5 sq. ft.

TEMCO GC-1B SWIFT   U.S.A.

Originally produced by the Globe Aircraft Corporation, the Swift was built under sub-contract by the Temco Aircraft Corporation until 1947, when the latter concern acquired the manufacturing rights of the GC-1B Swift from the Globe company. At that time, 329 Swifts had been produced under the sub-contract arrangement. The initial production model of the Swift built by Globe, the GC-1A, was powered by an 85 h.p. Continental C85 engine. The prototype, the GC-1, appeared in 1941 and employed bakelite-bonded plywood in its structure. The all-metal GC-1A flew in January 1945, and some 850 Swifts are currently active in the U.S.A.

Specification: Two-seat cabin monoplane. Engine: One 125 h.p. Continental C125. Weights: Empty, 1,139 lb.; loaded, 1,710 lb. Performance: Max. speed, 150 m.p.h.; cruising, 140 m.p.h.; initial climb rate, 1,000 ft./min. Dimensions: Span, 29 ft. 4 in.; length, 20 ft. 10¾ in.; height, 5 ft. 10½ in.; wing area, 131.63 sq. ft.

TEMCO TE-1A BUCKAROO U.S.A.

The Buckaroo all-purpose trainer is, in effect, a tandem-seat adaptation of the Swift, employing some eighty per cent of the earlier aircraft's tooling. Twenty examples of the Buckaroo were built: two prototypes, three as service test aircraft for the U.S.A.F. as the T-35A and later sold as surplus, ten delivered to Saudi-Arabia under M.D.A.P., and one each in Israel and Italy. The Buckaroo is powered by a 165 h.p. Franklin 6AF-165-B3 engine and can carry two 0.30-in. machine guns.

Max. speed, 156 m.p.h.; cruising, 125 m.p.h.; initial climb, 1,000 ft./min.; empty weight, 1,139 lb.; loaded, 1,710 lb.; span, 29 ft. 2 in.; length, 21 ft. 8 in.; height, 6 ft. 4 in.; wing area, 134 sq. ft.

THALMAN MODEL T-4 U.S.A.

The Model T-4 is an experimental four-seat cabin monoplane developed by the Thalman Aircraft, Inc. in 1953, and powered by a 135 h.p. Lycoming engine. An unusual feature of the design is the extension of the windscreen to the front of the engine cowling. Although there is no connection between the rudder and ailerons, the T-4 can be flown as a two-control aircraft except during landing and take-off. Access to the cabin is provided by four hinged sections, and a fully retractable nosewheel undercarriage is fitted.

Max. speed, 175 m.p.h.; cruising speed, 155 m.p.h.; range, 700 miles; service ceiling, 18,000 ft.; empty weight, 1,350 lb.; loaded, 2,400 lb.; span, 40 ft.; wing area, 164 sq. ft.

TIPSY JUNIOR BELGIUM

The first Belgian aircraft of new design to be built after W.W.2, the Junior is an ultra-light single-seat aircraft of extreme simplicity. All structural joints are at right angles, thus eliminating all other angle joints which call for more manufacturing skill, and any engine not weighing more than 135 lb. may be installed. Two prototypes were built, one (*illustrated*) with a 62 h.p. Walter Mikron and the other with a 35 h.p. J.A.P. engine. Specification relates to the Mikron-Junior.

Max. speed, 125 m.p.h.; cruising, 113 m.p.h.; initial climb, 1,200 ft./min.; range, 375 miles; empty weight, 403 lb.; loaded, 660 lb.; span, 22 ft. 7½ in.; length, 18 ft. 6½ in.; height, 5 ft. 10 in.

TEXAS BULLET 185 U.S.A.

The Bullet 185 is a modified, four-seat version of the Johnson Rocket 185. The Bullet incorporates what is referred to as a "jet assist" device which converts engine exhaust gases into useful thrust at speeds above 40 m.p.h. The Bullet is of all-metal construction and is powered by a 185 h.p. Continental E-185-1 engine. As compared to the original Rocket, the Bullet has redesigned tail surfaces, modified fuselage contours, and a retractable tailwheel undercarriage in place of the earlier machine's retractable nosewheel.

Max. speed, 210 m.p.h.; cruising speed, 183 m.p.h.; initial climb rate, 900 ft./min.; loaded weight, 2,300 lb.; span, 28 ft.; length, 23 ft.

TIMM PT-220-C TUTOR U.S.A.

Developed from the S-160-K of 1940, the PT-220-C Tutor was built almost entirely of plastic-bonded plywood. The PT-220-C appeared in 1942, powered by a 220 h.p. Continental W-670 engine, and was placed in production for schools operating under the Civilian Pilot Training Programme and, as the N2T-1, for the U.S. Navy. Some thirty-five surplus N2T-1 tandem two-seat primary trainers are operated in the U.S.A.

Max. speed, 144 m.p.h.; cruising, 124 m.p.h.; service ceiling, 16,000 ft.; range, 400 miles; empty weight, 1,940 lb.; loaded, 2,725 lb.; span, 36 ft.; length, 24 ft. 10 in.; height, 10 ft. 8 in.; wing area, 185 sq. ft.

TIPSY BELFAIR BELGIUM

The Tipsy Belfair was produced by Avions Fairey S.A., and designed by E. O. Tips. It is generally similar to the pre-war Tipsy B, apart from having an enclosed cockpit and raised rear fuselage decking. The few Belfairs produced were, in fact, assembled from existing components of the Tipsy B. One Belfair is registered in Australia, and a Belgian-owned Belfair established a new distance record for its class on August 4, 1955, by flying 1,647 miles. The Belfair is powered by a 62 h.p. Walter Mikron II. Seven pre-war Tipsy Bs are flying in the U.K. and two in France, one with a Train 6C-01 engine.

Max. speed, 110 m.p.h.; cruising, 100 m.p.h.; empty weight, 540 lb.; loaded, 1,100 lb.; span, 31 ft. 2 in.; length, 21 ft. 8 in.

T.N.C.A. TEZIUTLAN   MEXICO

Designed by Antonio Sea and built by the Talleres Nacionales de Construcciones Aeronauticas (T.N.C.A.), the Teziutlan primary trainer was produced in 1942, and forty-five machines were built for the Mexican Air Force. Powered by a 125 h.p. Lycoming engine, the Teziutlan was designed to operate from Mexico's high-altitude airfields and utilised some 95 per cent nationally-produced materials. Construction is all-wood and a few aircraft of this type are still used by Mexican private owners.

Max. speed, 108 m.p.h.; cruising, 102.5 m.p.h.; initial climb, 1,380 ft./min.; service ceiling, 22,960 ft.; empty weight, 986 lb.; loaded, 1,633 lb.; span, 38 ft. 5 in.; length, 23 ft. 10½ in.; height, 6 ft. 2¾ in.

TOYO TT-10   JAPAN

Japan's first post-war aircraft, the TT-10 tandem two-seat primary trainer was produced by the Toyo Aircraft Company and flown for the first time on December 30, 1952. Power is provided by a 135 h.p. Lycoming 0-290-D2 engine, and a scaled-up four-seat liaison and touring version was at one time projected. Only two prototypes of the TT-10 have been built, and quantity production is unlikely. Mixed construction is employed.

Max. speed, 137 m.p.h.; cruising, 119 m.p.h.; initial climb, 750 ft./min.; ceiling, 16,400 ft.; range, 472 miles; empty weight, 1,245 lb.; loaded, 1,764 lb.; span, 28 ft. 2 in.; length, 22 ft. 11 in.; height, 6 ft. 10 in.; wing area, 128 sq. ft.

TRAVEL AIR MODEL 4000   U.S.A.

Produced in considerable numbers between 1926 and 1930, when the Travel Air Company became a division of the Curtiss-Wright Airplane Corp., the Model 4000 three-seat biplane is generally similar to the Models 2000 (90 h.p. Curtiss OX-5), 3000 (180 h.p. Hispano-Suiza), 8000 (135 h.p. Fairchild-Caminez), and 9000 (125 h.p. Siemens-Halske), apart from engine. Some seventy Model 4000 biplanes are used for agricultural purposes, and the majority have either the 220 h.p. Continental or 300 h.p. Lycoming. Examples of the Models 2000, 3000, 6000, and the similar D4D (built by Curtiss-Wright) are active in the U.S.A.

Max. speed, 135 m.p.h.; cruising, 110 m.p.h.; loaded weight, 2,450 lb.; span, 34 ft. 8 in.; length, 24 ft. 2 in.; height, 8 ft. 11 in.

TRAVEL AIR MODEL 6000B   U.S.A.

The Model 6000 six-seat cabin monoplane was one of the last aircraft types produced by the Travel Air Company before it was absorbed by Curtiss-Wright. Powered by the 300 h.p. Wright Whirlwind radial engine, three Model 6000Bs are active in the U.S.A., and three others with the 450 h.p. Pratt & Whitney Wasp Junior. In addition, a Model 6000A powered by a Pratt & Whitney Wasp is also active. Production was continued by Curtiss-Wright as the Model 6B, and four Curtiss-Wright-built machines remain active.

Max. speed, 135 m.p.h.; range, 550 miles; empty weight, 2,608 lb.; loaded, 4,230 lb.; span, 48 ft. 7 in.; length, 31 ft. 5¼ in.; height, 9 ft. 3 in.; wing area, 282 sq. ft.

TRAVEL AIR MODEL 12Q   U.S.A.

The Model 12Q two-seat sports or training biplane was produced by the Curtiss-Wright Airplane Corporation during 1930–31, after the Travel Air Company had been absorbed. Of mixed construction with fabric covering, the Model 12Q was originally powered by a 90 h.p. Wright Gipsy engine, and at least one example is airworthy in the U.S.A. The Model 12W is generally similar but is powered by a 145 h.p. Warner engine.

Max. speed, 103 m.p.h.; initial climb, 600 ft./min.; service ceiling, 10,000 ft.; range, 484 miles; empty weight, 1,071 lb.; loaded, 1,725 lb.; span, 28 ft. 10 in.; length, 21 ft. 5 in.; height, 8 ft. 10 in.; wing area, 206.5 sq. ft.

TRAVEL AIR 16-E SPORT   U.S.A.

The Sport three-seat sporting biplane produced between 1930–33 was originally designed by the Travel Air Company which, in 1930, was combined with the Curtiss-Robertson Airplane Mfg. Co. under the name of Curtiss-Wright Airplane Company. Production of the Sport was continued in two versions: the 16-K "Light Sport" with a 125 h.p. Kinner radial (*illustrated*), and the 16-E "Sport Trainer" with a 175 h.p. Wright Whirlwind radial. Two examples of each version are currently flying in the U.S.A., and the specification relates to the higher-powered Model 16-E produced in 1932.

Max. speed, 135 m.p.h.; cruising, 115 m.p.h.; initial climb rate, 1,200 ft./min.; cruising range, 350 miles; empty weight, 1,357 lb.; loaded, 2,150 lb.; span, 28 ft. 10 in.; length, 21 ft. 1 in.; height, 8 ft. 10 in.

TUPOLEV TU-2   U.S.S.R.

The TU-2 tactical support bomber (N.A.T.O. identification name: *Bat*) first appeared in service in 1944, earning for its designer, Lt.-Gen. Andrei N. Tupolev, a Stalin Prize. Used in limited quantities during the closing stages of World War 2, the TU-2 continued in production until 1948, and still forms part of the first-line equipment of the Polish and Sino-Communist air forces. Two versions of a high-altitude reconnaissance bomber development, the TU-6, have been produced. These are similar to the TU-2 but have increased wing span and a modified nose section, one having a "solid" radar nose and the other a glazed TU-2-type nose.
Specification: Light attack bomber. Engines: Two 1,850 h.p. ASh-82FNV. Weights: Empty, 18,240 lb.; loaded, 28,224 lb. Performance: Max. speed, 360 m.p.h. at 19,000 ft.; climb to 18,000 ft., 9.5 minutes; ceiling, 36,000 ft.; max. range (3,300 lb. bomb load), 1,550 miles. Dimensions: Span, 61 ft. 10½ in.; length, 45 ft. 4 in.

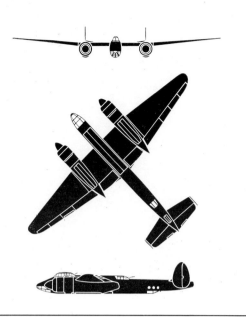

TUPOLEV (TYPE 35 BOSUN)   U.S.S.R.

A contemporary of the Ilyushin IL-28, the Tupolev naval attack bomber is in service in some numbers with the land-based units of the Soviet Naval Air Arm. The Soviet designation of this bomber is not known with certainty, but for identification purposes the *Type* number "35" and the code-name *Bosun* have been allocated to the aircraft by N.A.T.O. forces. Apart from its external appearance, little has been revealed concerning the *Bosun*, but it is believed that two 1,850-lb. naval torpedoes can be housed in its bomb-bay.
Specification: Three-seat attack bomber. Engines: Two 5,000 lb.s.t. RD-45 or VK-1 centrifugal turbojets. Weights: Approx. loaded, 45,000–50,000 lb.; Approx. performance: Max. speed, 560–580 m.p.h. at sea level; cruising, 500 m.p.h.; tactical radius, 850 miles. Approx. dimensions: Span, 70 ft.; length, 65 ft.; height, 20 ft.

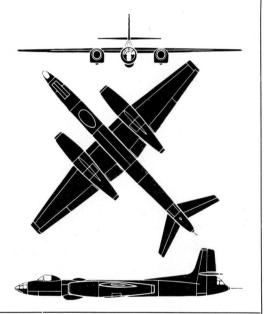

TUPOLEV (MYASISHCHEV BEAR)   U.S.S.R.

Dubbed Type 40 *Bear* by N.A.T.O. forces for identification purposes, this large, four-turboprop long-range heavy bomber was publicly demonstrated at Tushino on July 3, 1955, when a formation of seven machines participated in the Soviet Aviation Day display. The designers are believed to be A. N. Tupolev and his protégé, V. Myasishchev. The airscrew turbines are reputedly of the M-022 type, driving contra-rotating propellers, and the high aspect ratio wing has a leading edge sweep angle of 32° on the inboard sections, reducing to 28° on the outboard sections. The main bogie-type members of the undercarriage retract into inboard engine nacelle extensions.
Specifications: Long-range heavy bomber. Engines: Four airscrew turbines (possibly M-022 type delivering approx. 4,500 s.h.p. plus 1,200 lb. residual thrust). Weights: No details available. Performance: Approx. cruising speed, 400 m.p.h.; range, 5,000–6,000 miles. Approx. dimensions: Span, 150 ft.; length, 120 ft.; wing area, 2,800 sq. ft.

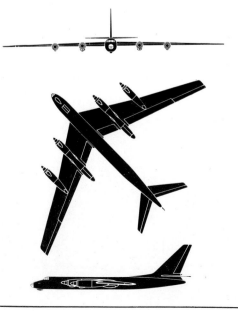

TUPOLEV-MYASISHCHEV TYPE 31   U.S.S.R.

Believed to be an interim bomber design built only in pre-production quantities and used to test the turboprop power plants later employed by the Type 40 *Bear*, the Type 31 *Barge* originally employed diesel engines believed to be of the 4,300 h.p. M-224 type, but these were later replaced by four propeller turbines believed to give some 4,500 s.h.p. plus 1,200 lb. residual thrust each. The Type 31 *Barge* is not thought to have entered service with Soviet strategic bombing units.

Approx. max. speed, 380 m.p.h.; approx. cruising, 340 m.p.h.; approx. max. range, 7,500 miles; approx. loaded weight, 210,000 lb.; estimated span, 185 ft.; length, 145 ft.; height, 38 ft.

VALMET VIIMA II   FINLAND

The Viima two-seat primary training biplane was first produced in 1935, and twenty-three machines of this type were delivered to the Finnish Air Force. A few of these, powered by 150 h.p. Bramo Sh 14 radials, are still employed by Finnish training elements, and one, the Viima IIB powered by a Cirrus Major III engine, is owned by Veljekset Karhumäki O/Y; this machine has enclosed seats. The Viima II is of mixed construction with fabric covering.

Max. speed, 110 m.p.h.; cruising, 87 m.p.h.; service ceiling, 13,120 ft.; range, 465 miles; empty weight, 1,300 lb.; loaded, 2,050 lb.; span, 34 ft. 5 in.; length, 25 ft. 10 in.; height, 9 ft. 10 in.; wing area, 297 sq. ft.

VALMET PYRY II   FINLAND

The Pyry tandem two-seat advanced training monoplane was first produced in 1939 by the Valtion Lentokonetehdas (the State Aircraft Factory), and forty-one machines were subsequently built for the Finnish Air Force, forty-one machines being produced during 1939–40. Powered by a 420 h.p. Wright Whirlwind R-975-E-3 radial engine, the Pyry is of mixed construction and carries an armament of one fixed machine gun firing through the airscrew disc. It is now being replaced in service by the Vihuri.

Max. speed, 205 m.p.h.; cruising, 180 m.p.h.; service ceiling, 19,000 ft.; range, 466 miles; loaded weight, 3,200 lb.; span, 32 ft. 3 in.; length, 24 ft. 10 in.; height, 8 ft. 2 in.; wing area, 136.7 sq. ft.

VULTEE 54 VALIANT   U.S.A.

Introduced in 1939, the Model 54 Valiant was ordered as the BT-13 and BT-15 by the U.S.A.A.F., and SNV-1 and SNV-2 by the U.S. Navy. Production continued after the merger of Vultee Aircraft and the Consolidated Aircraft Corp., in March 1943, 11,537 Valiants having been produced when contracts were completed in 1944. Powered by a 450 h.p. Pratt & Whitney Wasp Junior R-985-AN-1, the Valiant still serves with the Argentine Navy, and with the air forces of Bolivia, Haiti, Honduras, Guatemala, Mexico, Peru and Salvador.

Max. speed, 166 m.p.h.; cruising, 140 m.p.h.; range, 516 miles; empty weight, 3,345 lb.; loaded, 4,360 lb.; span, 42 ft. 2 in.; length, 28 ft. 8¼ in.; height, 12 ft. 4⅜ in.; wing area, 238 sq. ft.

VALMET VIHURI   FINLAND

The Vihuri (Squall) is being built for the Finnish Air Force by Valmet OY (State Metal Works, Aircraft Division) at Tampere. The prototype Vihuri flew for the first time on February 6, 1951, and the first production machine of an initial batch of thirty was flown on August 3, 1953. A second production batch is under consideration. A further post-war Valmet product was the Tuuli side-by-side two-seat low-wing primary training monoplane powered by a 150 h.p. Siemans-Halske Sh 14A and designed in 1941 but not built until 1951–52.

Specification: Two-seat advanced trainer. Engine: One 820 h.p. Bristol Mercury 8. Weights: Max. loaded, 6,345 lb. Performance: Max. speed, 268 m.p.h. at 12,140 ft.; economical cruising, 203 m.p.h. at 3,280 ft.; initial climb rate, 2,263 ft./min.; service ceiling, 29,190 ft. Dimensions: Span, 33 ft. 1 in.; length, 28 ft. 9 in.; height, 12 ft. 8 in.; wing area, 202.9 sq. ft.

VICKERS V.C.1 VIKING 1B   G.B.

Flown for the first time on June 22, 1945, the Viking was the first completely new post-war commercial aircraft. A number of Vikings have been delivered to the R.A.F. as the Viking C.1A, these originally being British European Airways airliners, and the Viking C.2 was a specially-equipped version employed by the Queen's Flight. Thirty Vikings were purchased by the Argentine Air Force in 1946, and several former B.E.A. Viking 1Bs are now employed by the Arab Legion Air Force. A total of 167 Vikings had been constructed when production terminated in 1949. *Specification: Twenty-four/thirty-eight passenger transport. Engines: Two 1,690 h.p. Bristol Hercules 634. Weights: Empty, 22,910 lb.; max. loaded, 34,000 lb. Performance: Cruising speed, 263 m.p.h. at 10,000 ft., (50 per cent power) 210 m.p.h.; initial climb rate, 1,500 ft./min.; max. range, 1,130 miles. Dimensions: Span, 89 ft. 5 in.; length, 65 ft. 4 in.; height, 24 ft.; wing area, 882 sq. ft.*

VICKERS VALETTA C.1   G.B.

Developed from the civil Viking 1B, the Valetta military transport has a strengthened floor, large loading doors in the fuselage port side, and higher-powered engines. As a troop carrier, the Valetta C.1 carries a maximum of thirty-six troops for a range of 290 miles. Alternatively, a 5,460 lb. freight load can be carried over 1,590 miles. The photograph depicts the prototype with pointed tail cone, production machines having a "sawn-off" rear fuselage. The C.2 is a V.I.P. version, and the T.3 (*silhouette*) is a navigational flying classroom with six astrodomes in the cabin roof. *Specification: Military transport. Engines: Two 1,975 h.p. Bristol Hercules 230. Weights: Empty, 25,061 lb.; loaded, 36,500 lb. Performance: Max. speed, 294 m.p.h. at 5,500 ft.; economical cruising, 172 m.p.h. at 10,000 ft.; climb to 10,000 ft., 8 minutes. Dimensions: Span, 89 ft. 3 in.; length, 62 ft. 11 in.; height, 24 ft.; wing area, 882 sq. ft.*

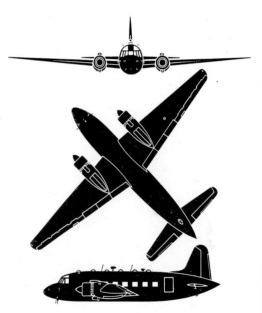

VICKERS VARSITY T.1   G.B.

Based upon the design of the Valetta military transport, the Varsity T.1 general-purpose crew trainer differs considerably in external appearance. The most noticeable external changes are the lengthened forward fuselage, nosewheel undercarriage, pannier-type bomb-bay and bomb-aiming station, and increased wing span. First flown in July 1949, the Varsity provides accommodation for two complete training crews, radar and radio operators, bomb aimers, navigators and pilots being trained simultaneously. *Specification: General-purpose crew trainer. Engines: Two 1,950 h.p. Bristol Hercules 264. Weights: Empty, 27,040 lb.; max. loaded, 37,500 lb. Performance: Max. speed, 288 m.p.h. at 10,000 ft.; max. cruising, 239 m.p.h.; initial climb rate, 1,400 ft./min.; service ceiling, 27,000 ft.; max. range, 2,648 miles. Dimensions: Span, 95 ft. 8 in.; length, 67 ft. 6 in.; height, 23 ft. 11 in.; wing area, 973 sq. ft.*

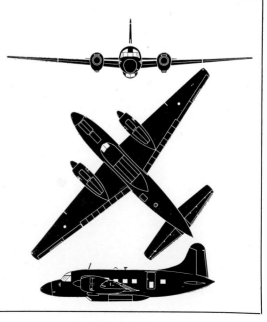

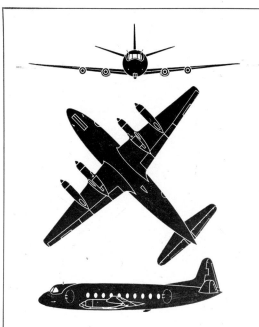

VICKERS V.C.2 VISCOUNT 760 SERIES   G.B.

The prototype Viscount, the Type 630, was first flown on July 16, 1948, becoming the world's first turboprop-powered commercial transport. The second prototype Viscount, the Type 663, was powered by two 6,250 lb.s.t. Rolls-Royce Tay R.Ta.1 turbojets for research purposes, and the third prototype, the Type 700, featured a 6 ft. 8 in. increase in fuselage length and a 5 ft. increase in wing span, and flew on August 28, 1950. Several variants of the Viscount 700 series have been produced, and the specification relates to the Type 745D as supplied to the U.S. Capital Airlines.
Specification: Forty/forty-eight passenger transport. Engines: Four 1,780 e.h.p. Rolls-Royce Dart 510. Weights: Empty, 38,580 lb.; loaded, 60,000 lb. Performance: Cruising speed, 320 m.p.h. at 15,000 ft.; max. initial climb rate, 1,500 ft./min.; max. still-air range (12,800 lb. payload), 1,450 miles. Dimensions: Span, 93 ft. 8½ in.; length, 81 ft. 2 in.; height, 26 ft. 9 in.; wing area, 963 sq. ft.

VICKERS VALIANT B.1   G.B.

Designed to meet the requirements of specification B.9/48, the first prototype Valiant, the Type 660, flew on May 18, 1951 powered by four 6,500 lb.s.t. Avon R.A.3 turbojets. This was followed on April 11, 1952, by a modified second prototype, the Type 667, with 7,500 lb.s.t. Avon R.A.7s. The initial production version for the R.A.F., the Type 674 Valiant B.1 is powered by 9,500 lb.s.t. Avon R.A.14s, but subsequent machines are powered by the 10,000 lb.s.t. Avon R.A.28. Progressive developments of the basic design include the Type 710 long-range photo-reconnaissance version.
Specification: Long-range medium bomber. Engines: Four 9,500 lb.s.t. Rolls-Royce Avon R.A.14. Weights: Loaded, 120,000–150,000 lb. Approx. performance: Cruising speed: Mach 0.9–0.95 (587–623 m.p.h.) at altitudes in excess of 50,000 ft.; normal range, 3,000 (plus) miles. Dimensions: Span, 114 ft. 4 in.; length, 108 ft. 3 in.

WACO MODEL SO   U.S.A.

When, in 1927, the first Waco biplane appeared, the manufacturer employed model numbers. In 1934, this system was replaced by a series of letters, the first of which indicated the engine and the second and third the aircraft model. The Model 10-T (220 h.p. Wright J-5) was redesignated Model ATO and (150 h.p. Hispano) DSO. Between 1927 and 1930 various engines were installed, and these models were retrospectively designated ASO (225 h.p. Wright Whirlwind), BSO (220 h.p. Continental), and CSO (either Wright or Continental). At least ten aircraft of this type are flying in Canada.
CSO: Max. speed, 152 m.p.h.; cruising, 134 m.p.h.; initial climb, 850 ft./min.; range, 500 miles; loaded weight, 3,200 lb.; span, 34 ft. 10 in.; length, 25 ft. 8 in.; height, 8 ft. 9½ in.

WACO MODEL VN   U.S.A.

The VN series were produced during 1937 and 1938, and differ from the thirty-seven other models produced by the Waco Aircraft Company between 1927 and 1942 in having a nosewheel undercarriage. All are four-seat cabin monoplanes with elliptical wings and pointed vertical tail surfaces. They are the only models to have flaps on both upper and lower wings. Versions flying include the 1937-built ZVN-7 (285 h.p. Jacobs L-5) and the 1938-built AVN-8 (*illustrated*) and ZVN-8 with 300 h.p. Jacobs L-6 and 285 h.p. Jacobs L-5 respectively.
AVN-8: Max. speed, 161 m.p.h.; cruising, 151 m.p.h.; initial climb, 900 ft./min.; service ceiling, 14,200 ft.; empty weight, 2,493 lb.; loaded, 3,800 lb.; span, 34 ft. 9 in.; length, 27 ft. 7 in.; height, 8 ft. 6 in.; wing area, 246 sq. ft.

WACO MODEL KS — U.S.A.

Introduced in 1934, the KS series of four/five-seat cabin biplanes still airworthy include the UKS-7 (225 h.p. Continental W670K), VKS-7 (240 h.p. Continental W670M), and ZKS-7 (285 h.p. Jacobs L-5). The VKS-7F (*illustrated*) is identical apart from having flaps. Generally similar apart from engine are the YKS-6 (225 h.p. Jacobs L-4), ZKS-6 (285 h.p. Jacobs L-5), and YKS-7 with the Jacobs L-4. Generally similar to the KS series are the Models C (DC, EC, JC, KC, OC, and UC) and F (MF and NF) series, examples of all of which are currently active.

YKS-7: Max. speed, 147 m.p.h.; cruising, 130 m.p.h.; initial climb, 1,150 ft./min.; range, 450 miles; loaded weight, 3,250 lb.; span, 33 ft. 3 in.; length, 25 ft. 4 in.; height, 6 ft. 7 in.; wing area, 240 sq. ft.

WACO MODEL PF — U.S.A.

The PF series two/three-seat biplane was introduced in 1935, and continued in production until 1942. These are the only Waco biplanes embodying constant-chord wings and pointed vertical tail surfaces. Two-seat versions flying include the UPF-7 (*illustrated*) with a 225 h.p. Continental W670K, and the VPF-7 (240 h.p. Continental W670M). Three-seaters include the CPF-1 and -6 (250 h.p. Wright R-760E), and ZPF-6 and -7 (285 h.p. Jacobs L-5). The latter are similar to the YPF-6 and -7 (225 h.p. Jacobs L-4).

UPF-7: Max. speed, 150 m.p.h.; cruising, 132 m.p.h.; initial climb, 1,150 ft./min.; range, 450 miles; loaded weight, 2,650 lb.; span, 30 ft.; length, 22 ft. 10 in.; height, 8 ft. 6 in.; wing area, 243 sq. ft.

WACO MODEL QC — U.S.A.

Produced between 1936 and 1938, cabin biplanes of the QC series still active include the four/five-seat DQC-6 (285 h.p. Wright R-760E2) and YQC-6 (225 h.p. Jacobs L-4). The ZQC-6 is similar to the latter model but has a 285 h.p. Jacobs L-5, and the AQC-6 and VQC-6 have 300 h.p. Jacobs L-6 and 250 h.p. Continental W670M-1 engines respectively. The EQC-6 (*photo*) has a 320 h.p. Wright R-760. All QC series biplanes have elliptical wings and pointed vertical tail surfaces, sharing this arrangement with the Model GC of 1937, including DGC-7, EGC-7, ZGC-7, YGC-7, EGC-8 and ZGC-8 which differ in engines.

YQC-6: Max. speed, 159 m.p.h.; cruising, 140 m.p.h.; initial climb, 760 ft./min.; range, 600 miles; loaded weight, 3,350 lb.; span, 35 ft.; length, 25 ft. 9 in.; height, 8 ft. 8 in.; wing area, 244 sq. ft.

WESTLAND WIDGEON III — G.B.

The Widgeon light parasol-wing monoplane appeared in 1924, and in 1926 it was decided to redesign the type for quantity production as the Widgeon III. The wing was made of constant chord and thickness, and the two cockpits were moved aft. Initially an 80 h.p. A.D.C. Cirrus II engine was installed (and the sole remaining airworthy example registered in Australia has this power plant), but later machines were powered with the Armstrong Siddeley Genet, the de Havilland Gipsy and the Cirrus Hermes. About two dozen production Widgeon IIIs were delivered.

Max. speed, 100 m.p.h.; cruising, 78 m.p.h.; landing speed, 42 m.p.h.; empty weight, 852 lb.; loaded, 1,400 lb.; span, 36 ft. 4½ in.; length, 23 ft. 5¼ in.; wing area, 200 sq. ft.

WESTLAND WYVERN S.4 — G.B.

The W.35 Wyvern was derived from the piston-engined Wyvern T.F.1, and four prototypes were ordered, one powered by the 4,030 e.h.p. Rolls-Royce Clyde R.C.3, and three powered by the 4,110 e.h.p. A.S. Python A.S.P.1. The Clyde-powered prototype flew on January 18, 1949, followed on March 22, 1949 by the first Python-powered prototype. Thirteen pre-production Wyvern T.F.2s were followed by the Wyvern S.4, the first version to enter service with the Fleet Air Arm which differs in having auxiliary tail fins, cut-back engine cowling and horn-balanced rudder. All Wyvern T.F.2s were subsequently brought up to S.4 standards.

Specification: Single-seat naval strike aircraft. Engine: One 4,110 e.h.p. Armstrong Siddeley Python A.S.P.3. Approx. weights: Empty, 15,290 lb.; loaded, 24,300 lb. Performance: Approx. max. speed, 550 m.p.h. Armament: Four 20-mm. Hispano cannon. Dimensions: Span, 44 ft.; length, 42 ft. 3 in.; height, 15 ft. 9 in.

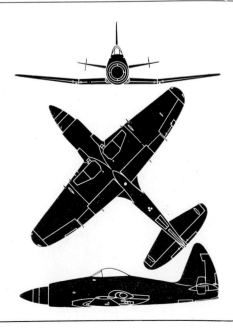

XL-14 MAYA PHILIPPINES

The XL-14 Maya has been developed by the Institute of Science and Technology in Manila, and has been built as part of a programme of research and study to investigate the possibilities of employing locally-available materials in aircraft construction. The XL-14 Maya is a three-seat experimental aircraft suitable for agricultural use and military air observation post and liaison roles. It is powered by a 100 h.p. Lycoming 0-235 engine, and employs a form of reinforced woven bamboo in its structure.

Max. speed, 115 m.p.h.; cruising, 90 m.p.h.; initial climb, 708 ft./min.; range, 300 miles; empty weight, 1,125 lb.; loaded, 1,720 lb.; span, 33 ft. 6 in.; length, 20 ft. 8 in.; height, 7 ft. 11 in.

XL-15 TAGAK PHILIPPINES

The XL-15 Tagak is the second aircraft of Philippine design and construction and, like the earlier XL-14 Maya, has been developed by the Institute of Science and Technology in Manila. Powered by a 190 h.p. Lycoming 0-425A engine, the Tagak is a general purpose monoplane which can be used for ambulance duties, and two stretchers and a medical attendant may be carried. Alternatively, the Tagak provides accommodation for four persons. The structure of the Tagak is entirely of locally-grown woods.

Max. speed, 135 m.p.h.; cruising, 105 m.p.h.; initial climb, 590 ft./min.; service ceiling, 13,120 ft.; range, 540 miles; empty weight, 1,716 lb.; loaded, 2,750 lb.; span, 39 ft. 5 in.; length, 27 ft. 2 in.; height, 9 ft. 3 in.

YAKOVLEV UT-2 U.S.S.R.

Designed in 1935 by A. S. Yakovlev and given the identification name *Mink* by N.A.T.O., the UT-2 primary trainer has been in service since 1937 and, although largely replaced in Soviet Air Force training elements by the YAK-18, the UT-2 is employed by numerous Russian civil flying schools and clubs and by several of the air forces of Russia's "satellites". The UT-2 is one of the last Soviet military aircraft to retain the pre-1940 system of designation which indicated the function of the aircraft. A few UT-2 primary trainers are still employed by flying clubs in Yugoslavia.
Specification: Two-seat primary trainer. Engine: One 110 h.p. M-11M or M-11G. Weights: Empty, 1,375 lb.; loaded, 2,075 lb. Performance: Max. speed, 122 m.p.h.; cruising speed, 97 m.p.h.; initial climb rate, 820 ft./min.; range, 465 miles. Dimensions: Span, 33 ft. 8 in.; length, 23 ft. 6 in.; wing area, 185 sq. ft.

YAKOVLEV YAK-9P U.S.S.R.

The YAK-9P (N.A.T.O. identification name: *Frank*) was the final development in a continuous line of single-seat fighters which commenced in 1939 with the YAK-1 (then designated I-26), and including the YAK-3 (initially designated YAK-1M), the YAK-7B and YAK-9, all progressive developments of the same basic design. The original production YAK-9 had a 1,210 h.p. VK-105PF engine, but the late production versions, such as the YAK-9P, have the more powerful VK-107A engine and dispense with the air intake fitted under the engine cowling of earlier YAK-9s, -9Ds, and -9Ts.
Specification: Single-seat fighter. Engine: One 1,600 h.p. Klimov VK-107A. Weights: Loaded, 6,985 lb. Performance: Max. speed, 370 m.p.h. at 16,400 ft.; cruising speed, 204 m.p.h. at 8,200 ft.; range, 505 miles. Armament: One 20-mm. cannon and two 12.7-mm. machine guns. Dimensions: Span, 30 ft. 11 in.; length, 27 ft. 10 in.

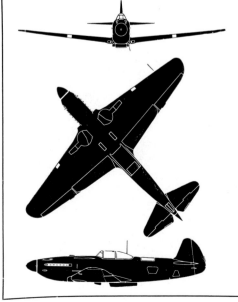

YAKOVLEV YAK-11   U.S.S.R.

The YAK-11 (N.A.T.O. identification name: *Moose*) advanced trainer began to enter service with the Soviet Air Force in 1946–47, and its design obviously owed much to Alexander Yakovlev's wartime series of fighters, the wing, tailplane and under-carriage being similar to those of the YAK-3 fighter. The YAK-11 holds a number of F.A.I.-recognised international records, including the 500-km. and 1,000-km. closed-circuit records in Class D. In addition to the Soviet Air Force, the YAK-11 is used by the air forces of Hungary, Rumania, Poland and China.
Specification: Two-seat advanced trainer. Engine: One 750 h.p. Schvetsov ASh-21. Weights: Approx. loaded, 4,900 lb. Performance: Max. speed, 295 m.p.h.; cruising speed, 210 m.p.h. Armament: One 7.62-mm. machine gun in engine cowling. Dimensions: Span, 30 ft. 9 in.; length, 28 ft.; wing area, 160 sq. ft.

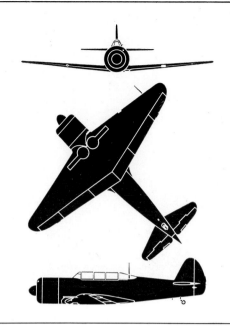

YAKOVLEV YAK-12   U.S.S.R.

The YAK-12 was first introduced in 1944 as a light military liaison monoplane to replace the obsolescent Polikarpov PO-2 biplane. The initial production version is illustrated by the photograph, but in 1947 a modified version, with a redesigned rear fuselage (*silhouette*) cut down aft of the wing, appeared, and this is used in large numbers in the Soviet Union. Given the identification name *Creek* by N.A.T.O. forces, the YAK-12 may be fitted with skis or floats. It is primarily employed for the air ambulance and communications roles.
Specification: Four-seat light cabin monoplane. Engine: One 145 h.p. M-11. Weights: Empty, 1,700 lb.; loaded, 2,650 lb. Performance: Max. speed, 115 m.p.h.; cruising speed, 103.6 m.p.h.; initial climb rate, 520 ft./min.; ceiling, 13,200 ft. Dimensions: Span, 39 ft. 6 in.; length, 27 ft. 7 in.; height, 8 ft.; wing area, 237 sq. ft.

YAKOVLEV YAK-16   U.S.S.R.

The YAK-16 (N.A.T.O. identification name: *Cork*) was first flown in 1946, and has since been produced for both commercial and military roles. The YAK-16 has been offered for sale at trade shows in Poland, Finland, Hungary and Czechoslovakia, but it is not believed that the YAK-16 is employed outside the Soviet Union. The YAK-16 is primarily an eight/ten passenger light feeder liner, but one crew training variant is known to have a glazed nose section and four astrodomes in the cabin roof. A small number of YAK-16s are employed by *Aeroflot*.
Specification: Eight/ten passenger light transport. Engines: Two 750 h.p. Schvetsov ASh-21. Weights: Empty, 11,400 lb.; loaded, 14,000. Performance: Max. speed, 190 m.p.h.; cruising speed, 173 m.p.h. at 5,600 ft.; ceiling, 16,000 ft.; normal range, 600 miles. Dimensions: Span, 65 ft. 7 in.; length, 49 ft. 6 in.; height, 12 ft.

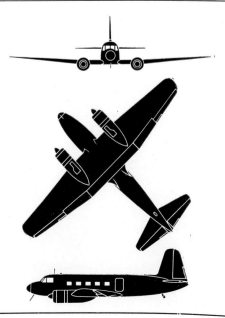

YAKOVLEV YAK-17   U.S.S.R.

The YAK-17 is a progressive development of Russia's first production single-seat jet fighter, the YAK-15. The YAK-17 (N.A.T.O. identification name: *Feather*) differs from its predecessor primarily in having a nosewheel undercarriage. A two-seat conversion trainer, the U-YAK-17 (N.A.T.O. identification name: *Magnet*), appeared in 1947. This variant is illustrated by the silhouette. Both single- and two-seat versions are believed to be employed in small numbers by conversion training units of the Soviet Air Force.

Specification: Single- and two-seat conversion trainer. Engine: One 2,200 lb.s.t. M-004 (Junkers Jumo 004B development). Weights: No details available. Performance: Approx. max. speed (single-seat), 505 m.p.h.; cruising, 370 m.p.h.; endurance, 1.5 hours. Armament: Two 20-mm. cannon. Approx. dimensions: Span, 30 ft.; length, 28 ft.; wing area, 177 sq. ft.

YAKOVLEV YAK-18   U.S.S.R.

Developed from and designed to replace the UT-2, the YAK-18 began to enter service with Soviet Air Force training elements in 1946–47, and has since been supplied to the air forces of Czechoslovakia, Poland, North Korea and China. The YAK-18 (N.A.T.O. identification name: *Max*) holds F.A.I.-recognised speed records for aircraft in its category over 500-km. and 2,000-km. courses. The YAK-18 has now largely replaced the UT-2 primary trainer and, in addition to being used by the Soviet Air Force as its standard elementary trainer, it is employed by many civil clubs and schools.

Specification: Tandem two-seat primary trainer. Engine: One 160 h.p. M-11RF-1. Weights: Empty, 1,665 lb.; loaded, 2,360 lb. Performance: Max. speed, 160 m.p.h.; cruising, 134 m.p.h.; ceiling, 16,400 ft.; range, 560 miles. Dimensions: Span, 34 ft. 9 in.; length, 26 ft. 4½ in.; height, 10 ft. 4 in.; wing area, 183 sq. ft.

YAKOVLEV YAK-23   U.S.S.R.

The YAK-23 fighter was derived from Alexander Yakovlev's earlier YAK-15-17 series of fighters and is contemporary to the MIG-15. Allocated the identification name *Flora* by N.A.T.O. forces, the YAK-23 is believed to have flown for the first time in the summer of 1947 powered by a Rolls-Royce Derwent engine acquired from Britain. While no longer first-line equipment with Soviet fighter elements, a number of YAK-23 fighters serve with the Polish and Bulgarian air forces, and others are probably employed as conversion trainers by Soviet training units.

Specification: Single-seat interceptor fighter. Engine: One 3,500 lb.s.t. R.D.500 (Russian production development of the Rolls-Royce Derwent). Weights: No details available. Approx. performance: Max. speed, 610 m.p.h.; initial climb rate, 6,000 ft./min.; service ceiling, 45,000 ft. Approx. dimensions: Span, 30 ft.; length, 29 ft.

YAKOVLEV YAK-3   U.S.S.R.

The YAK-3, initially known as the YAK-1M, was a "cleaned up" version of Alexander Yakovlev's initial fighter monoplane, the YAK-1, designed to take advantage of the 1,600 h.p. VK-107A engine. However, delays in the delivery of this engine resulted in the installation of the 1,210 h.p. VK-105PF engine in most wartime YAK-3s. A few YAK-3s remain in service with Russia's Balkan "satellites" and others are used as advanced trainers. An armament of one 20-mm. Sh-VAK motor cannon and two 12.7-mm. Beresin machine guns are carried.

Max. speed, 343 m.p.h.; range, 456 miles; climb to 16,400 ft., 4 minutes; loaded weight, 4,848 lb.; span, 31 ft.; length, 28 ft. 11 in.

ZAUNKOENIG LF-1   GERMANY

The Zaunkoenig (Wren) was built to the designs of Dr. Ing. H. Winter by the students of the Technical University of Brunswick. Two prototypes of the Zaunkoenig were built during the war, one of these being seriously damaged in an accident but rebuilt and flown in 1955 (*illustrated*), and the other being in the United Kingdom. The Zaunkoenig is powered by a 51 h.p. Zundapp Z9-92 engine and full-span slots and flaps are fitted. The aircraft was designed to convert sailplane pilots to powered flight.

Max. speed, 87 m.p.h.; initial climb rate, 562 ft./min.; service ceiling, 12,550 ft.; empty weight, 553 lb.; loaded, 776 lb.; span, 26 ft. 5 in.; length, 19 ft. 10¾ in.; height, 7 ft. 10¼ in.

ZLIN 22   CZECHOSLOVAKIA

The Zlin 22 appeared in 1947, and it was intended to power this two-seater with the Zlin Persy III engine of 57 h.p. However, when production of the Persy engine was discontinued, the Zlin 22 was re-engined with the 75 h.p. Praga D (Zlin 22D) and the 105 h.p. Walter Minor 4-III (Zlin 22M), the latter version being a three-seater. A projected version, of which only two prototypes were produced, was the three/four-seat Zlin 122 powered by a 105 h.p. Zlin Toma 4.

Specification (figures quoted in parentheses refer to the Zlin 22M)· Two-seat cabin monoplane. Engine: One 75 h.p. Praga D. Weights: Empty, 804 (926) lb.; loaded, 1,399 (1,588) lb. Performance: Max. speed, 112 (133.5) m.p.h.; cruising speed, 100 (121) m.p.h.; ceiling, 13,780 (18,040) ft.; range, 435 (620) miles. Dimensions: Span, 34 ft. 9 in.; length, 23 ft. 9 in.; height, 6 ft. 5 in.; wing area, 157.7 sq. ft.

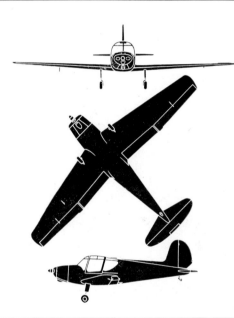

ZLIN 126 TRENER II   CZECHOSLOVAKIA

The Zlin 126 Trener II is an all-metal development of the wooden Zlin 26 two-seat primary trainer produced in 1948. Both the prototype and the production Zlin 126 flew in 1953, and the type is in quantity production at the Otrokovice works of the Czech nationalised aircraft industry (the former Zlin works). The Trener II has been delivered to primary training elements of the Czech Air Force and to the government-controlled flying training schools. The Zlin 126 has also been offered for export.

Specification: Two-seat primary trainer. Engine: One 105 h.p. Walter Minor 4-III. Weights: Empty, 1,113 lb.; loaded, 1,675 lb. Performance: Max. speed, 127 m.p.h. at sea level; cruising speed (70 per cent power), 102 m.p.h.; climb to 6,560 ft., 12 minutes, 15 seconds; range, 373 miles. Dimensions: Span, 33 ft. 9 in.; length, 24 ft. 7 in.; height, 6 ft. 9 in.; wing area, 160.38 sq. ft.

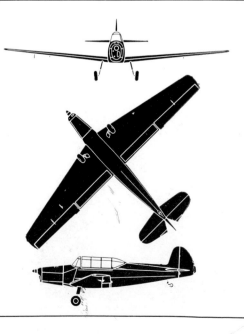

AEROTÉCNICA A.C.11   SPAIN

The unusual feature of this two-seat helicopter is the fact that its engine is mounted above and in front of the cockpit. The A.C.11 first flew in 1952 as the MATRA-Cantinieau M.C.101, powered by a 105 h.p. Hirth, and was a development of Jean Cantinieau's M.C.100. From the M.C.101 stemmed the M.C.101A (being developed as the A.C.13A). Production of the M.C.101 has been undertaken by Aerotécnica in Spain as the A.C.11. Power is provided by a 135 h.p. Lycoming 0-290-D2.

Max. speed, 67 m.p.h.; cruising, 50 m.p.h.; inclined climb rate, 356 ft./min.; endurance, 2 hours; service ceiling, 8,200 ft.; empty weight, 1,179 lb.; loaded, 1,687 lb.; rotor diameter, 27 ft. 10½ in.; length, 21 ft. 11¾ in.

AEROTÉCNICA A.C.13A   SPAIN

Differing considerably from the previously-described A.C.11, the A.C.13A is the first Spanish turbine-powered helicopter, being powered by a 260 e.h.p. Turboméca Artouste I turbine mounted above and behind the three-seat cockpit. The design is also being developed in France by the S.N.C.A. du Nord as the N.1750 Norelfe, and is a development of Jean Cantinieau's M.C.101A. Jet exhaust provides some 22 lb. thrust for anti-torque purposes.

Max. speed, 92 m.p.h.; cruising (80 per cent power), 87 m.p.h.; economical cruising, 50 m.p.h.; absolute ceiling, 29,000 ft.; endurance, 1 hour; empty weight, 1,265 lb.; loaded, 1,766 lb.; rotor diameter, 29 ft. 7½ in.; length, 25 ft. 7 in.; height, 9 ft. 0 in.

BAUMGARTL PB-63   BRAZIL

The Austrian engineer Paul Baumgartl developed "strap-on" type ultra-light helicopters such as the 45 lb. Heliofly for the *Wehrmacht* during World War 2. In August 1950, Baumgartl took his improved Model PB-59 to South America, and development continued with the backing of the Brazilian government, the PB-61 being produced at the Air Ministry workshops at Galeao Airport, Rio de Janeiro. From the PB-61 and intermediate PB-62 has been developed the PB-63 single-seater powered by an 85 h.p. Continental C-85-12 engine.

Cruising speed, 60 m.p.h.; inclined climb rate, 1,400 ft./min.; service ceiling, 7,500 ft.; loaded weight, 795 lb.; rotor diameter, 19 ft. 8 in.

BELL MODEL 47G (H-13G, HTL-6)   U.S.A.

The Model 47 was first flown on December 8, 1945, and the Model 47G is a progressive development of the earlier production models 47B and D. Built under licence in Italy and Japan, the Model 47G-1 is powered by a 200 h.p. Lycoming VO-435 engine and is a four-seater, the early 47G being a three-seater. U.S.A.F. and U.S. Navy variants are the H-13 and HTL respectively. The H-13G and HTL-6 have a 200 h.p. Franklin 6V4-200-C32 engine. The specification relates to the Model 47G.

Max. speed, 100 m.p.h.; cruising, 80 m.p.h.; inclined climb rate, 910 ft./min.; range, 212 miles; endurance, 3 hours, 54 minutes; hovering ceiling, 3,600 ft.; empty weight, 1,435 lb.; loaded, 2,350 lb.; rotor diameter, 35 ft. 1 in.; length, 41 ft. 5 in.; height, 9 ft. 4 in.

BELL MODEL 47H-1 (H-13H)   U.S.A.

Introduced in November 1954, the Model 47H retains the basic features of the earlier Model 47 helicopter series, but has a redesigned and enlarged cockpit seating three persons and is intended primarily for the executive commercial market. The engine of the commercial model is similar to that of the Model 47G, and a military version, the H-13H, has a 200 h.p. Lycoming VO-435. Twenty-one H-13Hs are on order for the U.S. Army Field Forces.

Max. speed, 100 m.p.h.; cruising, 90 m.p.h.; inclined climb rate, 1,130 ft./min.; range, 220 miles; hovering ceiling, 5,600 ft.; empty weight, 1,465 lb.; loaded, 2,200 lb.; rotor diameter, 35 ft. 1 in.; length, 41 ft. 5 in.; height, 9 ft. 4 in.

BELL MODEL 47J (HUL-1)   U.S.A.

Latest of the Model 47 helicopter series to be placed in production, the Model 47J is a four-seat general-purpose helicopter powered by a 200 h.p. Lycoming VO-435 engine. A service development contract for ten machines designated HUL-1 has been placed by the U.S. Navy, and it is proposed to replace the earlier HTL-1/6 series helicopters currently employed by the U.S. Navy with this type. Like the Model 47H, the Model 47J has improved streamlining, metal-covered rotor blades, and sheet-metal-covered rear fuselage.

Performance: No details available. Empty weight, 1,626 lb.; loaded, 2,550 lb.; rotor diameter, 35 ft. 1 in.; length, 45 ft. 1 in.; height, 9 ft. 4 in.

BELL MODEL 48 (YH-12B) U.S.A.

Essentially a scaled-up development of the Model 47, the eleven-seat Model 48 is a general-purpose helicopter powered by a 600 h.p. Pratt and Whitney Wasp R-1340-55 engine. The prototype Model 48, or XH-12, flew in 1947, and the final production version, the YH-12B for the U.S.A.F., flew on November 21, 1949. Of fourteen helicopters of this type ordered three were XH-12s, and one of these was relegated to static testing. Six stretcher patients and a nursing attendant can be carried when the type is used for casualty evacuation.
Max. speed, 105 m.p.h.; cruising, 85 m.p.h.; inclined climb rate, 1,000 ft./min.; range, 400 miles; service ceiling, 13,000 ft.; empty weight, 4,200 lb.; loaded, 6,515 lb.; rotor diameter, 47 ft. 6 in.; length, 58 ft. 8 in.; height, 19 ft. 3 in.

BELL MODEL 54 (XH-15) U.S.A.

The Model 54, or XH-15, is a further development of the basic Model 47 formula, and the first of three prototypes of this four-seat helicopter flew in March 1950. It was subsequently adapted as a two-seater and evaluated by the U.S. Army as a potential liaison and A.O.P. helicopter. Power is provided by a 285 h.p. Continental XO-470-5 engine. The design specification called for a service ceiling of 20,000 feet.
Max. speed, 100 m.p.h.; cruising, 85 m.p.h.; range, 100 miles; service ceiling, 20,000 ft.; empty weight, 2,000 lb.; loaded, 2,800 lb.; rotor diameter, 37 ft. 4 in.; length, 44 ft. 9 in.; height, 11 ft.

BELL MODEL 61 (HSL-1) U.S.A.

The Model 61, or HSL-1, is being supplied to the U.S. Navy and eight helicopters of this type are to be delivered to the Royal Navy under M.D.A.P. The first of three XHSL-1s was flown on March 4, 1953, and the type was designed specifically for anti-submarine duties. The HSL-1 carries "dipping sonar" equipment for detecting underwater craft, and the 4,000 lb. warload can include Fairchild Petrel self-homing missiles. The HSL-1 is powered by two 1,900 h.p. Pratt & Whitney Double Wasp R-2800-50 engines.
Max. speed, 138 m.p.h.; cruising, 100 m.p.h.; range, 350 miles; endurance, 3 hours, 30 minutes; loaded weight, 26,500 lb.; rotor diameter (each), 51 ft. 6 in.; length, 70 ft. 0 in.; height, 14 ft. 6 in.

BELL MODEL 200 (XV-3) U.S.A.

The Model 200 convertiplane was designed to meet a U.S. Army specification and a contract for its development was awarded in 1951. The Model 200 was initially designated XH-33, but the designation was later changed to XV-3. Powered by a 450 h.p. Pratt & Whitney R-985 engine, the XV-3 has two opposite-rotating three-blade rotors which lift the machine off the ground and forward until a speed above that of wing stalling is attained. The rotor heads then describe a 90° arc to form tractor airscrews. Ground tests commenced on February 10, 1955, and the first flight was made in August. The XV-3 provides accommodation for four persons.
Max. speed, 175 (plus) m.p.h.; rotor diameter (each), 24 ft.; span, 30 ft.; length, 30 ft.; height, 12 ft.

BELL MODEL 201 (XH-13F) U.S.A.

The Model 201 is a version of the Model 47G with a 425 e.h.p. Continental (Model 200) T51-T-3 gas turbine replacing the standard piston engine, and intended to furnish experience with jet transmissions for the new Model 204 (XH-40) four-seat utility helicopter for the U.S. Army. The T51-T-3 turbine (licence-built Turboméca Artouste II) drives both the two-blade main rotor and the anti-torque rotor, and provides 290 lb. residual thrust.
Rotor diameter, 35 ft. 1½ in.; overall length, 41 ft. 2½ in.; height, 9 ft. 6 in. Performance and weights: No details available for publication.

BENSEN MODEL B MID-JET U.S.A.

Designed and built by the Bensen Aircraft Corporation, the Mid-Jet is a single-seat ramjet-driven research helicopter. Built in 1953 and first flown in 1954, it is powered by a 40 e.h.p. 3R-1 ramjet at each rotor tip, and the manufacturers claim that it will lift approximately four times its empty weight. A three-wheel sprung undercarriage is attached to the open tubular framework, and a fuel tank is mounted immediately aft of the pilot's seat.
Max. speed, 80 m.p.h.; cruising, 75 m.p.h.; empty weight, 100 lb.; loaded, 372 lb.; rotor diameter, 15 ft.; overall length, 15 ft.; height, 4 ft. 11 in.

BENSEN MODEL B-4 SKY-SCOOTER   U.S.A.

The B-4 Sky-Scooter represents one of the first attempts to produce a simplified and inexpensive sports and general utility helicopter. The first prototype (*illustrated*), was tested in 1955, and this will be followed by a version with a totally enclosed cabin. Seating and control layout follow closely those of the contemporary motor scooter. Directional control is effected by a twist grip handlebar to the 40 h.p. motorcycle engine mounted on the rotor head. The Bensen Company has also produced the B-5 and B-6 Gyro-Gliders.
Max. speed, 60 m.p.h.; range, 118 miles; empty weight, 360 lb.; loaded, 730 lb.; rotor diameter, 26 ft. 2 in.

BRANTLEY MODEL B-2   U.S.A.

The two-seat B-2 helicopter appeared in 1952. Its 150 h.p. Lycoming engine drives a two-blade rotor and anti-torque tail rotor. The main blades are of a special design, their inner sections rigidly attached to the rotor hub, and were first tested on the co-axial Model B-1 designed in 1941, which helicopter was eventually flown in 1946. The B-2 is of simple, tubular steel construction, and no production plans have so far been announced.
Cruising speed, 100 (plus) m.p.h.; loaded weight, 1,350 lb.; rotor diameter, 23 ft. 0 in.

BRISTOL TYPE 171 MK.4   G.B.

First flown on July 24, 1947, the Type 171 was the first British helicopter to receive a commercial certificate. The two prototypes were powered by the 450 h.p. Pratt & Whitney Wasp Junior R-985, but subsequent machines are powered by the Alvis Leonides. The Type 171 has been supplied to the services as the Sycamore, and the current production model is the Type 171 Mk.4 with a 565 h.p. Alvis Leonides 524/1 engine, increased a.u.w., and redesigned undercarriage. Three Mk.4s have been purchased by the Belgian Air Force (*photo*).
Max. speed, 126 m.p.h.; cruising, 91 m.p.h.; inclined climb rate, 1,300 ft./min.; range, 268 miles; empty weight, 3,983 lb.; loaded, 5,400 lb.; rotor diameter, 48 ft. 6¼ in.; overall length, 46 ft. 2 in.

BRISTOL TYPE 173 MK.3   G.B.

The first British tandem-rotor helicopter, the Type 173 was flown for the first time on January 3, 1952. The two prototypes (*one of which is illustrated*) are designated Type 173 Mk.2, and are powered by two 545 h.p. Alvis Leonides Le.23 HMV Mk. 73 engines, but the Type 173 Mk.3 has two 850 h.p. Leonides Major ALe. M.1 engines. A further development of the Type 173 Mk.3 will be the Type 191 naval helicopter which has a shorter fuselage and, in one of its variants, will be employed for anti-submarine duties. Napier Gazelle turbines will be installed at a later stage.
Max. speed, 153 m.p.h.; cruising, 138 m.p.h.; inclined climb rate, 2,000 ft./min.; empty weight, 9,714 lb.; loaded, 13,496 lb.; rotor diameter (each), 48 ft. 6¼ in.; overall length, 77 ft. 7 in.

CANAMERICAN S.G.VI-E   U.S.A.

The three-seat utility S.G.VI-E originated in the S.G.IV helicopter of 1946, designed by Bernard Sznycer. The first S.G.VI was tested in July 1947, and was subsequently developed through successive A. B. C and D models by Engineering Products of Canada Ltd. Taken over by CanAmerican Inc., the latest variant is the S.G.VI-E which is essentially an improved model of the S.G.VI-D (*illustrated*) powered by a 200 h.p. Franklin 6A4-200-C6 engine.
Cruising speed, 78 m.p.h.; inclined climb rate, 760 ft./min.; loaded weight, 2,550 lb.; rotor diameter, 35 ft. 0 in.

CAPITAL MODEL C-1 FIREFLY   U.S.A.

Designed by Horace T. Pentecost, the pioneer of the strap-on type helicopter, development of the C-1 Firefly was commenced in 1949. In 1954, the Capital Helicopter Corporation was formed, and the Model C-1 Firefly was completed and test-flown in 1955. Power is provided by a 23 lb. thrust 4-in. diameter pulse-jet, mounted at each rotor tip and developed by the U.S. Naval Research Laboratory. Prior to the development of the Firefly, Pentecost had developed a series of light piston-engined machines.
Max. speed, 90 m.p.h.; cruising speed, 60 m.p.h.; inclined climb rate, 800 ft./min.; endurance, 1 hour, 30 minutes; empty weight, 130 lb.; loaded, 450 lb.; rotor diameter, 18 ft.

CESSNA CH-1   U.S.A.

First flown in July 1953, the Cessna CH-1 two-seat all-metal utility helicopter is a development of the Seibel S-3 of 1947, the Cessna Aircraft Company having absorbed the Seibel Helicopter Company in March 1952. The Cessna company also took over the experimental S-4A Skyhawk (YH-24) and the S-4B two-seat training helicopter, and these have served to provide experience for the CH-1. Two prototypes have been built, and these are powered by the 260 h.p. Continental FS0-470-A engine.

Max. speed, 122 m.p.h.; inclined climb rate, 1,330 ft./min.; service ceiling, 11,000 ft.; loaded weight, 3,000 lb.; rotor diameter, 35 ft.

CHU CJC-3   FORMOSA

The first successful Chinese helicopter is the two-seat Chu CJC-3 military liaison and air observation post for the Chinese Nationalist Army on Formosa. Designed by Major-General Chu, the CJC-3 began ground tests in 1952, tethered tests commencing in January 1955. The Chu CJC-3 is one of the very few small tandem-rotor helicopters, and is powered by a 190 h.p. Lycoming engine. Previously, Major-General Chu had designed and built the unsuccessful Yamman Humming Bird B.

Max. speed, 92 m.p.h.; cruising speed, 83 m.p.h.; inclined climb rate, 540 ft./min.; range, 130 miles; absolute ceiling, 16,800 ft.; loaded weight, 2,050 lb.; rotor diameter (each), 25 ft.

CIERVA C-30A AUTOGIRO   SPAIN

Senor Juan de la Cierva was a Spanish pioneer of rotating-wing aircraft. In 1923 he achieved success with a gyroplane for which he patented the name "Autogiro". The C-30A, of which airworthy examples exist in Britain, Sweden, Spain, Italy and Australia, was first produced in 1934, and during the following year the R.A.F. ordered a small number from A. V. Roe who produced the gyroplane under licence. The C-30A is powered by a 140 h.p. Armstrong Siddeley Civet I.

Max. speed, 110 m.p.h.; cruising speed, 95 m.p.h.; inclined climb rate, 900 ft./min.; range, 250 miles; service ceiling, 8,000 ft.; empty weight, 1,220 lb.; loaded, 1,800 lb.; rotor diameter, 37 ft.; length, 19 ft. 8½ in.; height, 11 ft. 2 in.

CONVERTAWINGS QUADROTOR A   U.S.A.

The Convertawings Quadrotor A is the only current example of a four-rotor helicopter. Powered by two 90 h.p. Continental C90 engines, the Quadrotor A is a single-seat research helicopter designed by Stanley J. Dubowski. Drive belts transmit power from the fore- and aft-mounted engines independently, and provision is made for over-ride clutches in case of power failure. The Quadrotor A is intended to provide data for several more advanced four-rotor helicopter projects, including the 40-passenger Quadrotor E.

Performance: No details available. Loaded weight, 1,950 lb.; rotor diameter (each), 15 ft. 0 in.; approx. fuselage length, 28 ft.

DE LACKNER DH-4 HELI-VECTOR   U.S.A.

The DH-4 Heli-Vector was test flown in free flight for the first time on January 22, 1955. In the same category as the Hiller "Flying Platform", the Heli-Vector was designed by L. C. McCarty and is powered by a 40 h.p. Kiekhaefer Mercury 325 outboard racing engine which drives the two counter-rotating rotors. Directional control is effected by the reflex movements of the pilot, and below the central sponson may be fitted gear for lifting a 60-lb. load.

Max. speed, 65 m.p.h.; range, 15–50 miles; ceiling, 5,000 ft.; empty weight, 180 lb.; loaded, 400 lb.; rotor diameter, 15 ft.

DOMAN LZ-5 (YH-31)   U.S.A.

The Doman LZ-5 is a seven-seat dual-purpose commercial and military helicopter powered by one 400 h.p. Lycoming S0-580-D engine. The LZ-5 features a special gimbal-mounted rotor hub first tested on a Sikorsky R-6 in 1953. The first of three LZ-5 prototypes flew on April 27, 1953, and Doman-Fleet Helicopters Ltd. has been formed to produce the LZ-5 in Canada. A development contract for the type, under the designation YH-31, has been awarded by the U.S. Army Transportation Corps.

Max. speed, 98 m.p.h.; cruising, 86 m.p.h.; inclined climb rate, 1,300 ft./min.; range, 245 miles; empty weight, 2,860 lb.; loaded, 5,000 lb.; rotor diameter, 48 ft.; length, 38 ft.; height, 10 ft. 3 in.

N*

FAIRCHILD XH-26 JET JEEP   U.S.A.

On April 1, 1954, the American Helicopter Company was absorbed by the Fairchild Engine and Airplane Company, and development work was continued with the single-seat, ultra-light, pulsejet-driven XH-26 Jet Jeep (formerly known as the A.H.C. XA-8). Five Jet Jeeps have been ordered by the U.S.A.F. on behalf of the U.S. Army, and two externally-mounted stretcher nacelles can be fitted. Powered by two 70 lb. thrust A.H.C. XAJ 7.5-in. pulsejets, the XH-26 was first flown on June 30, 1952.

Max. speed, 80 m.p.h.; cruising, 70 m.p.h.; range, 105 miles; empty weight, 300 lb.; loaded, 700 lb.; rotor diameter, 25 ft. 10 in.; length, 25 ft. 9 in.; height, 7 ft. 6 in.

FAIREY JET GYRODYNE   G.B.

The two-seat Jet Gyrodyne research helicopter is a direct development of the four-seat Gyrodyne helicopter of 1947, and a test vehicle for a number of design and power plant innovations which will be incorporated in the forty-seat Rotodyne. First flown on March 18, 1954, the Jet Gyrodyne is powered by a 550 h.p. Alvis Leonides piston engine which drives two pusher airscrews and also the compressor which forces air through the rotor blades to two Fairey "hot" pressure jets at the tips. Two prototypes of the Rotodyne are currently under construction, and these will be powered by two Napier Eland turbines, will weigh 33,000 lb., and will have rotor diameters of 90 ft.

FAIREY A.O.P.   G.B.

Developed as an ultra-light air observation post and liaison helicopter for the British Army, the first of four prototypes of the Fairey turbine-powered helicopter was flown on August 14, 1955. Powered by a 252 g.h.p. Blackburn-Turboméca Palouste 500 Bn. Pe.1 turbine, it seats two persons, the pilot being seated to starboard, while the observer has a 180° swivelling seat on the port side. Designed for rapid transportation in the field, the Fairey helicopter can be lifted manually and transported on a three-ton truck. The turbine supplies compressed air to the Fairey pressure jets at the rotor tips.

Rotor diameter, 28 ft. 3½ in.; fuselage length, 14 ft.; height, 7 ft. 11 in.

GLENVIEW GMP-1 FLYRIDE   U.S.A.

The GMP-1 Flyride two-seat utility helicopter of 1953 is a progressive development of the Teicher and Hunt Humming Bird of 1947. This embodies a simplified control system for the two-blade rotor head comprising only a twist-grip type control column and throttle. The second prototype of the Flyride, powered by a 140 h.p. Lycoming 0-290-D2, was flight-tested in the summer of 1954, the first prototype being stripped down for C.A.A. ground testing requirements.

Max. speed, 118 m.p.h.; cruising, 102 m.p.h.; inclined climb, 1,200 ft./min.; range, 300 miles; service ceiling, 15,500 ft.; empty weight, 1,150 lb.; loaded, 1,655 lb.; rotor diameter, fuselage length, 24 ft. 5 in.; height, 8 ft. 8½ in.

GOODYEAR GA-400R   U.S.A.

The GA-400R of 1954 is one of a number of single-seat ultra-light helicopters currently being developed for the U.S. Field Forces. It is, however, the only design which does not employ jet power (see Fairchild XH-26 Jet Jeep, Kellett Model KH-15, etc.), and employs a 31 h.p. Johnson outboard engine which is mounted immediately behind the rotor head. The GA-400R was designed by Paul Ziegler, and flight trials commenced at the Akron factory of the Goodyear Aircraft Corporation early in 1955.

Max. speed, 69 m.p.h.; cruising speed, 55 m.p.h.; endurance, 45 minutes; service ceiling, 12,000 ft.; empty weight, 245 lb.; loaded, 435 lb.; dimensions: No details available at the time of writing.

GYRODYNE MODEL G.C.A.2C   U.S.A.

The Model G.C.A.2C is a six-seat utility helicopter developed from the Bendix Model J of Helicopters Incorporated, and powered by a 450 h.p. Pratt & Whitney R-985-B4 Wasp Junior engine driving co-axial rotors. The earlier Model G.C.A.2A has two out-rigged 100 h.p. Continental engines. The Gyrodyne Company of American, Inc., is currently engaged in the development of convertiplanes, including the twin-turboprop Model 24 with a 40,000-lb. payload, and the ten-passenger G.C.A.7 Helidyne.

Max. speed, 87 m.p.h.; cruising, 70 m.p.h.; inclined climb, 1,030 ft./min.; range, 250 miles; empty weight, 3,800 lb.; loaded, 5,700 lb.; rotor diameter, 48 ft.; height, 14 ft. 4 in.

HILLER UH-12B (H-23B & HTE-2)   U.S.A.

Developed from the Model 360 of 1946, the UH-12B entered production in 1952, and has been supplied to the U.S. Army as the H-23B, and to the U.S. Navy and Royal Navy as the HTE-2. The earlier H-23A and HTE-1 had the 178 h.p. Franklin 6V4-178-B32 engine, but the later versions have the 200 h.p. Franklin VO-335 (6V4-200-C33). Dual controls may be fitted for training purposes, and external panniers may be carried. The UH-12B serves with the air forces of Thailand, Dominica, Guatemala, and Israel, as well as the U.S. Coast Guard.

Max. speed, 84 m.p.h.; cruising, 76 m.p.h.; inclined climb, 745 ft./min.; range, 140 miles; empty weight, 1,628 lb.; loaded, 2,500 lb.; rotor diameter, 35 ft.; length, 40 ft.; height, 9 ft. 6 in.

HILLER HJ-1 HORNET (HOE-1 & YH-32) U.S.A.

The first ramjet-driven helicopter to receive C.A.A. certification, the HJ-1 Hornet was first flown in 1950, and small-scale production is proceeding for the U.S. Marine Corps as the HOE-1, and as a trainer for the U.S. Army as the YH-32. The Hornet is a two-seat ultra-light machine powered by two 35 lb. thrust Hiller 8RJ2B ramjets, one mounted at each rotor tip. The small anti-torque rotor is gear-driven from the main rotor.

Max. speed, 80 m.p.h.; cruising, 70 m.p.h.; inclined climb, 830 ft./min.; range, 31 miles; empty weight, 360 lb.; loaded, 960 lb.; rotor diameter, 23 ft.; length (overall), 23 ft.; height, 8 ft.

HILLER (U.S.N./O.N.R.)   U.S.A.

One of the most unusual rotorcraft produced to-date is the Hiller "Flying Platform". Powered by two 50 h.p. piston engines, the "Flying Platform" has two counter-rotating rotor blades revolving inside a lipped cowl. Directional control is effected by movements of the pilot's body, the throttle controlling ascent and descent. The "Flying Platform", which might be termed an "inverted" helicopter appears to have a diameter of about 6 feet, but no details of the performance or weights of the machine have been divulged at the time of writing. It is being developed for the U.S. Navy's Office of Naval Research.

JACOBS MODEL 104   U.S.A.

Built by the Jacobs Aircraft Engine Company, the Model 104 is to be a five-seat convertiplane. The development prototype, with open framework and single seat for the pilot (*illustrated*), has undergone considerable flight testing, both with and without stub wings, and has a 350 h.p. Jacobs R-755-EH engine which supplies power to the three-blade main rotor for take-off, the pusher airscrew swivelling to the port side for anti-torque purposes. Power is then transferred to the rear airscrew for forward flight.

Max. speed, 175 m.p.h.; cruising, 157 m.p.h.; inclined climb, 1,400 ft./min.; range, 300 miles; empty weight, 2,360 lb.; loaded, 3,475 lb.; rotor diameter, 36 ft.; fuselage length, 22 ft.; height, 10 ft. 10 in.

KAMAN MODEL K-225 (YH-22)   U.S.A.

A progressive development of the K-125A and K-190 of 1947 and 1948 respectively, the K-225 three-seat utility helicopter entered production in 1949, and a small number were ordered by the U.S. Army as the YH-22. As a single-seat crop-duster, the K-225 has been supplied to the Turkish Department of Agriculture. The K-225 is powered by a 225 h.p. Lycoming O-435 engine, and an experimental version for the U.S. Navy was fitted with a 175 h.p. Boeing 502 (YT-50) turbine, flying on December 10, 1951.

Max. speed, 73 m.p.h.; cruising, 65 m.p.h.; inclined climb, 1,000 ft./min.; range, 194 miles; empty weight, 1,800 lb.; loaded, 2,700 lb.; rotor diameter, 38 ft.; fuselage length, 23 ft.; height, 11 ft. 6 in.

KAMAN MODEL K-240 (HTK-1)   U.S.A.

The Model 240, or HTK-1, is employed by the U.S. Navy and Marine Corps as a two/three-seat training helicopter, but can be employed for casualty evacuation with two externally-mounted panniers containing stretchers. The HTK-1 is powered by a 245 h.p. Lycoming 0-435-4 engine, and was first flown in 1951. On March 26, 1954, an HTK-1 was test flown with coupled turbines—two 190 s.h.p. Boeing Model 501-10Bs, and another participated in a remotely-controlled helicopter research programme.

Max. speed, 81 m.p.h.; cruising, 70 m.p.h.; inclined climb, 700 ft./min.; range, 194 miles; empty weight, 1,750 lb.; loaded, 3,100 lb.; rotor diameter (each), 42 ft.; fuselage length, 20 ft. 6½ in.; height, 12 ft. 6 in.

KAMAN MODEL K-3 (HOK-1)   U.S.A.

Developed concurrently with the smaller K-240, the Model K-3 or HOK-1, incorporates the same patented servo control for the inter-meshing twin rotors, and is a four-seat liaison helicopter powered by a 600 h.p. Pratt & Whitney Wasp R-1340-48 engine. Possessing an unusual twin-boom tail configuration, initial production models had twin endplate fins, but an additional central fin is fitted on the latest machines. The HOK-1 may be employed for casualty evacuation duties, accommodating two stretchers and one sitting casualty. In-flatable pontoons may be fitted.
Loaded weight, 3,500 lb.; rotor diameter (each), 47 ft.; fuselage length, 22 ft. 7 in.; height, 12 ft. 6 in.

KAMOV KA-10 VERTOLET   U.S.S.R.

The only known Russian ultra-light post-war helicopter produced in the U.S.S.R. since the war, the KA-10 is powered by a 50 h.p. converted Pobieda engine and is developed from the K-17 Vertolet powered by a 17 h.p. Aubier-Dunne engine and first demonstrated at Tushino in 1947. The work of N. I. Kamov, the KA-10 has been demonstrated with twin floatation bags, and several different types of tail assembly have been fitted. It is possible that the KA-10 single-seat helicopter is employed by the Soviet Navy for observation duties from submarines.
Max. speed, 74 m.p.h. No further details available for publication.

KAYABA   JAPAN

Licencees of the Cierva gyroplanes in pre-war years, the Kayaba concern has adapted the fuselage of a Cessna Model 170 light plane for use as a ramjet-driven convertiplane, a Kayaba ramjet at each rotor tip and a 185 h.p. Continental E-180 providing forward propulsion. Primarily a four-seat research convertiplane, the Kayaba appeared in 1954.
Rotor diameter, 24 ft. 3¼ in.; fuselage length, 10 ft. 6 in.; height, 9 ft. 2¼ in.

KELLETT KD-1A   U.S.A.

Produced by the Kellett Autogiro Company, the KD-1A was a pro-gressive development of the KD-1 of 1934. The KD-1 was the first gyroplane to utilise the Kellett direct control principle, and followed closely the Cierva designs of the period. Powered by a 225 h.p. Jacobs L-4-MA engine, one example of the KD-1A is flying in Canada. A current application of the KD-1A is the U.S. Navy's KH-17A con-vertiplane fitted with a wing carrying two 140 h.p. Lycoming engines. The KH-17A was due to fly at the end of 1955.
Max. speed, 125 m.p.h.; cruising, 103 m.p.h.; inclined climb, 1,000 ft./min.; range, 360 miles; empty weight, 1,345 lb.; loaded, 2,050 lb.; rotor diameter, 40 ft.; length, 25 ft. 6 in.; height, 10 ft. 6 in.

KELLETT MODEL KH-15   U.S.A.

The single-seat KH-15 research helicopter, powered by two 16 lb. thrust Reaction Motors XLR-32, was flown for the first time on May 13, 1954, four weeks after the Rotor-Craft RH-1, the World's first rocket-driven helicopter. The development contract for the KH-15 was placed by the U.S. Navy's Office of Naval Research to promote Kellett's gyratory stabilised rotor control system. The hydrogen peroxide fuel for the tip-mounted rocket motors is contained in tanks either side of the pilot. There is a small anti-torque rotor.
Empty weight, 234 lb.; loaded, 644 lb.; rotor diameter, 18 ft. 0 in.; overall length, 18 ft. 0 in.; height, 8 ft.

LAR-3 (TYPE 36 HOUND)   U.S.S.R.

Although unofficially credited to the designer Mikhail I.Mil', this helicopter, given the *Type* number "36" and the code-name *Hound* by N.A.T.O., is designated LAR-3 in the U.S.S.R. Powered by a 1,000 h.p. M-62-IR radial, the LAR-3 was first publicly demonstrated on August 28, 1953, and reputedly carries a crew of two and fourteen troops or a 4,400 lb. disposable load. Clam-shell type doors under the tail boom provide access to the cargo hold, and permit loading of a Jeep-type land truck, etc. The following specification is quoted from German sources.
Max. speed, 130 m.p.h. at 4,920 ft.; range (at 109 m.p.h. at 4,920 ft.), 155 miles; service ceiling, 11,800 ft.; normal loaded weight, 12,015 lb.; max., 13,998 lb.; rotor diameter, 56 ft. 6 in.; fuselage length, 45 ft. 4 in.

LUALDI-TASSOTTI E.S.53   ITALY

Designed by Carlo Lualdi and Sergio Tassotti, the single-seat E.S.53 is the precursor of two- and three-seat variants powered by 125 h.p. and 140 h.p. engines respectively. The E.S.53 is powered by an 85 h.p. Continental C-85 engine, and test flights commenced in March, 1954. The weights quoted in the following specification relate to the two-seat second prototype.

Max. speed, 68 m.p.h.; range, 155 miles; service ceiling, 6,560 ft.; duration, 2 hours, 15 minutes; empty weight, 882 lb.; loaded, 1,874 lb.; rotor diameter, 24 ft. (two-seater: 29 ft. 7 in.); length, 21 ft. 6 in.; height, 8 ft. 6 in.

McCULLOCH MC-4C (YH-30)   U.S.A.

A progressive development of the Jovanovich JOV-3 of 1946, the two-seat McCulloch MC-4C was designed by D. K. Jovanovich, and was flown for the first time on March 20, 1949. The MC-4C has been evaluated for the U.S. Army Transportation Corps as the YH-30, and the helicopter received a commercial Approved Type Certificate on February 17, 1953. It is powered by a 200 h.p. Franklin 6A4-200-C6 engine from which a central shaft is driven by a vee-belt.

Max. speed, 105 m.p.h.; cruising, 85 m.p.h.; inclined climb, 800 ft./min.; range, 200 miles; service ceiling, 8,000 ft.; empty weight, 1,600 lb.; loaded, 2,500 lb.; rotor diameter, 23 ft.; length, 32 ft. 5 in.; height, 9 ft. 3 in.

MCDONNELL MODEL 82 (XV-1)   U.S.A.

The XV-1, or Model 82, is a four-seat convertiplane under development for the U.S. Army as an experimental liaison and reconnaissance machine. Powered by one 550 h.p. Continental R-975-19 engine which drives a pusher airscrew for level flight and also feeds the three McDonnell "hot pressure-jet" units at the rotor tips, the XV-1 commenced flight trials on April 29, 1955, and was the first U.S. military convertiplane to fly. The designer primarily responsible for the XV-1 is Friedrich Doblhoff, the Austrial jet helicopter pioneer who produced the wartime WNF 342.

Max. speed, 190–210 m.p.h.; span, 26 ft.; fuselage length, 30 ft.; height, 10 ft.

MIL' MI-2 (TYPE 32 HARE)   U.S.S.R.

Believed to be the first Russian post-war helicopter to have been placed in quantity production for military liaison and air observation post duties, this three/five-seat general purpose helicopter was designed by Mikhail I.Mil', and was demonstrated publicly for the first time on July 8, 1951 at Tushino. The MI-2 has been allocated the *Type* number "32" and the code-name 'Hare' by N.A.T.O. forces. It is powered by a Shvetsov air-cooled radial engine, believed to be of the 640 h.p. ASh-21 type. The MI-2 is employed by the Soviet Forestry Commission for fire-fighting and, together with the larger LAR-3, was used on the 1954 Soviet polar expeditions painted orange overall. No dimensions, weights, or performance figures are available.

MIL' MI-4 (HORSE)   U.S.S.R.

The most recent Soviet military helicopter to be revealed, this machine was initially thought to be the work of Alexander Yakovlev. However, Soviet publications have credited the design to Mikhail I.Mil', and quoted the official designation as being MI-4. The MI-4 has been given the code-name *Horse* by N.A.T.O. forces, and was first publicly revealed on July 3, 1955, when four assault helicopters of this type participated in the Soviet Aviation Day celebrations at Tushino airfield. It is credited with being capable of carrying forty fully-armed troops, and is powered by two radial engines, these possibly being conversions of the 1,850 h.p. ASh-82FNV. A rear-loading ramp is fitted and, apart from a cabin length of 33 ft., no dimensions, weights, or performance figures are available.

PIASECKI PV-3 (HRP-1 RESCUER)   U.S.A.

The PV-3 was the World's first tandem-rotor helicopter to enter production, twenty being delivered to the U.S. Navy as the HRP-1 Rescuer in 1949. The prototype was first flown in March 1945, and the production HRP-1 is powered by a 600 h.p. Pratt & Whitney Wasp R-1340-AN-1. With a crew of two, this fabric-covered general utility helicopter carries eight troops. The U.S. Marine Corps has twelve for assault training, and three are employed by the U.S. Coast Guard as HRP-1Gs.

Max. speed, 120 m.p.h.; cruising, 85 m.p.h.; inclined climb, 800 ft./min.; range, 300 miles; empty weight, 5,000 lb.; loaded, 6,900 lb.; rotor diameter (each), 41 ft.; fuselage length, 48 ft.; height, 12 ft. 6 in.

PIASECKI PV-17 HRP-2 (RESCUER)   U.S.A.

Incorporating the experience gained with the earlier fabric-covered HRP-1, the all-metal PV-17, or HRP-2 Rescuer, was ordered by the U.S. Navy in June 1948. The overall configuration differs in detail from that of the earlier machine, including a lengthened fuselage, redesigned rotor heads, cleaner contours and improved directional control. The HRP-2 is powered by a 600 h.p. Pratt & Whitney Wasp R-1340-AN-1 engine, and carries a crew of two and eight passengers. It is also employed by the U.S. Marine Corps for airborne assault development.

Max. speed, 105 m.p.h.; cruising, 85 m.p.h.; inclined climb, 830 ft./min.; range, 300 miles; empty weight, 5,025 lb.; loaded, 7,129 lb.; rotor diameter (each), 41 ft.; fuselage length, 54 ft.; height, 14 ft. 10 in.

PIASECKI PV-15 (YH-16)   U.S.A.

The World's largest helicopter, the PV-15 was first flown on October 23, 1953 powered by two 1,650 h.p. Pratt & Whitney R-2180-11 piston engines. In this form it was known as the YH-16 Transporter and carried forty troops. A second machine, the YH-16A (*illustrated*), was flown in the summer of 1955 and is powered by two 2,925 s.h.p. Allison T38-A-6 shaft turbines, and the first machine is being re-engined with two 3,750 s.h.p. Allison T-56 shaft turbines as the YH-16V. Specification relates to the YH-16A Turbo-Transporter.

Max. speed, 130 m.p.h.; combat radius, 200 miles; ceiling, 18,000 ft.; empty weight, 23,000 lb.; loaded, 35,000 lb.; rotor diameter (each), 85 ft.; fuselage length, 77 ft. 10 in.; height, 31 ft. 1 in.

PIASECKI PV-14 & PD-18 (HUP)   U.S.A.

The Piasecki PV-14 was conceived as a carrier-borne utility helicopter. Originally designated XHJP-1 in its U.S. Navy version, the PV-14 entered production as the HUP-1 Retriever, powered by a 525 h.p. Continental R-975-34 and carrying five passengers in addition to two crew members. Three prototypes and twenty-two production machines were built during 1948–52. Discarding the endplate fins and with a 550 h.p. Continental R-975-46, it became the PD-18 of 1951, and was produced as the HUP-2 and HUP-2S, the latter for anti-submarine warfare.

Max. speed, 108 m.p.h.; cruising, 80 m.p.h.; inclined climb, 650 ft./min.; range, 340 miles; empty weight, 4,132 lb.; loaded, 5,750 lb.; rotor diameter (each), 35 ft.; overall length, 56 ft. 11 in.

PIASECKI PD-18 (H-25A ARMY MULE)   U.S.A.

Third and last of the U.S. Navy's HUP-series is the HUP-3 which incorporates several refinements over the HUP-2. Ordered in quantity by the U.S. Army as the H-25A Army Mule, the military version carries five/six troops and is powered by a 550 h.p. Continental R-975-46 engine. The HUP-4 is a "retrofit" of the HUP-3 fitted with an 800 h.p. Wright R-1300-13 radial. Three hundred and thirty-six HUP/H-25 helicopters were built, and all will be brought up to HUP-4 standards. The specification relates to the H-25A.

Max. speed, 105 m.p.h.; cruising, 80 m.p.h.; inclined climb, 720 ft./min.; range, 490 miles; empty weight, 3,928 lb.; loaded, 5,750 lb.; rotor diameter (each), 35 ft.; length, 56 ft. 11 in.; height, 12 ft. 6 in.

PIASECKI PD-22 (H-21 WORK-HORSE)   U.S.A.

First flown on April 11, 1952, the PD-22 has been produced for the U.S.A.F. and U.S. Army as the H-21A Work-Horse. Powered by a 1,425 h.p. Lycoming-Wright R-1820-103 engine, the H-21B (PH-42) and H-21C are respectively twenty-two seater and sixteen seater variants for the U.S.A.F. and the U.S. Army. A 16/19-seat commercial version of the PH-42 is being developed and is undergoing C.A.A. certification procedures at the time of writing. A number of H-21As have been supplied to the R.C.A.F. for rescue duties.

Max. speed, 140 m.p.h.; cruising, 104 m.p.h.; inclined climb, 1,420 ft./min.; range, 400 miles; empty weight, 8,600 lb.; loaded, 13,300 lb.; rotor diameter (each), 44 ft.; fuselage length, 52 ft. 6 in.; height, 16 ft.

PITCAIRN PA-18   U.S.A.

Still flying in Canada is an example of the Pitcairn PA-18 gyroplane, contemporary of the Kellett KD-1A, and first produced in 1934. Like the Kellett gyroplanes, the Pitcairn machines followed closely on the lines of those designed by Juan de Cierva. The PA-18 was produced by the Pitcairn Autogiro Company and is powered by a 160 h.p. Kinner R-5 radial engine. Originally a tandem two-seater, the last remaining example has the front cockpit deleted. Construction is of wood and steel-tube with fabric covering.

Max. speed, 100 m.p.h.; cruising, 80 m.p.h.; inclined climb, 680 ft./min.; ceiling, 10,500 ft.; empty weight, 1,355 lb.; loaded, 1,910 lb.; rotor diameter, 40 ft.; fuselage length, 19 ft. 4 in.; height, 11 ft. 4 in.

ROTOR-CRAFT RH-1 PINWHEEL   U.S.A.

The first rocket-propelled helicopter to be successfully flown, the single-seat RH-1 Pinwheel began flight tests on April 15, 1954. Representing an intermediate stage in the development of a practical "strap-on" military helicopter, the RH-1 Pinwheel has a Rotor-Craft liquid-fuel rocket motor mounted at each rotor blade tip. Initial tests were conducted with two 16 lb. thrust Reaction Motors XLR-32RM rockets. The only control is a motor-cycle-style twist-grip throttle positioned on the ventral control column. Design of the RH-1 commenced in 1950 under the U.S.N. Office of Naval Research and has now been taken over by the U.S.N. Bureau of Aeronautics.

SAUNDERS-ROE W.14 SKEETER MK.6   G.B.

The two-seat Skeeter was originally designed by the Cierva Autogiro Company and, powered by a 105 h.p. Jameson engine, first flew on October 8, 1948. In 1951, development of the Skeeter was taken over by Saunders-Roe, and several variants appeared, including the marks 2 and 3 with the 145 h.p. de Havilland Gipsy Major 8 and 10, the marks 3A, 3B, 4 and 5 with the 180 h.p. Blackburn Cirrus Bombardier 702, and, in 1955, the Skeeter Mk.6 with a 200 h.p. Gipsy Major Srs.200. A small development batch of Skeeter Mk.6s has been ordered by the Ministry of Supply.
Max. speed, 106 m.p.h.; cruising, 101 m.p.h.; inclined climb, 940 ft./min.; empty weight, 1,590 lb.; loaded, 2,150 lb.; rotor diameter, 32 ft.; overall length, 31 ft. 1½ in.; height, 10 ft.

SIKORSKY VS-316A (H-4B)   U.S.A.

The first U.S. helicopter to be placed in quantity production, the Sikorsky VS-316 flew on January 13, 1942 as the XR-4. The XR-4 prototype was followed by three YR-4A for service evaluation, twenty-seven YR-4Bs, and one hundred R-4Bs which differed from their predecessors primarily in having a 200 h.p. Warner R-550-3 replacing the 180 h.p. Warner R-550-1. At least one privately-owned R-4B is active in the U.S.A., and a few are used by the U.S. Coast Guards to train cadets.
Max. speed, 82 m.p.h.; cruising, 65 m.p.h.; range, 200 miles; service ceiling, 8,000 ft.; empty weight, 2,010 lb.; loaded, 2,600 lb.; rotor diameter, 38 ft.; overall length, 48 ft. 1 in.; height, 12 ft. 5 in.

SIKORSKY R-6A   U.S.A.

Two examples of the all-metal, two-seat Sikorsky R-6A helicopter are currently active in the U.S.A. Designed in 1942, the R-6A observation helicopter was also supplied to the U.S. Navy. The XR-6 proto-type was followed by five XR-6As, twenty-six YR-6As, and 193 R-6As, thirty-six of the latter being supplied to the U.S. Navy as HOS-1s. The R-6A is powered by a 240 h.p. Franklin 0-405-9 engine.

Max. speed, 100 m.p.h.; service ceiling, 10,000 ft.; loaded weight, 2,600 lb.; rotor diameter, 38 ft.; length, 47 ft. 11 in.

SIKORSKY S-51 (DRAGONFLY)   U.S.A.

The four-seat S-51 general utility helicopter had been produced in several commercial and military variants when production was terminated by the parent company in 1951 after three hundred had been built. The S-51 serves with the U.S.A.F. as the H-5H, and the U.S. Navy and Coast Guard as the H03S-1 with a 450 h.p. Pratt & Whitney Wasp Junior R-985-AN-7 engine. Licence production of the S-51, as the Westland-Sikorsky Dragonfly, is continuing in the U.K., and the specification refers to the 520 h.p. Leonides-powered version.
Max. speed, 105 m.p.h.; cruising, 81 m.p.h.; inclined climb, 970 ft./min.; range, 302 miles; empty weight, 4,397 lb.; loaded, 5,870 lb.; rotor diameter, 49 ft.; length, 57 ft. 6½ in.

SIKORSKY S-52-2 (YH-18A & HO5S-1G)   U.S.A.

Developed from the two-seat, all-metal S-52-1 of 1946, the S-52-2 four-seater was flown in May 1950, and small numbers have been delivered to the U.S. Army as the YH-18A, U.S. Marine Corps (HO5S-1) and Coast Guard (HO5S-1G). Powered by a 300 h.p. Franklin 0-425-13 engine, the S-52 was the first U.S. helicopter to have all-metal rotor blades. As an ambulance, two stretchers and a medical attendant may be carried, and dual controls may be fitted.
Max. speed, 110 m.p.h.; cruising, 95 m.p.h.; inclined climb, 1,100 ft./min.; range, 415 miles; empty weight, 1,825 lb.; loaded, 3,000 lb.; rotor diameter, 33 ft.; length, 27 ft. 6 in.; height, 9 ft. 10 in.

SIKORSKY S-55 (WHIRLWIND) U.S.A.

One of the most widely-used helicopters, the S-55 is built under licence in the U.K. by Westland Aircraft as the Whirlwind, and is assembled in France by S.N.C.A. du Sud-Est as the *Elephant Joyeux*. The variants, both commercial and military, are too numerous to list here, but the version to which the specification refers is powered by a 600 h.p. Pratt and Whitney R-1340-57 engine, and is employed by the U.S.A.F. as the H-19A, by the U.S. Army as the H-19C, by the U.S. Navy as the HO4S-1 and the U.S. Marine Corps as the HRS-1 and -2.

Max. speed, 110 m.p.h.; cruising, 85 m.p.h.; inclined climb, 1,100 ft./min.; range, 290 miles; empty weight, 4,395 lb.; loaded, 6,835 lb.; rotor diameter, 53 ft.; length, 41 ft. 9 in.; height, 13 ft.

SIKORSKY S-56 (H-37A & HR2S-1) U.S.A.

The S-56 is a heavy assault helicopter for the U.S. Marine Corps carrying twenty-six troops of three Jeep-type land vehicles. The U.S. Marine Corps designation is HR-2S1 and an U.S. Army version is designated H-37A. Flown for the first time on December 18, 1953, the S-56 is powered by two 1,900 h.p. Pratt & Whitney R-2800-50 Double Wasp engines. A 35-passenger commercial version is projected. The Jeep-type vehicles (Marine Corps' 1,500 lb. MM-100 "Mighty Mite" airborne trucks) are loaded through clamshell-type nose doors.

Max. speed, 156 m.p.h.; range, 200 miles; loaded weight, 28,500 lb.; rotor diameter, 90 ft.; fuselage length, 59 ft.

SIKORSKY S-58 (H-34A, HSS-1 & HUS-1) U.S.A.

Developed from the S-55, the S-58 will carry twelve passengers or a 4,000 lb. payload. Powered by a 1,525 h.p. Lycoming-Wright R-1820-84 engine, the S-58 is in production for the U.S. Navy for anti-submarine warfare under the designation HSS-1, for the U.S. Marine Corps as the HUS-1, and as a general purpose transport for the U.S. Army as the H-34A. A commercial version is projected, and certification is scheduled for completion in 1956. The HSS-1 carries dipping sonar equipment and offensive weapons.

Max. speed, 132 m.p.h.; cruising, 104 m.p.h.; max. inclined climb, 1,100 ft./min.; normal range, 270 miles; ferry range, 972 miles; empty weight, 7,530 lb.; loaded, 11,867 lb.; rotor diameter, 56 ft.; fuselage length, 47 ft. 2 in.; height, 14 ft. 2 in.

SIKORSKY S-59 (H-39A) U.S.A.

The 1954 Sikorsky S-59 is derived from the extensively modified S-52-5 of 1947, and is a two/four-seat utility helicopter ordered by the U.S.A.F. on behalf of the U.S. Army as the H-39A. Powered by a 400 s.h.p. Continental T51-T-3 shaft turbine, the S-59 is unusual among comparatively small helicopters in having a fully-retractable undercarriage. The S-59 gained world records for height (24,500 ft.) and speed (156 m.p.h.) in 1954.

Max. speed, 156 m.p.h.; cruising, 138 m.p.h.; inclined climb, 800 ft./min.; range, 250 miles; service ceiling, 16,000 ft.; empty weight, 2,200 lb.; loaded, 3,560 lb.; rotor diameter, 35 ft.; length, 30 ft. 3 in.; height, 9 ft. 8 in.

SUD-OUEST S.O.1120 ARIEL III FRANCE

The S.O. 1120 Ariel III is a progressive development of the S.O.1100 Ariel I and S.O.1110 Ariel II of 1949. Both earlier machines were powered by a Mathis G8 piston engine driving a compressor to provide air for rotor-tip burners, but the Ariel III, which first flew on April 18, 1951, employs a Turboméca Arrius turbine as the source of compressed air. The Ariel III is purely a research machine, and no production of the type has been undertaken.

Cruising speed: 105.5 m.p.h.; service ceiling, 14,430 ft.; range (with 660 lb. useful load), 155 miles; empty weight, 1,496 lb.; loaded, 2,750 lb.; rotor diameter, 35 ft. 5 in.; length, 24 ft. 7 in.

SUD-OUEST S.O.1310 FARFADET FRANCE

The S.O.1310 Farfadet (Hobgoblin) is a three-seat convertiplane powered by a 400 e.h.p. Turboméca Arrius II turbine to drive the rotor head and a 400 s.h.p. Turboméca Marcadau to drive the tractor airscrew. Flown for the first time on May 8, 1953, the Farfadet was tested as a helicopter initially, but a Turboméca Artouste II driving the tractor airscrew was tested for the first time on July 1, 1953. During high-speed level flight, the three-blade rotor head is off-loaded in autorotation. The Artouste has now been replaced by the later Marcadau turbine. Only one prototype of the Farfadet has been constructed at the time of writing.

Approx. max. speed, 150 m.p.h.; range, 240 miles; rotor diameter, 36 ft. 8½ in.

SUD-OUEST S.O.1221 DJINN FRANCE

The two-seat S.O.1221 Djinn is a lightweight two/three-seat general utility helicopter powered by a 250 g.h.p. Turboméca Palouste shaft turbine. The two prototypes (S.O.1220) were single-seaters, and the first was flown on January 2, 1953. The first two-seat S.O.1221 flew on December 15, 1953, being followed by twenty-two pre-production Djinns, ten of which were delivered to the *Armee de Terre* and *Aeronavale*. A further hundred Djinns are on order for civil and military roles.
Max. speed, 81 m.p.h.; cruising, 62 m.p.h.; inclined climb, 1,500 ft./min.; range, 155 miles; empty weight, 686 lb.; loaded, 1,550 lb.; rotor diameter, 36 ft.; fuselage length, 16 ft. 2 in.; height, 7 ft. 2¼ in.

SUD-EST S.E.3120 ALOUETTE I FRANCE

The S.E.3120 Alouette I three-seat utility helicopter flew for the first time on July 31, 1951. The Alouette I is powered by a 200 h.p. Salmson 9 NH engine, and ten production machines have been completed. From the basic design has been evolved the turbine-powered S.E.3130 Alouette II. The Alouette I was designed primarily as an agricultural aircraft, but two external panniers may be fitted to suit it for use as a casualty evacuation helicopter.
Max. speed, 78 m.p.h.; cruising, 62 m.p.h.; inclined climb, 500 ft./min.; range, 340 miles; empty weight, 1,650 lb.; loaded, 2,750 lb.; rotor diameter, 38 ft.; length, 34 ft. 3 in.; height, 9 ft. 6 in.

SUD-EST S.E.3130 ALOUETTE II FRANCE

The five-seat Alouette II is powered by a 400 s.h.p. Turboméca Artouste II shaft turbine, and features a simplified clutchless rotor transmission. The first prototype captured the Absolute Altitude Record for helicopters by attaining 26,933 ft. on June 6, 1955. Seventy-five Alouette IIs have been ordered by the French Government, and twenty are to be delivered to the French Navy. In September 1955, the Alouette II landed and took-off from Mt. Blanc.
Cruising speed, 106 m.p.h.; inclined climb, 1,180 ft./min.; range, 323 miles; service ceiling, 14,765 ft.; loaded weight, 3,307 lb.: rotor diameter, 32 ft. 9½ in.; length, 31 ft. 10 in.

TRANSCENDENTAL MODEL 1-G U.S.A.

The Transcendental Model 1-G convertiplane is powered by one 160 h.p. Lycoming GO-290-A engine, and test flying commenced in December 1954. The twin rotor heads move through an 84° arc on the ground and through 90° while airborne. The Model 1-G is primarily a test vehicle for the tilting mechanism, and a larger enclosed utility model is currently projected.
Cruising speed (as helicopter), 115 m.p.h.; loaded weight, 1,640 lb.; overall span, 38 ft.; rotor diameter (each), 17 ft.

WESTLAND WIDGEON G.B.

The Widgeon is basically the licence-built Sikorsky S.51 with a redesigned forward fuselage, increasing seating capacity to five, and an S.55-type rotor head. The Widgeon prototype, flown for the first time on August 23, 1955, is a rebuilt Westland-Sikorsky S.51 powered by a 550 h.p. Alvis Leonides engine. For use as a trainer dual controls may be fitted, and for the ambulance role two stretchers can be carried internally. Stretchers are loaded via a clamshell-type nose door.
Max. speed, 96 m.p.h.; cruising, 81 m.p.h.; inclined climb, 970 ft./min.; range, 301 miles; empty weight, 4,424 lb.; loaded, 5,900 lb.; rotor diameter, 49 ft. 2 in.; overall length, 57 ft. 7½ in.; height, 12 ft. 11½ in.

YOMIURI Y-1 JAPAN

The first post-war Japanese helicopter designed for quantity production, the Yomiuri Y-1 powered by a 150 h.p. Jinphu radial engine. It is anticipated that production will commence by mid-1956.
Max. speed, 96 m.p.h.; weights: No details available; rotor diameter, 32 ft. 10 in.; overall length, 40 ft. 2 in.

Index